D0944281

FUNDAMENTAL CONCEPTS OF ALGEBRA

PURE AND APPLIED MATHEMATICS

A SERIES OF MONOGRAPHS AND TEXTBOOKS

EDITED BY

PAUL A. SMITH AND SAMUEL EILENBERG

Columbia University, New York

I: A. SOMMERFELD, Partial Differential Equations in Physics, 1949 (Lectures on Theoretical Physics, Volume VI)

II: R. BAER, Linear Algebra and Projective Geometry, 1952

III: H. BUSEMANN AND P. J. KELLY, Projective Geometry and Projective Metrics, 1953

IV: S. BERGMAN AND M. SCHIFFER, Kernel Functions and Elliptic Differential Equations in Mathematical Physics, 1953

V: R. P. BOAS, JR., Entire Functions, 1954

VI: H. BUSEMANN, The Geometry of Geodesics, 1955

VII: CLAUDE CHEVALLEY, Fundamental Concepts of Algebra, 1956

ACADEMIC PRESS INC • PUBLISHERS • NEW YORK

FUNDAMENTAL CONCEPTS OF
ALGEBRA

By

CLAUDE CHEVALLEY
Columbia University, New York

1956

ACADEMIC PRESS INC • PUBLISHERS • NEW YORK

ACADEMIC PRESS INC.
111 FIFTH AVENUE
NEW YORK 3, N. Y.

First Printing, 1956
Second Printing, 1961

LIBRARY OF CONGRESS CATALOG CARD NUMBER:
56-8682

United Kingdom Edition
Published by
ACADEMIC PRESS INC. (London) LTD.
17 OLD QUEEN STREET, LONDON SW 1

PRINTED IN UNITED STATES OF AMERICA

Preface

Algebra is not only a part of mathematics; it also plays within mathematics the role which mathematics itself played for a long time with respect to physics. What does the algebraist have to offer to other mathematicians? Occasionally, the solution of a specific problem; but mostly a language in which to express mathematical facts and a variety of patterns of reasoning, put in a standard form. Algebra is not an end in itself; it has to listen to outside demands issued from various parts of mathematics. This situation is of great benefit to algebra; for, a science, or a part of a science, which exists in view of its own problems only is always in danger of falling into a peaceful slumber and from there into a quiet death. But, in order to take full advantage of this state of affairs, the algebraist must have sensitive ears and the ability to derive profit from what he perceives is going on outside his own domain, Mathematics is changing constantly, and algebra must reflect these changes if it wants to stay alive. This explains the fact that algebra is one of the most rapidly changing parts of mathematics: it is sensitive not only to what happens inside its own boundaries, but also to the trends which originate in all other branches of mathematics.

This book represents an attempt to adapt the teaching of algebra to at least a part of what present day mathematics requires. The most important new demands on algebra come from topology, analysis, and algebraic geometry. These demands are of various kinds; but to all of them the general notion of a module seems to be absolutely essential. This is why the theory of modules occupies such an important place in this book. The concept of a module unites and generalizes those of an additive group and of a vector space; it differs from them by the generality which is allowed for the domain of operators, which may be an arbitrary ring instead of the ring of integers (in additive groups) or a field (in vector spaces). This generality is not there for its own merits, but because it is actually needed in many cases. The operations from the general theory of modules which are considered here are essentially the construction of the group of linear mappings of a module into another one and the construction of the tensor product of two modules. These concepts are not, by far, the only useful ones; but we believe that they contain "what everybody must know" from the theory of modules. The last part of the book is concerned with the theory of algebras and mostly of exterior algebras; the latter have become essential to analysts because of the frequent use they make of the calculus of differential forms.

We are far from even hinting that this book represents a complete survey of those parts of algebra whose knowledge is essential to contemporary mathematicians; the most glaring lacuna is that of field theory, which is not touched on in this book. The principle which has presided over our choice of material is that it is better to acquire a complete familiarity with a few fundamental notions than to have a superficial knowledge of many. The contents of this book (with a few omissions) have been taught by the author in a one year first graduate course in algebra; we think that it would be impossible to cram any more matter into the program of such a course without destroying its usefulness. The presentation of the material will perhaps incur the reproach of being too dogmatic in its methods. To this possible objection, we would like to make two answers. Firstly that what the student may learn here is not designed to help him with problems he has already met but with those he will have to cope with in the future; it is therefore impossible to motivate the definitions and theorems by applications of which the reader does not know the existence as yet. Secondly, that one of the important pedagogical problems which a teacher of beginners in mathematics has to solve is to impart to his students the technique of rigorous mathematical reasoning; this is an exercise in rectitude of thought, of which it would be futile to disguise the austerity.

PARIS, JUNE 1956. CLAUDE CHEVALLEY.

Contents

Prerequisite Knowledge and Terminological Conventions

The reader will be assumed to be familiar with the general principles of set theory, including Zorn's lemma, which will be used in the following form. Let E be a set and S a set of subsets of E. Assume that for any subset S' of S with the property that, for any two sets X and Y belonging to S', one is contained in the other, there exists a set in S which contains all sets in S'; then every set in S is contained in some maximal set X of S (i. e. in a set X such that the only set in S which contains X is X itself). From the theory of cardinals, we require the following results: to every set I there is associated an object card I, in such a way that a necessary and sufficient condition for I and I' to be equipotent is that card I $=$ card I'; there is an order relation among the cardinals such that card I $\leqslant$ card I' if and only if I is equipotent to a subset of I'; if to every element i of an infinite set I there is associated a finite subset F_i of a set I', and if every element of I' belongs to at least one of the sets F_i, then card $I' \leqslant$ card I. A mapping f of a set A into a set B is called injective if the condition $a \neq a'$ (where a, a' are in A) implies $f(a) \neq f(a')$; f is called surjective if, for any b in B, there exists at least one a in A such that $f(a) = b$; a mapping which is both injective and surjective is called bijective. An injective (resp.: surjective, bijective) mapping is also called an injection (resp.: surjection, bijection). A mapping of a set I into a set A is also called a family of elements of A indexed by I; if this terminology is used, then the image under the mapping of an element i is generally denoted by f_i (instead of the usual notation $f(i)$); the mapping itself is often denoted by $(f_i)_{i \in I}$.

The set of all integers (positive, null or negative) will always be denoted by $\underline{Z}$. If m is an integer > 0, the factor group $\underline{Z}/m\underline{Z}$ (to be defined in chapter II) will be denoted by $\underline{Z}_m$. A family of elements of a set A which is indexed by the set of integers > 0 will be called a sequence of elements of A; a family of elements of A which is indexed by the set of all integers > 0 which are at most equal to an integer n will be called a finite sequence (of length n) of elements of A. Such a sequence will often be denoted by $(a_i)_{1 \leqslant i \leqslant n}$ or by $(a_1, \cdots, a_n)$. The elements a_i are called the terms of the sequence.

The formula $a \in A$ will mean that a is an element of the set A. The empty set will be denoted by $\emptyset$. If a is an object, then the set whose unique element is a is denoted by $\{a\}$. If $(a_1, \cdots, a_n)$ is a finite sequence, the set whose elements are $a_1, \cdots, a_n$ will be denoted by $\{a_1, \cdots, a_n\}$; if a, b are objects, $\{a, b\}$ denotes the set whose elements are a, b. The notation $A \subset B$ means that every element of A is an element of B; this does not exclude the possibility that $A = B$. If A and B are sets, $A \cup B$ represents the set whose elements are all objects which are elements either of A or of B (the union of A and B); $A \cap B$ represents the set of elements which belong to both A and B (the intersection of A and B). If a, b are objects, the finite sequence of length 2 which maps 1 upon a and 2 upon b is called the pair (a, b). If A and B are sets, the set of all pairs (a, b) such that $a \in A$ and $b \in B$ is called the *(Cartesian) product of A and B*, and is denoted by $A \times B$.

Let $(A_i)_{i \in I}$ be a family of sets. The union of these sets (i. e. the set of elements a such that there exists an $i \in I$ for which $a \in A_i$) is denoted by $\bigcup_{i \in I} A_i$. The intersection of the sets A_i (i. e. the set of elements a such that $a \in A_i$ for every $i \in I$) is denoted by $\bigcap_{i \in I} A_i$. The product of the sets A_i (i. e. the set of families $(a_i)_{i \in I}$, indexed by I, such that $a_i \in A_i$ for every $i \in I$) is denoted by $\prod_{i \in I} A_i$. If $(A_1, \cdots, A_n)$ is a finite sequence of sets, the union of the sets A_i is also denoted by $A_1 \cup \cdots \cup A_n$, their intersection by $A_1 \cap \cdots \cap A_n$ and their product by $A_1 \times \cdots \times A_n$.

Let f be a mapping of a set A into a set B. If $X \subset A$, then the set of elements b such that there exists an x such that $x \in X$ and $f(x) = b$ is denoted by $f(X)$. If $(X_i)_{i \in I}$ is a family of subsets of A, then

$$f(\bigcup_{i \in I} X_i) = \bigcup_{i \in I} f(X_i).$$

If Y is a subset of B, the set of elements a such that $a \in A$ and $f(a) \in Y$ is denoted by $\overset{-1}{f}(Y)$. If $(Y_i)_{i \in I}$ is a family of subsets of B, then we have

$$\overset{-1}{f}(\bigcup_{i \in I} Y_i) = \bigcup_{i \in I} \overset{-1}{f}(Y_i) \text{ and } \overset{-1}{f}(\bigcap_{i \in I} Y_i) = \bigcap_{i \in I} \overset{-1}{f}(Y_i).$$

If g is a mapping of B into a set C, then the mapping of A into C which assigns $g(f(a))$ to every $a \in A$ is denoted by $g \circ f$. If f is a bijection, then the mapping of B into A which maps any element b of B upon the unique element a of A such that $f(a) = b$ is denoted by $\overset{-1}{f}$. If $E(a)$ is an expression involving a letter a and which has a meaning whenever a stands for an element of a set A, then $a \to E(a)$ represents the mapping which assigns to every element a of A the value of the expression $E(a)$. If $(A_i)_{i \in I}$ is a family of sets and j an element of I, then the mapping of $\prod_{i \in I} A_i$ into A_j which assigns a_j to any element $(a_i)_{i \in I}$ of $\prod_{i \in I} A_i$ is called the j-th projection, or, if there is no danger of confusion, the projection on A_j.

CHAPTER I

Monoids

1. Definition of a monoid

An *internal law of composition*, or *law of composition*, on a set A is a mapping of $A \times A$ into A, i. e. a mapping which assigns to every ordered pair (a, b) of elements of A an element c of A, called their *composite*.

We shall have to consider a great variety of laws of composition. However we shall have only three notations for the composite of a and b: either $a + b$, ab, or $a \circ b$. If the composite is denoted by $a + b$, then it is called the sum of a and b, and we say that we have an additive law of composition. If the composite is denoted by ab or $a \circ b$, then it is called the product of a and b, and we say that we have a multiplicative law of composition. However, in the beginning of this discussion, we shall not make any distinction between additive and multiplicative laws of composition; therefore, we shall use the notation $a \tau b$ for a composite, which may be either a sum or a product.

A law of composition τ on the set A is called *associative* if it is true that

$$(a \tau b) \tau c = a \tau (b \tau c)$$

for all a, b, c in A.

EXAMPLES: *a*) A is the set $\underline{Z}$ of integers, and τ stands either for addition or multiplication: τ is then associative.

b) Let S be any set and A the set of all mappings of S into itself, with the law of composition $(f, g) \to f \circ g$ (where $(f \circ g)(x) = f(g(x))$ for any $x \in S$). This law of composition is associative, for if f, g, h are in A, then

$$((f \circ g) \circ h)(x) = (f \circ g)(h(x)) = f(g(h(x)))$$
$$(f \circ (g \circ h))(x) = f((g \circ h)(x)) = f(g(h(x)))$$

for any $x \in S$, which proves our assertion.

c) In the set of integers, subtraction, i. e. the law of composition $(a, b) \to a - b$, is not associative.

An element e is called *a neutral element* for a law of composition τ in A if we have

$$a \tau e = e \tau a = a$$

for all $a \in A$.

EXAMPLES: *a*) In the set of integers, 0 is a neutral element for addition and 1 a neutral element for multiplication.

b) In the law of composition of example *b*) above, the identity mapping e (i. e. the mapping $x \to x$) is a neutral element.

c) We have, for any integer a, $a - 0 = a$ but, in general, $0 - a \neq a$; thus 0 is not a neutral element for subtraction. It is easy to see that there does not exist *any* neutral element for subtraction.

Theorem 1. *If there is a neutral element for a law of composition τ in A, there is only one.*

Assume that e and e' are neutral elements. Then we have $e\tau e' = e'$ but also $e\tau e' = e$, whence $e = e'$.

The neutral element for an additive law of composition is always denoted by 0; the neutral element for a multiplicative law of composition is most often denoted by 1.

A *monoid* is a set A which has a law of composition that is associative and has a neutral element.

In what follows, unless ortherwise stated, A shall denote a monoid, in which the law of composition is denoted by τ.

Composite of finite sequences. Let $(a_1, \cdots, a_n)$ be a finite sequence of elements of A; we shall then define the composite, $a_1\tau \cdots \tau a_n$, of this sequence in the following inductive manner. If the sequence is the empty sequence $(n = 0)$, then the composite is by definition the neutral element e. If $n > 0$ and if the composites of sequences of less than n terms are already defined, then we define $a_1\tau \cdots \tau a_n$ by

$$a_1\tau \cdots \tau a_n = (a_1\tau \cdots \tau a_{n-1})\tau a_n.$$

EXAMPLES: The composite of a sequence (a) of a single term is this term a. We have $a\tau b\tau c = (a\tau b)\tau c$, $a\tau b\tau c\tau d = (a\tau b\tau c)\tau d = ((a\tau b)\tau c)\tau d$.

For an additive law of composition, the composite of $(a_1, \cdots, a_n)$ is denoted by $\sum_{i=1}^{n} a_i$; for a multiplicative law of composition, by $\prod_{i=1}^{n} a_i$. There are many variations in the notational conventions, with which the reader will familiarize himself by usage. Examples:

$$\sum_{i=6}^{9} a_i = a_6 + a_7 + a_8 + a_9,$$

$$\sum_{i=-3,\, i \text{ odd}}^{5} a_i = a_{-3} + a_{-1} + a_1 + a_3 + a_5,\ \sum_{i=2}^{0} a_i = 0, \text{ etc.}$$

Theorem 2. (General associativity theorem) *Let $(a_1, \cdots, a_n)$ be a sequence of elements of A. Let $k_1, \cdots, k_h$ be integers such that $1 = k_1 \leqslant \cdots \leqslant k_h \leqslant n$. Let $b_1 = a_1\tau \cdots \tau a_{k_2 - 1}$, $b_2 = a_{k_2}\tau \cdots \tau a_{k_3 - 1}, \cdots, b_h = a_{k_h}\tau \cdots \tau a_n$. Then we have $a_1\tau \cdots \tau a_n = b_1\tau \cdots \tau b_h$.*

EXAMPLES: (case $n=4$). We have

$$a\tau b\tau c\tau d = a\tau(b\tau c)\tau d = a\tau(b\tau c\tau d) = a\tau b\tau(c\tau d) = (a\tau b)\tau c\tau d = (a\tau b)\tau(c\tau d) = \text{etc.}$$

Proof. We proceed by induction on n. If $n=0$, then, necessarily, $h=0$, and both sides are equal to the neutral element. Assume that $n>0$ and that the theorem is true for sequences of at most $n-1$ terms.

Case 1. Assume first that $k_h=n$, whence $b_h=a_n$. We have, by definition, $a_1\tau\cdots\tau a_n=(a_1\tau\cdots\tau a_{n-1})\tau a_n$. By the inductive assumption, we have $a_1\tau\cdots\tau a_{n-1}=b_1\tau\cdots\tau b_{h-1}$, whence

$$a_1\tau\cdots\tau a_n=(b_1\tau\cdots\tau b_{h-1})\tau b_h=b_1\tau\cdots\tau b_h.$$

Case 2. Assume now that $k_h<n$. We have $b_1\tau\cdots\tau b_h=(b_1\tau\cdots\tau b_{h-1})\tau b_h$. Let $b'_h=a_{k_h}\tau\cdots\tau a_{n-1}$, whence $b_h=b'_h\tau a_n$. Then we have, using the assumed associativity of the law of composition τ,

$$\begin{aligned} b_1\tau\cdots\tau b_h &= (b_1\tau\cdots\tau b_{h-1})\tau(b'_h\tau a_n) \\ &= ((b_1\tau\cdots\tau b_{h-1})\tau b'_h)\tau a_n = (b_1\tau\cdots\tau b_{h-1}\tau b'_h)\tau a_n. \end{aligned}$$

But we have $a_1\tau\cdots\tau a_{n-1}=b_1\tau\cdots\tau b_{h-1}\tau b'_h$ by our inductive assumption, whence $b_1\tau\cdots\tau b_h=(a_1\tau\cdots\tau a_{n-1})\tau a_n=a_1\tau\cdots\tau a_n$. This concludes the proof.

Consider now the case where $a_1,\cdots,a_n$ are all equal to one and the same element a. Then the composite of the sequence $(a_1,\cdots,a_n)$ is denoted by na if the law of composition is additive, by a^n if the law of composition is multiplicative.

Let m and n be non-negative integers, and a an element of A. If the law of composition is additive, then we have

$$(1)\qquad 0a=0,\ 1a=a,\ (m+n)a=ma+na,\ (mn)a=m(na):$$

if the law of composition is multiplicative, we have

$$(2)\qquad a^0=1,\ a^1=a,\qquad a^{m+n}=a^m a^n,\qquad a^{mn}=(a^m)^n.$$

These formulas follow easily from the definitions and from the general associativity theorem.

Commutative monoids. The monoid A is called *commutative* or *Abelian* if we have $a\tau b=b\tau a$ for any elements a and b of A.

EXAMPLES: *a*) The set Z of integers is a commutative monoid under both addition and multiplication.

b) Let R be the set of real numbers, and A the set of mappings of R into itself. Denote by f the mapping $x\to x+1$ and by g the mapping $x\to x^2$. Then $(f\circ g)(x)=x^2+1$, $(g\circ f)(x)=x^2+2x+1$; thus, the law of composition $\circ$ in A is not commutative.

Theorem 3. (general commutativity theorem). *Let A be a commutative monoid, $(a_1, \cdots, a_n)$ a finite sequence of elements of A and ϖ any permutation of the set $\{1, \cdots, n\}$. Then we have*

$$a_1\tau \cdots \tau a_n = a_{\varpi(1)}\tau \cdots \tau a_{\varpi(n)}.$$

EXAMPLES: We have

$$a\tau b\tau c = a\tau c\tau b = b\tau a\tau c = b\tau c\tau a = c\tau a\tau b = c\tau b\tau a.$$

Proof. We proceed by induction on n. There is nothing to prove if $n = 0$. Assume that $n > 0$ and that the statement is true for sequences of $n-1$ terms.

Case 1. Consider first the case where $\varpi(n) = n$. Then we have, by the inductive assumption, $a_1\tau \cdots \tau a_{n-1} = a_{\varpi(1)}\tau \cdots \tau a_{\varpi(n-1)}$. Thus,

$$\begin{aligned} a_1\tau \cdots \tau a_n &= (a_1\tau \cdots \tau a_{n-1})\tau a_n = (a_{\varpi(1)}\tau \cdots \tau a_{\varpi(n-1)})\tau a_{\varpi(n)} \\ &= a_{\varpi(1)}\tau \cdots \tau a_{\varpi(n-1)}\tau a_{\varpi(n)}. \end{aligned}$$

Case 2. Assume now that $\varpi(n) < n$. Let k be the integer such that $\varpi(k) = n$. Then we have

$$a_{\varpi(1)}\tau \cdots \tau a_{\varpi(n)} = (a_{\varpi(1)}\tau \cdots \tau a_{\varpi(k-1)})\tau(a_{\varpi(k)}\tau(a_{\varpi(k+1)}\tau \cdots \tau a_{\varpi(n)})),$$

and this is equal to

$$(a_{\varpi(1)}\tau \cdots \tau a_{\varpi(k-1)})\tau((a_{\varpi(k+1)}\tau \cdots \tau a_{\varpi(n)})\tau a_{\varpi(k)}) = a_{\varpi'(1)}\tau \cdots \tau a_{\varpi'(n)}$$

where we have set $\varpi'(i) = \varpi(i)$ if $i \leqslant k-1$, $\varpi'(i) = \varpi(i+1)$ if $k \leqslant i \leqslant n-1$, $\varpi'(n) = \varpi(k) = n$. But ϖ' is again a permutation of $\{1, \cdots, n\}$, and, this time, $\varpi'(n) = n$. Thus $a_{\varpi'(1)}\tau \cdots \tau a_{\varpi'(n)} = a_1\tau \cdots \tau a_n$ by case 1. This complete the proof.

Assume that we have a commutative monoid where the law of composition is additive. Let I be any finite set, and $i \to a_i$ a mapping of I into A. If n is the number of elements of I, let us number these elements by the integers from 1 to n; denote by $i(k)$ the element of I to which we have assigned the number k. Then $(a_{i(1)}, \cdots, a_{i(n)})$ is a finite sequence, and has therefore a sum $\sum_{k=1}^{n} a_{i(k)}$. It follows from the general commutativity theorem that the value of this sum does not depend on the manner in which we have numbered the elements of I; this value is denoted by $\sum_{i \in I} a_i$.

Let I' be a subset of I and assume that $a_i = 0$ for all $i \in I$ not belonging to I'. Then we have $\sum_{i \in I} a_i = \sum_{i \in I'} a_i$ (i. e., in a sum, we may drop any number of terms all equal to 0). For, we may assume that we number I in such a way that the elements of I' come first; assume that $i(1), \cdots, i(m)$

are the elements of I' and $i(m+1), \cdots, i(n)$ the others. Then it is clear that $\Sigma_{i \in I} a_i = \Sigma_{i \in I'} a_i + (a_{i(m+1)} + \cdots + a_n)$, and we have only to prove that a sum of terms all equal to 0 has the value 0, which is easily done by induction on the number of terms.

This allows us to extend the notation $\Sigma_{i \in I} a_i$ to certain cases where the set I may be infinite. In fact, assume that there are only a finite number of elements i of I for which a_i is $\neq 0$. Then I admits at least one *finite* subset I' such that a_i is 0 for all i not in I'; the value of the sum $\Sigma_{i \in I'} a_i$ does not depend on the choice of the set I' satisfying these conditions. For, let I'' be another set satisfying the same conditions. Then $I' \cup I''$ is again a finite set, and we have $a_i = 0$ for all i in $I' \cup I''$ but not in I', whence $\Sigma_{i \in I'} a_i = \Sigma_{i \in I' \cup I''} a_i$, and we see in the same way that

$$\Sigma_{i \in I''} a_i = \Sigma_{i \in I' \cup I''} a_i,$$

which proves our assertion. The common value of the sums $\Sigma_{i \in I'} a_i$ for all sets I' satisfying the stated conditions is denoted by $\Sigma_{i \in I} a_i$.

Assume that we have subsets J_k of I, indexed by an index k which runs over a certain set K, and which satisfy the following conditions: they are pairwise disjoint, and the union of all of them is the whole of I (this is called a *partition* of I). Then, for each k, the sum $b_k = \Sigma_{i \in J_k} a_i$ is defined (i. e., it has only a finite number of terms $\neq 0$); moreover, the sum $\Sigma_{k \in K} b_k$ is defined, and we have the equality

$$\Sigma_{i \in I} a_i = \Sigma_{k \in K} b_k.$$

For, let I' be the set of indices $i \in I$ such that $a_i \neq 0$. Then I' is finite, and so, for each $k \in K$, $I' \cap J_k$ is finite, which shows that each sum $\Sigma_{i \in J_k} a_i$ is defined. Since the sets J_k are mutually disjoint, only a finite number of them can meet the set I' (this number is at most equal to the number of elements of I'). Now, if J_k does not meet I', we have $a_i = 0$ for *all* i in J_k, whence $b_k = 0$. This shows that the sum $\Sigma_{k \in K} b_k$ is defined. For each k, let $J'_k = J_k \cap I'$; then, by definition, $b_k = \Sigma_{i \in J'_k} a_i$. Let K' be the set of indices k for which $J'_k \neq \emptyset$; then we have

$$\Sigma_{k \in K} b_k = \Sigma_{k \in K'} b_k = \Sigma_{k \in K'} (\Sigma_{i \in J'_k} a_i),$$

and we have reduced the proof to establishing the formula

$$\Sigma_{i \in I'} a_i = \Sigma_{k \in K'} (\Sigma_{i \in J'_k} a_i)$$

where I' and K' are now finite sets. This is easily accomplished by means of the general associativity theorem.

Let $(a_i)_{i \in I}$ and $(b_i)_{i \in I}$ be families indexed by the same set I and for which $\sum_{i\in I} a_i$ and $\sum_{i\in I} b_i$ are defined. Then $\sum_{i\in I}(a_i + b_i)$ is defined, and we have

$$\sum_{i\in I}(a_i + b_i) = \sum_{i\in I} a_i + \sum_{i\in I} b_i. \tag{3}$$

For, it is clear that there exists a finite set $I' \subset I$ such that $a_i = b_i = 0$ for all i not in I', whence

$$\sum_{i\in I}(a_i + b_i) = \sum_{i\in I'}(a_i + b_i),\ \sum_{i\in I} a_i = \sum_{i\in I'} a_i,\ \sum_{i\in I} b_i = \sum_{i\in I'} b_i.$$

Thus, we need only prove (3) in the case where I is finite. Let then $i(1), \cdots, i(n)$ be its elements. Let $c_{2j-1} = a_j$, $c_{2j} = b_j$ $(1 \leqslant j \leqslant n)$. Then $\sum_{i\in I}(a_i + b_i) = \sum_{j=1}^{n}(c_{2j-1} + c_{2j})$. This is equal by the general associativity theorem to $c_1 + \cdots + c_{2n}$, and, by the general commutativity and associativity theorems, to

$$(c_1 + c_3 + \cdots + c_{2n-1}) + (c_2 + c_4 + \cdots + c_{2n}) = \sum_{i\in I} a_i + \sum_{i\in I} b_i.$$

Similar considerations apply to the case of a commutative monoid A in which the law of composition is multiplicative, and lead to the definition of the symbol $\prod_{i\in I} a_i$ in the case where there are only a finite number of indices $i \in I$ for which $a_i \neq 1$.

Let A be a commutative additive monoid, n an integer $\geqslant 0$ and a, b elements of A. Then we have

$$n(a + b) = na + nb;$$

this follows immediately from formula (1) above.

Similarly, if A is a commutative multiplicative monoid, then we have $(ab)^n = a^n b^n$.

If A is any monoid, two elements a and b of A are said to *commute with each other* if we have $a \top b = b \top a$. For instance, the neutral element commutes with every element of the monoid.

2. Submonoids. Generators

A subset B of a monoid A (in which the law of composition is denoted by $\top$) is called *stable* if we have $a \top b \in B$ whenever a and b are in B.

Examples: In the additive monoid $\underline{Z}$ of integers, the set of integers $\geqslant k$ (where k is any integer) is stable under addition if $k \geqslant 0$ but not if $k < 0$. The set $\{-1, 1\}$ is stable under multiplication, but not under addition. In the set of all mappings of the set of real numbers into itself (with the law of composition $\circ$), the set of all mappings of the form $x \to x^n$ (n an integer $\geqslant 0$) is stable.

If B is stable, the restriction to $B \times B$ of the law of composition τ in A is a law of composition in B, called the *induced law of composition.* If τ is associative, then so is its induced law of composition. If τ admits a neutral element e and $e \in B$, then e is a neutral element for the induced law of composition.

Thus, if we assume that B contains e and is stable, then it constitutes a monoid when equipped with the induced law of composition. In that case, B is called a *submonoid* of A.

If B is a submonoid of A, then it is clear that the composite in A of a finite sequence of elements of B belongs to B and is also the composite of this sequence in B.

Theorem 4. *Let $(B_i)_{i \in I}$ be a family of submonoids of A, I being any (non empty) set of indices. Then the intersection B of all B_i's is a submonoid.*

Since $e \in B_i$ for all i, we have $e \in B$. Let a and b be in B; then, for each i, a and b are in B_i, whence $a \tau b \in B_i$; it follows that $a \tau b \in B$.

Let S be any subset of A. Then S is contained in at least one submonoid of A, viz. A itself. By theorem 4, the intersection B of all submonoids of A containing S is a submonoid; B is the smallest submonoid of A containing S (in the sense that it is contained in any submonoid which contains S). It is called the *submonoid generated by S.*

For instance, if $S = \emptyset$, then B is the submonoid $\{e\}$ consisting of the neutral element e alone. If $\underline{Z}$ is the monoid of integers under addition, and k any integer, the submonoid generated by the set $\{k\}$ consists of all elements nk, where n runs over the integers $\geqslant 0$.

Theorem 5. *Let U be any subset of a monoid A. Then the set C of those elements of A which commute with every element of U is a submonoid of A.*

It is clear that C contains the neutral element. Let a, b be elements of C, and u any element of U. Then we have

$$(a \tau b) \tau u = a \tau (b \tau u) = a \tau (u \tau b) = (a \tau u) \tau b = (u \tau a) \tau b = u \tau (a \tau b),$$

which shows that $a \tau b$ commutes with u; C is therefore stable.

Corollary 1. *If all elements of a subset S of A commute with all elements of U, then all elements of the submonoid A' generated by S commute with all elements of U.*

For, we have $S \subset C$ (in the notation of theorem 5), whence $A' \subset C$, since A' is the smallest submonoid containing S.

Corollary 2. *If the elements of a subset S of A commute with each other, then the submonoid A' generated by S is Abelian.*

For, any element of S commutes with any element of A', by corollary 1. Applying corollary 1 again, with A' taking the place of U, we see that any element of A' commutes with any element of A'.

3. Homomorphisms

Let A and B be monoids. A mapping f of A into B is called a *homomorphism* if the following conditions are satisfied:

a) f maps the neutral element e_A of A upon the neutral element e_B of B;

b) if a, b are any elements of A, we have

$$f(a \tau b) = f(a) \tau f(b).$$

(We use the same notation τ for the laws of composition in A and in B; but the reader should remember that it may happen that the law of composition in A is additive and that in B multiplicative.)

EXAMPLES: a) Let A be a commutative additive monoid, and let n be an integer $\geqslant 0$; then the mapping $x \rightarrow nx$ is a homomorphism of A into itself.

b) Let R be the set of real numbers. Then the mapping $x \rightarrow e^x$ is a homomorphism of the additive monoid $\underline{R}$ into the multiplicative monoid $\underline{R}$.

If f is a homomorphism of A into B and g a homomorphism of B into a third monoid C, then $g \circ f$ is a homomorphism of A into C. The proof is obvious.

Let f be a homomorphism of A into B. If $(a_1, \cdots, a_n)$ is a finite sequence of elements of A, then we have

$$f(a_1 \tau \cdots \tau a_n) = f(a_1) \tau \cdots \tau f(a_n).$$

This is easily proved by induction on n. In particular, if A and B are both additive, we have $f(na) = nf(a)$; if they are both multiplicative, we have $f(a^n) = (f(a))^n$; if A is additive and B multiplicative, we have $f(na) = (f(a))^n$.

Theorem 6. *Let f be a homomorphism of A into B. Then the image under f of a submonoid of A is a submonoid of B. If S is a subset of A, the image of the submonoid of A generated by S is the submonoid of B generated by $f(S)$. If B' is a submonoid of B, then $\overset{-1}{f}(B')$ (the set of elements $x \in A$ such that $f(x) \in B'$) is a submonoid of A.*

The first assertion follows immediately from the definitions. Let B' be a submonoid of B; since $f(e_A) = e_B \in B'$, we have $e_A \in \overset{-1}{f}(B')$; if a, b are in $\overset{-1}{f}(B')$, then $f(a)$ and $f(b)$ are in B', whence $f(a \tau b) = f(a) \tau f(b) \in B'$ and $a \tau b \in \overset{-1}{f}(B')$; this proves that $\overset{-1}{f}(B')$ is a submonoid of A. Let S be a subset of A and A' the submonoid generated by S. Then $f(A')$ is a submonoid of B and contains $f(S)$. Let B' be any submonoid of B containing $f(S)$; then $\overset{-1}{f}(B')$ is a submonoid of A and obviously contains S. Since A' is the *smallest* submonoid of A containing S, we have $A' \subset \overset{-1}{f}(B')$, which means that

$f(A') \subset B'$. This shows that $f(A')$ is the smallest submonoid of B containing $f(S)$, i. e. that it is generated by $f(S)$.

Theorem 7. *Let f and f' be homomorphisms of a monoid A into a monoid B, and let S be a set of generators of A. If we have $f(s) = f'(s)$ for all $s \in S$, then we have $f = f'$.*

For, let A' be the set of *all* elements a of A such that $f(a) = f'(a)$. Then A' contains S. We shall see that A' is a submonoid of A. If e is the neutral element of A, then $f(e)$ and $f'(e)$ are both equal to the neutral element of B, whence $e \in A'$. If a and a' are elements of A', we have

$$f(a \top a') = f(a) \top f(a') = f'(a) \top f'(a') = f'(a \top a'),$$

whence $a \top a' \in A'$, and A' is stable. Thus, A' is a submonoid. Since $S \subset A'$, we have $A' = A$, whence $f' = f$.

Corresponding to the classification of mappings, we have a classification of homomorphisms. A homomorphism which is injective is called a *monomorphism*; a homomorphism which is surjective is called an *epimorphism*.

Theorem 8. *Let f be a homomorphism of A into B. If f is a bijection, then $\overset{-1}{f}$ is a homomorphism of B into A.*

For, since $f(e_A) = e_B$, we have $\overset{-1}{f}(e_B) = e_A$. Let c and d be elements of B, and set $a = \overset{-1}{f}(c)$, $b = \overset{-1}{f}(d)$. Then, since $c = f(a)$, $d = f(b)$, we have $c \top d = f(a \top b)$, whence $a \top b = \overset{-1}{f}(c \top d)$ and $\overset{-1}{f}$ is a homomorphism.

A homomorphism which is a bijection is called an *isomorphism*. If there exists an isomorphism of A with B, then A and B are said to be isomorphic to each other.

A homomorphism of a monoid A into itself is called an *endomorphism* of A; if it is an isomorphism of A with itself, it is called an *automorphism* of A.

The set of all endomorphisms of a monoid A is a submonoid of the set of all mappings of A into itself, under the law of composition $\circ$.

Theorem 9. *Any homomorphism f of A into B may be represented in the form $g \circ h$, where h is an epimorphism of A into a monoid B' and g a monomorphism of B' into B.*

The set $f(A) = B'$ is a submonoid of B (theorem 5); thus we may take for h the mapping f itself, considered as a mapping of A into B', and for g the identity mapping of B' into B.

Theorem 10. *Let f be a homomorphism of A into B. Assume that there exists a mapping g of B into A with the following properties: $g \circ f$ is the* *identity mapping of A and $f \circ g$ is the identity mapping of B. Then f is an isomorphism of A with B.*

If a and b are elements of A such that $f(a) = f(b)$, then we have $a = (g \circ f)(a) = g(f(a)) = g(f(b)) = (g \circ f)(b) = b$, or $a = b$: this proves that f is an injection. Let c be any element of B: if we set $x = g(c)$, then we have $f(x) = f(g(c)) = (f \circ g)(c) = c$, or $f(x) = c$, which shows that f is a surjection.

Let A be a monoid; assume that we have a bijection f of A on a certain set B. Then we may (in a unique manner) define a law of composition in B such that B, with this law of composition, becomes a monoid, and f is an isomorphism of A with this monoid. For, if b and b' are any two elements of B, we *define* their composite $b \top b'$ to be $f(a \top a')$, where a and a' are the elements of A such that $f(a) = b$, $f(a') = b'$. It is then easy to check that this law of composition defines a monoid on B and that f is an isomorphism of A with this monoid.

Let A, B and C be monoids and f a homomorphism of A into C. Let φ be a homomorphism of A into B. Then we say that φ is right-factorable in f if there exists a homomorphism ψ of B into C such that $f = \psi \circ \varphi$. Similarly, a homomorphism θ of B into C is said to be left-factorable in f if there exists a homomorphism ζ of A into B such that $f = \theta \circ \zeta$.

Diagrams. It is often convenient to represent a system of various homomorphisms by a diagram in which the monoids which occur are represented by dots and a homomorphism of, say, A into B by an arrow pointing from the representative dot of A towards the representative dot of B. Thus

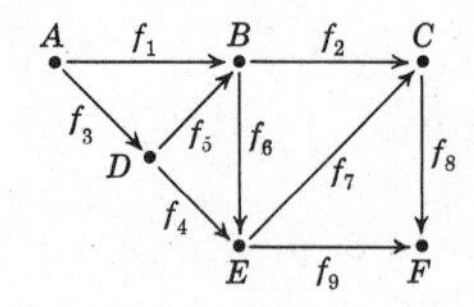

is such a diagram.

Assume that we have a diagram. To every path leading from one monoid, say K, of the diagram to another one, say L, there is associated a homomorphism of K into L, obtained by composing together the homomorphisms corresponding to the arrows of which the path is composed. For instance, in the preceding diagram f_1, $f_5 \circ f_3$ are homomorphisms of A into B; $f_2 \circ f_1$, $f_2 \circ f_5 \circ f_3$, $f_7 \circ f_4 \circ f_3$ are homomorphisms of A into C, etc.

A diagram is called commutative if, for any two paths leading from each monoid A in the diagram to any monoid B, the resulting homomorphisms of A into B are identical.

4. Quotient monoids

Let A be any set. By a *quotient* of the set A, we mean a set Q which has the following properties:

a) The elements of B are non empty subsets of the set A;

b) Two distinct elements of B are disjoint subsets of A;

c) Every element of A belongs to one (and only one, in virtue of *b*) subset belonging to B.

This is just another name for the notion of a partition of A into mutually exclusive, non empty subsets. If Q is a quotient set of A, then there is a mapping π of A into Q which assigns to every element $a \in A$ the (unique) element q of Q such that $a \in q$; π is called the *natural mapping* of A into Q; this mapping is clearly a surjection.

Now, let A be a monoid. A monoid Q is called a *quotient monoid* of A if the following conditions are satisfied:

a) The set of elements of Q is a quotient set of A;

b) The natural mapping of A on Q is a homomorphism.

Let f be a homomorphism of A into a monoid B. Then, for any element b belonging to $f(A)$, $\overset{-1}{f}(b)$ is a non empty subset of A. If b and b' are distinct elements of $f(A)$, then an element $a \in \overset{-1}{f}(b)$ is distinct from an element $a' \in \overset{-1}{f}(b')$, since $f(a) = b \neq b' = f(a')$. Thus the sets $\overset{-1}{f}(b)$ are mutually disjoint. Finally, any element $a \in A$ belongs to one of these sets, for, if $b = f(a)$, then a belongs to $\overset{-1}{f}(b)$. Thus, the sets $\overset{-1}{f}(b)$, for $b \in f(A)$, form a quotient set Q of A. Let π be the natural mapping of A on Q. We shall see that f may be factored in the form

$$f = g \circ \pi$$

where g is an injection of Q into B. We define g as follows: any element q of Q is a set of the form $\overset{-1}{f}(b)$, where b is some element of $f(A)$, and b is the image under f of any element of the set q; we set $g(q) = b$. It is then clear that $f = g \circ \pi$. If q, q' are distinct elements of Q, then $q = \overset{-1}{f}(b)$, $q' = \overset{-1}{f}(b')$, where b and b' are distinct elements of $f(A)$; it follows that $g(q) \neq g(q')$, which shows that g is an injection.

The set $g(Q)$ is obviously identical with $f(A)$, which is a submonoid of B; g is a bijection of Q on $f(B)$. Thus, it is possible to define a law of composition in Q in such a way that Q becomes a monoid and g an isomorphism of this monoid with the submonoid $f(A)$ of B. We shall see that the monoid defined in this manner is a quotient monoid of A. It suffices to check that π is a homomorphism. Let a and a' be elements of A; then we have

$$g(\pi(a\tau a')) = f(a\tau a') = f(a)\tau f(a') = g(\pi(a)\tau\pi(a'))$$

since g is a homomorphism; g being an injection, it follows that $\pi(a\tau a') = \pi(a)\tau\pi(a')$. On the other hand, if e is the neutral element of A, then $f(e) = g(\pi(e))$ is the neutral element of $f(A)$; and, since g is an isomorphism, $\pi(e)$ is the neutral element of Q. This completes the proof that Q is a quotient monoid. We shall say that it is *the quotient monoid associated with the homomorphism* f. We have proved

Theorem 11. *Any homomorphism f of a monoid A into a monoid B may be represented in the form $f = g \circ \pi$, where π is the natural homomorphism of A on the quotient monoid Q determined by f, while g is a monomorphism of Q into B.*

It should be observed that, if Q is any quotient monoid of A, then Q is identical to the quotient monoid associated with the natural homomorphism of A onto Q.

Let A be a monoid, Q a quotient *set* of A and π the natural mapping of A onto Q. Then it is not always possible to define a law of composition in Q relative to which Q becomes a quotient monoid of A. But, if it is possible, then it is possible in only one way. For, let q and q' be elements of Q, a an element of q and a' an element of q'; if τ is a law of composition in Q relative to which Q is a quotient monoid, then, since $q = \pi(a)$, $q' = \pi(a')$, we must have $q\tau q' = \pi(a\tau a')$, i. e. $q\tau q'$ must be the (uniquely determined) set of Q which has $a\tau a'$ as an element, which shows that $q\tau q'$ is uniquely determined. At the same time, we see a necessary condition for our problem to have a solution, namely the following: *If q and q' are sets of Q, then all elements $a\tau a'$ formed by taking the composite (in A) of any element a of q with any element a' of q' must lie in one and the same set of Q.*

We shall now prove that this condition is not only necessary but also sufficient. Assume that it is satisfied. Then, given sets q and q' belonging to Q, *define* $q\tau q'$ to be the subset of Q which contains all the elements $a\tau a'$ for a in q and a' in q'. We obtain in this way a law of composition in Q relative to which, we assert, Q is a quotient monoid of A. Indeed, if a and a' are any elements of A, we have $\pi(a\tau a') = \pi(a)\tau\pi(a')$; for, if $\pi(a) = q$, $\pi(a') = q'$, then a belongs to q, a' belongs to q', whence $a\tau a' \in q\tau q'$, and therefore $\pi(a\tau a') = q\tau q'$. Let q, q', q'' be elements of Q; select elements a, a', a'' of A belonging to q, q', q'' respectively. Then we have

$$(q\tau q')\tau q'' = \pi((a\tau a')\tau a'') \quad \text{and} \quad q\tau(q'\tau q'') = \pi(a\tau(a'\tau a''));$$

since $(a\tau a')\tau a'' = a\tau(a'\tau a'')$, we have $(q\tau q')\tau q'' = q\tau(q'\tau q'')$, which shows that the law τ in Q is associative. Let ε be the element $\pi(e)$; if q is any element of Q, and a an element of q, then $\varepsilon\tau q = \pi(e\tau a) = \pi(a) = q$, and we see in the same way that $q\tau\varepsilon = q$; thus ε is a neutral element for the law τ, and this law makes a monoid out of the set Q. We have $\pi(e) = \varepsilon$ and

$\pi(a\tau a') = \pi(a)\tau\pi(a')$ for any $a, a' \in A$; thus π is a homomorphism, and Q a quotient monoid. This completes the proof of the sufficiency of our condition.

5. Products

Let A and B be monoids, in both of which the law of composition is denoted by τ. Consider the set $A \times B$ of all ordered pairs (a, b), with $a \in A$ and $b \in B$. We define a law of composition, also denoted by τ, in $A \times B$ by the formula

$$(a, b)\tau(a', b') = (a\tau a', b\tau b').$$

If e_A and e_B are the neutral elements in A and in B, then (e_A, e_B) is the neutral element for the law of composition on $A \times B$. Moreover, it is immediate that this law of composition is associative. It endows $A \times B$ with the structure of a monoid; this monoid is called the *product* of the monoids A and B.

The mappings of $A \times B$ into A and B which map any pair (a, b) upon its first term a and its second term b are called respectively the *first* and the *second* projection of $A \times B$. They are obviously epimorphisms of $A \times B$ on A and on B.

Let A, B and C be monoids. Then there is a natural bijection φ of $(A \times B) \times C$ on $A \times (B \times C)$ defined by

$$\varphi(((a, b), c)) = (a, (b, c)) \quad (a \in A, b \in B, c \in C).$$

It is clear that φ is an isomorphism of $(A \times B) \times C$ with $A \times (B \times C)$. It is often convenient not to distinguish between the elements of $(A \times B) \times C$ and their images under φ in $A \times (B \times C)$. When this is done, the elements $((a, b), c)$ and $(a, (b, c))$ are both represented by the symbol (a, b, c). However, it is worth observing that, by so doing, the terms "first projection" and "second projection" become ambiguous; for, the first projection of $((a, b),c)$ is (a, b), while that of $(a, (b, c))$ is a.

Similar considerations would apply for any finite number of monoids, instead of 2. But we may go further. Let $(A_i)_{i \in I}$ be any family of monoids, indexed by indices belonging to a set I. Then the product $\prod_{i \in I} A_i$ of the sets A_i is by definition the set of all families $(a_i)_{i \in I}$ indexed by the set I such that $a_i \in A_i$ for all $i \in I$. (The case of the product of two sets is the case in which I has only 2 elements.) Now, we may define a law of composition in $\prod_{i \in I} A_i$ by the formula

$$(a_i)_{i \in I}\tau(b_i)_{i \in I} = (a_i\tau b_i)_{i \in I}.$$

We verify immediately that $\prod_{i \in I} A_i$ becomes a monoid under this law of composition with neutral element $(e_i)_{i \in I}$ where e_i is the neutral element of A_i for each $i \in I$. For each $j \in I$ there is a mapping π_j of $\prod_{i \in I} A_i$ into A_j which maps any family $(a_i)_{i \in I}$ belonging to the product upon its term a_j of index j; π_j is called the *projection of index j* of the product. It is obviously an epimorphism of $\prod_{i \in I} A_i$ upon A_j.

Let there be given a partition of the set I into mutually disjoint sets J_k, k running over a set K. Let $B_k = \prod_{i \in J_k} A_i$. If $(a_i)_{i \in I}$ is any element of $\prod_{i \in I} A_i$, set $\varphi_k((a_i)_{i \in I}) = (a_i)_{i \in J_k}$ and

$$\varphi((a_i)_{i \in I}) = (\varphi_k((a_i)_{i \in I}))_{k \in K}.$$

Then φ is a mapping of $\prod_{i \in I} A_i$ into $\prod_{k \in K} B_k$. It is easily checked that φ is actually an isomorphism of the first of these monoids with the second; we leave it to the reader to provide a complete proof of this fact.

Theorem 12. *Let f be a mapping of a monoid M into the product $A = \prod_{i \in I} A_i$ of the monoids A_i. Denote by π_i the projection of index i of A. In order for f to be a homomorphism, it is necessary and sufficient that, for each j, $\pi_j \circ f$ should be a homomorphism of M into A_j. Conversely, let there be given for each $j \in I$ a homomorphism θ_j of M into A_j. Then there exists a unique homomorphism θ of M into A such that $\pi_j \circ \theta = \theta_j$ for every $j \in J$.*

If f is a homomorphism, then so is $\pi_j \circ f$, since it is a composite of homomorphisms. Assume conversely that each $\pi_j \circ f$ is a homomorphism. Let μ and μ' be elements of M. Then $f(\mu)$ and $f(\mu')$ are families whose terms of index i are $(f(\mu))_i = (\pi_i \circ f)(\mu)$ and $(f(\mu'))_i = (\pi_i \circ f)(\mu')$. The term of index i of $f(\mu\tau\mu')$ is $(\pi_i \circ f)(\mu\tau\mu') = (\pi_i \circ f)(\mu)\tau(\pi_i \circ f)(\mu') = (f(\mu))_i\tau(f(\mu'))_i$. Moreover, if e_M is the neutral element of M, then, for each i, the term of index i of $f(e_M)$ is $(\pi_i \circ f)(e_M)$, which is the neutral element of A_i; this shows that $f(e_M)$ is the neutral element of A; f is therefore a homomorphism.

Now, let the homomorphisms θ_j be given. For each $\mu \in M$, $(\theta_i(\mu))_{i \in I}$ is a family belonging to $\prod_{i \in I} A_i$; denote this family by $\theta(\mu)$. Then θ is a mapping of M into A, and, for each j, we have $\pi_j \circ \theta = \theta_j$. Since each θ_j is a homomorphism, it follows from the first part of the proof that θ is a homomorphism. If θ is any homomorphism of M into A such that $\pi_j \circ \theta = \theta_j$, then, for any element μ in M, $\theta(\mu)$ is a family whose term of index i is $\theta_i(\mu)$; hence $\theta(\mu) = (\theta_i(\mu))_{i \in I}$ and so θ is unique.

For any fixed index j, let ψ_j be the mapping of A_j into $\prod_{i \in I} A_i$ which assigns to any element $a_j \in A_j$ the family $(b_i)_{i \in I}$ whose term of index j is a_j, while, for any $i \neq j$, b_i is the neutral element of A_i. Then ψ_j is an injection of A_j into $\prod_{i \in I} A_i$, and it is moreover a monomorphism. The mapping $\pi_j \circ \psi_j$ is the identity mapping of A_j onto itself. We call ψ_j the *natural injection* of A_j into $\prod_{i \in I} A_i$.

The set of elements $(a_i)_{i\in I}$ of the product $\prod_{i\in I}A_i$ with the property that, except for at most a finite number of indices i, a_i is the neutral element of A_i, is clearly a submonoid of the product. It is called the *weak product* of the monoids A_i, and is denoted by $\prod^w_{i\in I}A_i$ In case I is finite, the weak product coincides with the product. The submonoids $\psi_j(A_j)$ are all contained in the weak product.

If j and j' are distinct elements of I, any element of $\psi_j(A_j)$ commutes with any element of $\psi_{j'}(A_{j'})$. For, let a_j, $a_{j'}$ be in A_j, $A_{j'}$ respectively, and set $\psi_j(a_j) = (b_i)_{i\in I}$, $\psi_{j'}(a_{j'}) = (b'_i)_{i\in I}$. Then, since $j \neq j'$, for any $i \in I$, at least one of b_i, b'_i is the neutral element of A_i, which shows that $b_i\tau b'_i = b'_i\tau b_i$. It follows that $(b_i)_{i\in I}$ commutes with $(b'_i)_{i\in I}$.

Theorem 13. *Let N be a commutative monoid, whose law of composition is additive. Let there be given for each j a homomorphism θ_j of a monoid A_j into N; denote by ψ_j the natural injection of A_j into the weak product $A^w = \prod^w_{i\in I}A_i$. Then there exists a unique homomorphism θ of A^w into N such that $\theta\circ\psi_j = \theta_j$ for every j; θ maps the element $(a_i)_{i\in I}$ of A^w upon $\sum_{i\in I}\theta_i(a_i)$.*

Let $a = (a_i)_{i\in I}$ be any element of A^w; for any j, denote by α_j the element $(\psi_j\circ\pi_j)(a)$ of A^w: its term of index j is a_j, while, for $i \neq j$, its term of index i is the neutral element e_i of A_i. There is by assumption a finite subset I' of I such that $a_i = e_i$ for all i not in I'. Let $i(1), \cdots, i(n)$ be the distinct elements of I', numbered in an arbitrary manner by the integers from 1 to n. We shall see that $\alpha_{i(1)}\tau\cdots\tau\alpha_{i(n)} = a$. Since the projection π_i of index i is a homomorphism, it is sufficient to prove that, for each i,

$$a_i = \pi_i(a) = \pi_i(\alpha_{i(1)})\tau\cdots\tau\pi_i(\alpha_{i(n)}).$$

If i is not in I', then $a_i = e_i$ and $\pi_i(\alpha_{i(1)}) = \cdots = \pi_i(\alpha_{i(n)}) = e_i$ since i is distinct from $i(1), \cdots, i(n)$. If $i \in I'$, then there exists a unique k $(1 \leqslant k \leqslant n)$ such that $i = i(k)$. We then have $\pi_i(\alpha_{i(k)}) = a_i$ but $\pi_i(\alpha_{i(k')}) = e_i$ if $k \neq k'$. In both cases, our formula is true. This being so, assume that there exists a homomorphism θ with the required properties. Then we have

$$\theta(a) = \sum^n_{k=1}\theta(\alpha_{i(k)}) = \sum^n_{k=1}(\theta\circ\psi_{i(k)})(a_{i(k)}).$$

On the other hand, if i is not in I', then $a_i = e_i$, $\psi_i(a_i)$ is the neutral element of A_i and $(\theta\circ\psi_i)(a_i) = 0$. It follows that $\theta(a) = \sum_{i\in I}(\theta\circ\psi_i)(a_i) = \sum_{i\in I}\theta_i(a_i)$, which shows that θ is uniquely determined.

Now, for each $a \in A^w$, the sum $\sum_{i\in I}\theta_i(a_i)$ is defined, since, for all but a finite number of indices i, $a_i = e_i$, whence $\theta_i(a_i) = 0$. Denote the value of this sum by $\theta(a)$. Then θ is a mapping of A^w into N. Let $a = (a_i)_{i\in I}$ and $a' = (a'_i)_{i\in I}$ be elements of A^w. Then

$$\theta(a\tau a') = \sum_{i\in I}\theta_i(a_i\tau a'_i) = \sum_{i\in I}(\theta_i(a_i) + \theta_i(a'_i)) = \sum_{i\in I}\theta_i(a_i) + \sum_{i\in I}\theta_i(a'_i)$$

(cf. formula (1), Sect. 1). This shows that $\theta(a\tau a') = \theta(a) + \theta(a')$. It is clear that θ maps the neutral element of A^w upon 0; it is therefore a homomorphism.

Remarks on terminology. In a product $\prod_{i\in I} A_i$, any element a is a family $(a_i)_{i\in I}$. The terms of this family are also called the *coordinates* of a. Thus: coordinate of index i of a = image of a under the projection of index i. If a is any element of $\prod^w_{i\in I} A_i$, the elements $\psi_i(\pi_i(a))$ are also called the *components* of a. Thus, if each A_i is a commutative additive monoid, then we may say that any element of A^w is the sum of its components.

6. Free monoids

Let S be any set. Assume that we are given a monoid F and a mapping ψ of S into F. We shall say that F (together with ψ) is a *free monoid on the set S* if the following condition is satisfied:

If φ is any mapping of S into any monoid A, then there exists a unique homomorphism f of F into A such that $f \circ \psi = \varphi$:

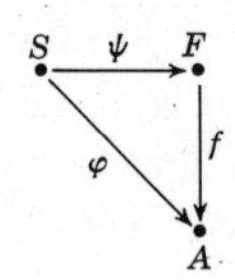

Assume that this is the case. We shall see that $\psi(S)$ is a set of generators of F. For, let F' be the submonoid of F generated by $\psi(S)$. Then, considering the mapping ψ of S into F', we see that there exists a homomorphism f of F into F' such that $f \circ \psi = \psi$. We may consider f as a homomorphism of F into F; but we have also $I \circ \psi = \psi$ if I is the identity mapping of F on itself. By the uniqueness requirement in our condition, we have $f = I$, whence $F' = F$. Moreover, the notation being as in the condition above, $f(F)$ is the submonoid of A generated by the set $\varphi(S)$. For, since F is generated by $\psi(S)$, $f(F)$ is generated by $f(\psi(S)) = (f \circ \psi)(S) = \varphi(S)$ (theorem 6, Sect. 3). In particular, if $\varphi(S)$ is a set of generators of A, then f is an epimorphism.

Theorem 14. *Assume that (F, ψ) and (F', ψ') are free monoids on the same set S; then F and F' are isomorphic. More precisely, there exists a unique isomorphism J of F with F' such that $J \circ \psi = \psi'$.*

There corresponds to the mapping ψ' of S into F' a unique homomorphism J of F into F' such that $J \circ \psi = \psi'$. Similarly, there corresponds to ψ a homomorphism J' of F' into F such that $J' \circ \psi' = \psi$. It follows that $J' \circ (J \circ \psi) = J' \circ \psi' = \psi$, i. e. $(J' \circ J) \circ \psi = \psi$, which means that $(J' \circ J)(x) = x$ for any element $x \in \psi(S)$. Let I be the identity mapping of F into itself, which is a homomorphism of F into F; then $(J' \circ J)(x) = I(x)$ for all $x \in \psi(S)$. Since $\psi(S)$ generates F, we have $J' \circ J = I$ by theorem 7, Sect. 3. We see in the same way that $J \circ J'$ is the identity mapping I' of F' onto itself. Then, it follows from theorem 10, Sect. 3, that J is an isomorphism of F with F'.

We shall now prove that there exists at least one free monoid on S by actually constructing one. Let F_0 be the set of all finite sequences of elements of S (including the empty sequence, which we shall denote by σ_0). We shall define a law of composition τ in F_0 as follows. If $\sigma = (a_1, \cdots, a_m)$ and $\sigma' = (b_1, \cdots, b_n)$ are finite sequences of elements of S, we denote by $\sigma\tau\sigma'$ the sequence $(c_1, \cdots, c_{m+n})$, where

$$c_1 = a_1, \cdots, c_m = a_m, c_{m+1} = b_1, \cdots, c_{m+n} = b_n.$$

Thus we have $\sigma_0\tau\sigma = \sigma\tau\sigma_0 = \sigma$ for any sequence σ, so that σ_0 is a neutral element for our law of composition. Now, let

$$\sigma = (a_1, \cdots, a_m), \sigma' = (b_1, \cdots, b_n), \sigma'' = (c_1, \cdots, c_p)$$

be finite sequences of elements of S; then it is easily verified that $(\sigma\tau\sigma')\tau\sigma''$ and $\sigma\tau(\sigma'\tau\sigma'')$ are both equal to the sequence $(d_1, \cdots, d_{m+n+p})$, where

$$d_1 = a_1, \cdots, d_m = a_m, d_{m+1} = b_1, \cdots, d_{m+n} = b_n,$$
$$d_{m+n+1} = c_1, \cdots, d_{m+n+p} = c_p.$$

This shows that our law of composition endows F_0 with the structure of a monoid.

If $a \in S$, denote by $\psi_0(a)$ the sequence with a single term a. Then ψ_0 is a mapping of S into F_0.

Let φ be any mapping of S into a monoid B. If $\sigma = (a_1, \cdots, a_n)$ is any finite sequence of elements of S, define $f_0(\sigma)$ to be the composite in B of the sequence $(\varphi(a_1), \cdots, \varphi(a_n))$:

$$f_0(\sigma) = \varphi(a_1)\tau \cdots \tau\varphi(a_n).$$

Then it follows immediately from the general associativity theorem that we have $f_0(\sigma\tau\sigma') = f_0(\sigma)\tau f_0(\sigma')$ for any two finite sequences σ, σ' in F_0. On the other hand, the neutral element of F_0 is the empty sequence σ_0, and, by definition, $f_0(\sigma_0)$ is the neutral element of B. Thus, f_0 is a homomorphism of F_0 into B. If $a \in S$, then $\psi_0(a)$ is the sequence (a), and $f_0(\psi_0(a))$ is the element $\varphi(a)$, whence $f_0 \circ \psi_0 = \varphi$. Moreover, it is clear that f_0 is the only homomorphism f of F_0 into A such that $f \circ \psi_0 = \varphi$. This proves that (F_0, ψ_0) is a free monoid on S.

Obviously, ψ_0 is an injection of S into F. From this, and from theorem 14, it follows immediately that, for any free monoid (F, ψ) on S, ψ is an injection.

Theorem 15. *Let A be any monoid and S a set of generators of A. Then every element of A may be written as the composite of a finite sequence of elements of S. If (F, ψ) is a free monoid on S, then A is isomorphic to a quotient monoid of A.*

Using the same notation as above, there is a homomorphism f_0 of F_0 into A such that $f_0 \circ \psi_0$ is the identity mapping of S into A. Since S generates A, f_0 is an epimorphism. Thus, for every $a \in A$, there is a finite sequence $\sigma = (a_1, \cdots, a_n)$ such that $a = f_0(\sigma)$. Using the definition of f_0, we see that a is the composite $a_1 \tau \cdots \tau a_n$. If (F, ψ) is a free monoid on S, then there is an epimorphism f of F on A. Let Q be the quotient monoid associated with f and π the natural homomorphism of A on Q; then we know that $f = g \circ \pi$, where g is an isomorphism of Q with $f(F) = A$; thus, A is isomorphic to Q.

Let S be any set, and (F, ψ) a free monoid on S. Consider the set Σ of all those quotient monoids Q of F which are commutative; we index this set by a set of indices I, and denote by Q_i the element of Σ of index i and by π_i the natural mapping of F on Q_i. Let C be the monoid $\prod_{i \in I} Q_i$; denote by ω_i the projection of index i of C on Q_i. Then C is commutative. For, let γ and γ' be elements of C. Then, for any index $i \in I$, we have

$$\omega_i(\gamma \tau \gamma') = \omega_i(\gamma) \tau \omega_i(\gamma') = \omega_i(\gamma') \tau \omega_i(\gamma) = \omega_i(\gamma' \tau \gamma)$$

(because Q_i is commutative); this clearly implies that C is commutative. By theorem 12, Sect. 5, there exists a homomorphism θ of F into C such that $\omega_i \circ \theta = \pi_i$ for every index i. Denote by $\bar{F}$ the submonoid $\theta(F)$ of C, and by $\bar{\psi}$ the mapping $\theta \circ \psi$ of S into $\bar{F}$.

We shall prove that, if $\bar{\varphi}$ is any mapping of S into a commutative monoid B, then there is a homomorphism $\bar{f}$ of $\bar{F}$ into B such that $\bar{f} \circ \bar{\psi} = \bar{\varphi}$. There is a homomorphism f of F into B such that $f \circ \psi = \bar{\varphi}$. Let Q be the quotient monoid associated with f; then we may write $f = g \circ \pi$, where π is the natural mapping of F on Q and g a monomorphism of Q into B. We may regard g as an isomorphism of Q with a submonoid of B; since B is commutative, so is Q, whence $Q \in \Sigma$. Let $\bar{i}$ be an index such that $Q = Q_{\bar{i}}$. The restriction of $\omega_{\bar{i}}$ to the submonoid $\bar{F}$ of C is a homomorphism $\bar{\omega}$ of $\bar{F}$ into $Q_{\bar{i}}$; set $\bar{f} = g \circ \bar{\omega}$. Then $\bar{f}$ is a homomorphism of $\bar{F}$ into B. We have

$$\bar{f} \circ \bar{\psi} = g \circ \bar{\omega} \circ \bar{\psi} = g \circ \bar{\omega} \circ \theta \circ \psi.$$

But we have $\bar{\omega} \circ \theta = \pi$ by definition of θ and $g \circ \pi = f$, whence

$$\bar{f} \circ \bar{\psi} = f \circ \psi = \bar{\varphi}.$$

Moreover, $\bar{\psi}(S)$ is a set of generators of $\bar{F}$; for, $\bar{\psi}(S) = \theta(\psi(S))$, and we know that $\psi(S)$ is a set of generators of F and that θ is an epimorphism. It follows that $\bar{f}$ is the only homomorphism of $\bar{F}$ into B such that $\bar{f} \circ \bar{\psi} = \bar{\varphi}$.

In general, we call a *free commutative monoid* on S a system formed by a commutative monoid $\overline{F}$ and a mapping $\overline{\psi}$ of S into $\overline{F}$ which has the following property:

if $\overline{\varphi}$ is any mapping of S into a commutative monoid B, then there is a unique homomorphism $\overline{f}$ of $\overline{F}$ into B such that $\overline{f} \circ \overline{\psi} = \overline{\varphi}$.

Proceeding as above, we see that this implies that $\overline{\psi}(S)$ is a set of generators of $\overline{F}$.

As in the case of free monoids, we see that, in the notation above, if $\overline{\varphi}(S)$ generates B, then $\overline{f}$ is an epimorphism. Moreover:

Theorem 14a. *Let $(\overline{F}, \overline{\psi})$ and $(\overline{F}', \overline{\psi}')$ be free commutative monoids on the same set S. Then there is an isomorphism $\overline{J}$ of $\overline{F}$ with $\overline{F}'$ such that $\overline{J} \circ \overline{\psi} = \overline{\psi}'$.*

The proof is analogous to the proof of theorem 14.

Theorem 15a. *Let A be a commutative monoid and S a set of generators of A. Then every element of A is the composite of a finite family of elements of S.*

We shall now construct another free commutative monoid on S. Let $\underline{N}$ be the additive monoid of integers $\geqslant 0$. For any $x \in S$, set $\underline{N}_x = \underline{N}$, and form the weak product $\prod_{x \in S}^{w} \underline{N}_x$. This is a commutative monoid $\overline{F}$. Let ζ_x be the natural injection of $\underline{N}$ into $\overline{F}$ corresponding to the index x; if $x \in S$, set $\overline{\psi}(x) = \zeta_x(1)$. Then $\overline{\psi}$ is a mapping of S into $\overline{F}$. Let B be any commutative monoid and $\overline{\varphi}$ a mapping of S into B. For any $x \in S$, there exists a homomorphism of $\underline{N}$ into B, say $\overline{f}_x$, which maps 1 upon $\overline{\varphi}(x)$, namely, the mapping $n \rightarrow n\overline{\varphi}(x)$ $(n \in \underline{N})$. There exists a homomorphism $\overline{f}$ of $\overline{F}$ into B such that $\overline{f} \circ \zeta_x = \overline{f}_x$ for every $x \in S$. If $x \in S$, we have

$$\overline{f}(\overline{\psi}(x)) = (\overline{f} \circ \zeta_x)(1) = \overline{f}_x(1) = \overline{\varphi}(x),$$

whence $\overline{f} \circ \overline{\psi} = \overline{\varphi}$; moreover, the homomorphism $\overline{f}$ is obviously uniquely determined by this condition. Thus we see that $(\overline{F}, \overline{\psi})$ is a free commutative monoid.

Theorem 16. *Let $(\overline{F}, \overline{\psi})$ be a free commutative monoid on S; assume that the law of composition on $\overline{F}$ is additive. Let $(a_1, \cdots, a_m)$ and $(b_1, \cdots, b_n)$ be finite sequences of elements of S; set $\bar{a}_i = \overline{\psi}(a_i)$, $\bar{b}_j = \overline{\psi}(b_j)$. If $\sum_{i=1}^{m} \bar{a}_i = \sum_{j=1}^{n} \bar{b}_j$, we have $m = n$ and, for every $x \in S$, there are exactly as many indices i such that $a_i = x$ as there are indices j such that $b_j = x$.*

We may assume that $(\overline{F}, \overline{\psi})$ is the free commutative monoid we have just constructed. Let x be any element of S; denote by π_x the projection of index x of $\overline{F} = \prod_{x \in S}^{w} \underline{N}_x$ on $\underline{N}$. This is a homomorphism; therefore, $\pi_x(\sum_{i=1}^{n} \bar{a}_i) = \sum_{i=1}^{n} \pi_x(\bar{a}_i) = \sum_{i=1}^{n} \pi_x(\overline{\psi}(a_i))$. But $\overline{\psi}(a_i) = \zeta_{a_i}(1)$, and

$$(\pi_x \circ \zeta_a)(k) = 0 \text{ if } a \neq x, \ (\pi_x \circ \zeta_a)(k) = k \text{ if } a = x$$

(for any $k \in \underline{N}$). Thus $\pi_x(\sum_{i=1}^n \bar{a}_i)$ is equal to $m_x 1 = m_x$ if m_x is the number of indices i for which $a_i = x$. Similarly, $\pi_x(\sum_{j=1}^n \bar{b}_j) = n_x$ if n_x is the number of indices j for which $b_j = x$. Thus, if $\sum_{i=1}^m a_i = \sum_{j=1}^n \bar{b}_j$, then $m_x = n_x$ for every x. But it is clear that $m = \sum_{x \in S} m_x$, $n = \sum_{x \in S} n_x$; thus we have $m = n$.

Exercises on Chapter I

1. Construct a finite number of monoids $A_1, \cdots, A_h$, each containing 4 elements, such that every monoid with 4 elements is isomorphic to one and exactly one of $A_1, \cdots, A_h$.

2. Let n be an interger > 0 and k an integer such that $0 \leqslant k < n$. Show that there exists a monoid $A_{n,k}$ with n elements, generated by a single element a, such that $na = ka$.
   Let A' be any monoid generated by a single element. Show that, if A' is infinite, then A' is isomorphic to the additive monoid of integers $\geqslant 0$ and is a free monoid on a set of one element, while, if A' is finite, there exist uniquely determined integers n, k such that $0 \leqslant k < n$ and A' is isomorphic to $A_{n,k}$.

3. *a*) Prove that there exists a countable set of monoids A_n ($n = 1, 2, \cdots$) such that every finite monoid is isomorphic to at least one of the monoids $A_1, \cdots, A_n \cdots$.
   b) Let A be a monoid with a finite set of generators. Show that the set of distinct finite quotient monoids of A is countable [use part *a*].
   c) Show by an example that there exists a monoid A with a countable set of generators such that the set of quotient monoids of A is not countable.

4. Let $(A_i)_{i \in I}$ be a family of monoids, A the product of the monoids A_i and A^w their weak product; let ψ_i be the natural injection of A_i into A^w. Show that the union of the sets $\psi_i(A_i)$ is a set of generators of A^w.

5. Generalize theorem 13 to the case where it is not assumed that N is commutative, but only that, for any two distinct indices j and j', every element of $\theta_j(A_j)$ commutes with every element of $\theta_{j'}(A_{j'})$.

6. An ordering for a set A is defined to be a subset Ω of $A \times A$ which satisfies the following conditions : if a, b, c are elements of A such that $(a, b) \in \Omega$ and $(b, c) \in \Omega$, then (a, c) is in Ω; if (a, b) is in Ω, then (b, a)

is not in Ω. An ordered monoid is defined to be a monoid A, given together with an ordering set Ω for A which satisfies the following condition: if a, b, c are elements of A such that $(a, b) \in \Omega$, then we have $(a\tau c, b\tau c) \in \Omega$ and $(c\tau a, c\tau b) \in \Omega$. Prove that, if A is furthermore assumed to be finite, then Ω must be empty. [Let A_k be the composite of k elements equal to a and B_h the composite of h elements equal to b; show that, if $(a, b) \in \Omega$, then $(A_k\tau B_{n-k}, A_{k-1}\tau B_{n-k+1}) \in \Omega$ if $0 < k \leqslant n$.]

7. Let $\underline{N}^*$ be the multiplicative monoid of integers > 0. Prove that $\underline{N}^*$ is isomorphic to the weak product of a countable family of monoids all identical to the additive monoid $\underline{N}$ of integers $\geqslant 0$ [use the decomposition of an integer into prime numbers].

CHAPTER II

Groups

1. Definition of a group

An element s of a monoid A is called invertible if there exists an element s' of A such that $s \tau s' = s' \tau s = e$ (were e is the neutral element). In that case, there is only one element s' with this property. For, assume that $s \tau s'' = e$; then

$$s'' = (s' \tau s) \tau s'' = s' \tau (s \tau s'') = s'.$$

The element s' is called the inverse of S.

If A is multiplicative, then the inverse of an invertible element s is denoted by s^{-1}; if A is additive, it is denoted by $-s$.

EXAMPLES: *a*) In any monoid A, the neutral element is invertible.

b) If s is any invertible element of A, and s' its inverse, then s' is invertible, and its inverse is s. Thus, if A is multiplicative, we have $(s^{-1})^{-1} = s$, and, if A is additive, $-(-s) = s$.

c) Let S be any set; then the set M of mappings of S into itself is a monoid (under the law of composition $(f, g) \to f \circ g$). The invertible elements of this monoid are the bijections of S on itself (which are also called permutations of S). If f is a permutation of S, then its inverse is $\overset{-1}{f}$.

d) In the monoid of integers under addition, every element is invertible; in the monoid of integers under multiplication, the only invertible elements are $+1$ and -1; in the monoid of rational numbers under multiplication, the invertible elements are all rational numbers $\neq 0$.

Theorem 1. *If s and t are invertible elements of a monoid A, and s', t' their inverses, then $s \tau t$ is invertible and its inverse is $t' \tau s'$.*

Let e be the neutral element. Then we have

$$(t' \tau s') \tau (s \tau t) = t' \tau (s' \tau s) \tau t = t' \tau e \tau t = t' \tau t = e$$

and we see in the same way that $(s \tau t) \tau (t' \tau s') = e$.

It follows immediately from this, by induction on n, that, if $s_1, \cdots, s_n$ are invertible elements of A, and $s'_1, \cdots, s'_n$ their inverses, then $s_1 \tau \cdots \tau s_n$ is invertible and its inverse is $s'_n \tau \cdots \tau s'_1$.

If A is a multiplicative monoid, then theorem 1 gives the formula $(st)^{-1} = t^{-1}s^{-1}$ (if s and t are invertible); if A is additive, then

$$-(s + t) = (-t) + (-s).$$

Theorem 2. *Let s be an invertible element of a monoid A, and s' its inverse. Then, if a is any element of A, each one of the equations $x\tau s = a$, $s\tau y = b$ has a unique solution; the solution is $x = a\tau s'$ for the first equation, $y = s'\tau b$ for the second equation.*

We have $(a\tau s')\tau s = a\tau(s'\tau s) = a\tau e = a$, and similarly $s\tau(s'\tau b) = b$. Conversely, assume that x is an element such that $x\tau s = a$; then

$$x = x\tau(s\tau s') = (x\tau s)\tau s' = a\tau s',$$

and $a\tau s'$ is the only solution of our first equation. We see in the same way that $s'\tau b$ is the only solution of the second equation.

If s is an invertible element of an additive monoid A, then $a + (-s)$ is also denoted by $a - s$. Thus we have $(a - s) + s = a$. On the other hand, the element $(-s) + a$ is denoted by $-s + a$, whence $s + (-s + a) = a$. If s and t are invertible elements of the additive monoid A, then it is easily verified that $-(s - t) = t - s$, $-(-s + t) = -t + s$.

Let A be an additive monoid and s an invertible element of A. Then we have, for any integer $n \geqslant 0$, $n(-s) = -(ns)$. This element is also denoted by $(-n)s$. Thus, for such an element, ps is now defined for every integer p. If p and q are any integers, then we have

$$(1) \qquad ps + qs = (p + q)s.$$

We know already that this is true if $p \geqslant 0$, $q \geqslant 0$. Now, assume that $p \geqslant 0$, $q \leqslant 0$, $p + q \geqslant 0$. Then $(p + q)s + (-q)s = (p + q + (-q))s = ps$, whence, by theorem 2, $(p + q)s = ps + (-(-qs)) = ps + qs$. To prove the formula in general, select an integer m such that $m \geqslant 0$, $m + p \geqslant 0$, $m + q \geqslant 0$, $m + p + q \geqslant 0$. Then we have

$$ms + (p + q)s = (m + p + q)s = (m + p)s + qs = ms + (ps + qs),$$

whence $(p + q)s = ps + qs$. Formula (1) means that the mapping $p \rightarrow ps$ is a homomorphism of the monoid of integers into A.

We shall also prove the formula

$$(2) \qquad p(qs) = (pq)s.$$

We know that this formula is true if p, q are $\geqslant 0$. If $p \geqslant 0$, $q < 0$, then $p(qs) = p(-(-q)s) = (p(-(-q)))s = pqs$. If p is < 0, then

$$p(qs) = -((-p)(qs)) = -(((-p)q)s) = -((-pq)s) = -(-pqs) = pqs.$$

If we assume further that A is commutative and that s, t are invertible, then we have, for any integer p, $p(s+t) = ps + pt$. We know that this is true if $p \geqslant 0$. If $p < 0$, then

$$p(s+t) = -((-p)(s+t)) = -((-p)s + (-p)t)$$
$$= -(-p)t + (-(-p)s) = pt + ps = ps + pt.$$

If s, t are invertible elements of a multiplicative monoid, then we have, for any integers p and q,

$$s^{p+q} = s^p s^q, \qquad s^{pq} = (s^p)^q,$$

and, if the monoid is commutative,

$$(st)^p = s^p t^p.$$

Let B be a submonoid of a monoid A. If an element s of B is invertible in B, then it is invertible in A, and its inverse in A is the same as its inverse in B. However, an element s of B may well be invertible in A without being invertible in B.

Let G be the set of all invertible elements of a monoid A. Then G contains the neutral element, and it follows from theorem 1 that G is a submonoid. If $s \in G$, then the inverse s' of G is invertible, whence $s' \in G$, and s' is the inverse of s in G. Thus, every element of the monoid G is invertible.

A monoid whose elements are all invertible is called a *group*.

Examples: *a*) The permutations of any set A form a group under the law of composition $(f, g) \to f \circ g$.

b) The additive monoid of integers is a group. The multiplicative monoid of rational numbers $\neq 0$ is a group.

If a group G has a finite number of elements, then the number of elements of G is also called the *order* of G.

2. Subgroups

All groups in this section will be denoted multiplicatively.

Let G be a group and H a subset of G which is a submonoid and is such that the inverse in G of any element of H lies in H. Then it is clear that any element of H is invertible and has the same inverse in H as in G; thus H is a group. We use the term *subgroup* for a group which may be defined in this manner.

Examples: *a*) Let A be a monoid. Then the set of automorphisms of A is a subgroup of the set of all permutations of A.

b) Let $\underline{Z}$ be the set of integers, and let k be any element of $\underline{Z}$. Then the set of multiples of k, i. e. the set of all elements pk, for all $p \in \underline{Z}$, is a subgroup of $\underline{Z}$. For, we have, for any p, q in $\underline{Z}$, $pk + qk = (p + q)k$, $-pk = (-p)k$, and we have $0 \cdot k = 0$.

c) Let S be a set, and S' any subset of S. Then the set of permutations ϖ of S such that $\varpi(S') = S'$ is a subgroup P' of the group P of permutations of S. The set P'' of permutations ϖ such that $\varpi(x) = x$ for every $x \in S'$ is a subgroup of P'.

Theorem 3. *If* $(G_i)_{i \in I}$ *is a family of subgroups of a group* G *(with* $I \neq \emptyset$*), then* $\bigcap_{i \in I} G_i$ *is a subgroup of* G.

We know already that it is a submonoid. If s is an element of this intersection, then we have $s^{-1} \in G_i$ for every $i \in I$, and s^{-1} belongs to the intersection.

If S is any subset of a group G, then the intersection of all subgroups of G which contain the subset S is a group H, which is called the subgroup *generated by* S; we say that S is a set of generators of H. It is important to observe that the submonoid of G generated by S is contained in H, but is in general $\neq H$. However, we have the following result:

Theorem 4. *Let* S *be a subset of a group* G*; assume that the inverse of any element of* S *belongs to* S*. Then the submonoid* H *of* G *generated by* S *is a subgroup, and is the subgroup generated by* S.

For, let H' be the set of elements s of H such that $s^{-1} \in H$. Then it follows from theorem 1, Sect. 1, that H' is a submonoid of H. Since $S \subset H'$ by assumption, we have $H \subset H'$, and H is a subgroup of G. It is obvious that it is the subgroup generated by S.

Corollary. *If* H *is the subgroup of a group* G *generated by* S*, then every element of* H *is the product of a finite sequence of elements of* G *whose terms are either elements of* S *or inverses of elements of* S.

For, let S' be the set of inverses of elements of S. Then the inverse of any element of $S \cup S'$ lies in $S \cup S'$, and it follows from theorem 4 that H is the subgroup generated by $S \cup S'$. Our result therefore follows from theorem 15, Chapter I, Sect. 6.

If a is any element of a group G, the elements a^m, for all integers m, form a subgroup of G. For, a^0 is the unit element of G, we have $a^m a^n = a^{m+n}$ for any integers m and n, and $(a^m)^{-1} = a^{-m}$. This group is obviously generated by the set $\{a\}$; it is also said to be generated by the element a. Any group which is generated by a single element is called *cyclic*. If the subgroup generated by an element a is finite, then we call its order the *order of* a; if not, then we say that a is of *infinite order*.

Let G be a group, and u an element of G. Then, if an element s of G commutes with u, s^{-1} likewise commutes with u. For we have $su = us$, whence $u = s^{-1}su = s^{-1}us$, and $us^{-1} = s^{-1}uss^{-1} = s^{-1}u$. Making use of theorem 5, Chapter I, Sect. 2, we obtain

Theorem 5. *If S is any subset of a group G, the set of elements of G which commute with all elements of S is a subgroup.*

This subgroup is called the *centralizer* of S.

Corollary. *If the elements of a subset S of a group G all commute with each other, then the subgroup generated by S is commutative.*

3. Homomorphisms. Quotient groups

Here again, all groups and monoids will be denoted multiplicatively.

A mapping f of a group G into a monoid H is called a homomorphism if it is a homomorphism of the monoid G.

EXAMPLES: *a*) Let G be any group, and $\underline{Z}$ the additive group of integers. If a is any element of G, the mapping $m \to a^m$ ($m \in \underline{Z}$) is a homomorphism of $\underline{Z}$ into G.

b) Let S be a set, S' a subset of S, P the group of all those permutations ϖ of S which are such that $\varpi(S') = S'$. If $\varpi \in P$, denote by $\rho(\varpi)$ the restriction of ϖ to S'; then ρ is a homomorphism of P into the group of permutations of S'.

Theorem 6. *Let f be a homomorphism of a group G into a monoid H. Then $f(G)$ is a subgroup of H, and we have $f(s^{-1}) = (f(s))^{-1}$ for any $s \in G$.*

Let e_G and e_H be the unit elements of G and H. If $s \in G$, then we have $e_H = f(e_G) = f(ss^{-1}) = f(s)f(s^{-1})$ and also $e_H = f(s^{-1})f(s)$. Thus, $f(s)$ is invertible in H, and its inverse is $f(s^{-1})$. Since $f(G)$ is a submonoid of H (theorem 6, Chapter I, Sect. 3), theorem 6 is proved.

Corollary 1. *The notation being as in theorem 6, let S be any subset of G and L the subgroup of G generated by S. Then $f(L)$ is the submonoid of H generated by $f(S \cup S^{-1})$.*

Corollary 2. *Any quotient monoid Q of a group G is a group.* For, the natural mapping of G on Q is an epimorphism.

The quotient monoids of a group are called its *quotient groups* (or *factor groups*).

The notions of monomorphism, epimorphism, isomorphism, endomorphism, and automorphism are defined for groups in the same way as for monoids. It is clear that any group isomorphic to a finite group G is also finite, and has the same order as G. Similarly, any group isomorphic to a cyclic group is cyclic, and any group isomorphic to a commutative group is commutative.

Theorem 7. *Let f be a homomorphism of a group G into a group H, and H' a subgroup of H. Then the set $\overset{-1}{f}(H')$ is a subgroup of G.*

We know this set to be a submonoid of G. If s is any one of its elements, we have $f(s^{-1}) = (f(s))^{-1} \in H'$, whence $s^{-1} \in \overset{-1}{f}(H')$.

If f is a homomorphism of a group G into a group H, then there is associated with f a quotient group Q of G. We shall determine the elements of Q. Let e_H be the unit element of H. Then $\overset{-1}{f}(e_H)$, which is a subgroup of G by theorem 7, is also an element of Q (the elements of Q being the elements $\overset{-1}{f}(t)$, for all t in $f(G)$). The group $\overset{-1}{f}(e_H)$ is called the *kernel* of the homomorphism f. Let us denote it by G'. Now, if A is any subset of a group G and s an element of G, we denote by sA (resp.: As) the set of elements sa (resp.: as) for all $a \in A$. This being said, we shall prove

Theorem 8. *Let G' be the kernel of a homomorphism f of the group G. Then, for any $s \in G$, we have $sG' = G's = \overset{-1}{f}(f(s))$. The sets $sG' = G's$ (for all $s \in G$) are the elements of the quotient group Q of G associated with f, and the natural homomorphism π of G on Q is defined by $\pi(s) = sG' = G's$.*

Let s' be any element of $\overset{-1}{f}(s)$. Then $f(s') = f(s)$, whence $f(s^{-1}s') = e_H$, $s^{-1}s' \in G'$ and $s' = s(s^{-1}s') \in sG'$. Conversely, let t be any element of G', and $s' = st$; then $f(s') = f(s)f(t) = f(s)e_H = f(s)$, whence $s' \in \overset{-1}{f}(f(s))$. This shows that $\overset{-1}{f}(f(s)) = sG'$. An entirely similar argument shows that $\overset{-1}{f}(f(s)) = G's$. Thus the elements of Q are the sets $sG' = G's$, for all $s \in G$. If $s \in G$, we have $\pi(s) = \overset{-1}{f}(f(s)) = sG'$.

The notation being as in theorem 8, we say that the sets $sG' = G's$ (for $s \in G$) are the *cosets* of G modulo G'.

A necessary and sufficient condition for a homomorphism f of G into a group to be a monomorphism is that the kernel G' of f should contain only the unit element of G. In general, not every subgroup of G is the kernel of a homomorphism of G. A subgroup G' of G which is the kernel of some homomorphism of G is called a *normal* (or invariant, or distinguished) subgroup of G.

Let G' be a normal subgroup of G, and f a homomorphism of G whose kernel is G'. Then it follows from theorem 8 that the quotient group Q of G associated with f depends only on the group G' itself, since its elements are the cosets modulo G'. This group is called the *quotient group* (or factor group) of G by G', and is denoted by G/G'. It is clear that G' is the kernel of the natural homomorphism of G on G/G'. If two elements s and s' are in the same coset modulo G', then we say that s and s' are congruent to each other modulo G', and we write $s \equiv s' \pmod{G'}$. This relation of congruence modulo G' has the following properties:

1. *If f is any homomorphism of a group G whose kernel is G', then the condition $s \equiv s' \pmod{G'}$ is equivalent to the condition that $f(s) = f(s')$;*

2. *The conditions "$s \equiv s' \pmod{G'}$", "$s^{-1}s' \in G'$", "$s'^{-1}s \in G'$", "$s's^{-1} \in G'$", "$ss'^{-1} \in G'$" are all equivalent to each other; in particular, e being the unit element of G, the condition "$s \equiv e \pmod{G'}$" is equivalent to "$s \in G'$";*

3. *We have $s \equiv s \pmod{G'}$ for any $s \in G'$; the conditions "$s \equiv s' \pmod{G'}$"* and *"$s' \equiv s \pmod{G'}$" are equivalent to each other; if s, s', s'' are elements such that $s \equiv s' \pmod{G'}$* and *$s' \equiv s'' \pmod{G'}$, then we have $s \equiv s'' \pmod{G'}$;*

4. *If s, s', t, t' are elements of G such that $s \equiv s' \pmod{G'}$ and $t \equiv t' \pmod{G'}$, then we have $s^{-1} \equiv s'^{-1} \pmod{G'}$, $st \equiv s't' \pmod{G'}$, $st^{-1} \equiv s't'^{-1} \pmod{G'}$, $s^{-1}t \equiv s'^{-1}t' \pmod{G'}$.*

If our groups were denoted additively instead of multiplicatively, then the statements (2), (4) would read as follows:

2'. *The conditions "$s \equiv s' \pmod{G'}$," "$-s + s' \in G'$", "$-s' + s \in G'$", "$s' - s \in G'$", "$s - s' \in G'$" are all equivalent to each other; the condition "$s \equiv 0 \pmod{G'}$" is equivalent to "$s \in G'$".*

4'. *If s, s', t, t' are elements of G such that $s \equiv s' \pmod{G'}$ and $t \equiv t' \pmod{G'}$, then we have $-s \equiv -s' \pmod{G'}$, $s + t \equiv s' + t' \pmod{G'}$, $s - t \equiv s' - t' \pmod{G'}$ and $-s + t \equiv -s' + t' \pmod{G'}$.*

We shall now give a direct characterization of normal subgroups of a group G. If $s \in G$, we denote by $J(s)$ the mapping of G into itself which assigns sts^{-1} to any element $t \in G$. If s and s' are elements of G, then $J(ss') = J(s) \circ J(s')$. For, we have

$$(ss')t(ss')^{-1} = ss'ts'^{-1}s^{-1} = s(s'ts'^{-1})s^{-1} = J(s)\,(J(s')\,(t)).$$

Moreover, it is clear that, e being the unit element of G, $J(e)$ is the identity mapping of G. Thus the mapping $J : s \to J(s)$ is a homomorphism of G into the monoid of all mappings of G into itself. Making use of theorem 6, we see that, for any $s \in G$, $J(s)$ is a permutation of the set G. Moreover, $J(s)$ is an endomorphism of G; for we have, for t and t' in G,

$$s(tt')s^{-1} = stt's^{-1} = stet's^{-1} = sts^{-1}st's^{-1} = (sts^{-1})\,(st's^{-1}),$$

and $ses^{-1} = e$. It follows that $J(s)$ is an automorphism of G. Those automorphisms of G which are representable in the form $J(s)$, for some $s \in G$, are called *inner automorphisms.*

Theorem 9. *Let G' be a subgroup of G. Then the following conditions are equivalent to each other:*

a) G' is mapped into itself by any inner automorphism of G;

b) $sG' = G's$ *for any* $s \in G$;

c) G' *is a normal subgroup of* G.

Assume that *a*) is satisfied; if $s \in G$, we have, for any $t \in G'$, $sts^{-1} \in G'$, whence $st = (sts^{-1})s \in G's$, which shows that $sG' \subset G's$. We have also $s^{-1}ts = s^{-1}t(s^{-1})^{-1} \in G'$, whence $ts = s(s^{-1}ts) \in sG'$, and $G's \subset sG'$. This shows that *a*) implies *b*). Assume now that *b*) is satisfied. Then, if $t \in G'$, $s \in G$, st is an element $t's$ of $G's$ (for some $t' \in G'$), whence $sts^{-1} = t' \in G'$, and *a*) is satisfied. Moreover, we shall see that the sets sG', for all $s \in G$, form a quotient group of G. These sets are not empty; e being the unit element of G, we have $s = se \in sG'$, whence $\bigcup_{s \in G} sG' = G$. Now, let t be any element of sG'; then $t = su$, for some $u \in G'$, and, if $t' \in G'$, $tt' = s(ut')$, $ut' \in G'$, whence $tG' \subset sG'$. On the other hand, we have $s = tu^{-1}$, $u^{-1} \in G'$, whence $s \in tG'$ and therefore $sG' \subset tG'$, which shows that $sG' = tG'$. It follows that, if the sets sG', $s'G'$ (where s, s' are in G) have an element t in common, they are both identical to tG'. This shows that the sets sG', for all $s \in G$, form a quotient set Q of G'. Let sG' and $s'G'$ be two of these sets; we shall see that the product of any element st of sG' by any element $s't'$ of $s'G'$ is in $(ss')G'$; in fact, we have $sts't' = (ss')((s'^{-1}ts')t')$, and $s'^{-1}ts'$, t' are both in G', whence $(s'^{-1}ts')t' \in G'$, which proves our assertion. It follows that Q is a quotient monoid (and therefore a quotient group) of G. Let π be the natural mapping of G on Q; since $s \in sG'$ for any $s \in G$, we have $\pi(s) = sG'$; thus, $\pi(e) = G'$, whence $G' = \overset{-1}{\pi}(\bar{e})$, where $\bar{e}$ is the unit element of Q, and the kernel of π is G'. This shows that *b*) implies *a*) and *c*). We know already that *c*) implies *b*); theorem 9 is thereby proved.

Corollary. *Any intersection of normal subgroups of a group* G *is normal.* This follows immediately from condition *a*) in theorem 9.

Let G be a group. Then the intersection D of all normal subgroups G' of G such that G/G' is commutative is a normal subgroup of G. This group is called the *derived* group. It is clearly contained in the kernel of any homomorphism of G into a commutative group. Moreover, G/D is itself commutative. For, let s and t be any elements of G; then, if G' is any normal subgroup of G such that G/G' is commutative, we have $st \equiv ts \pmod{G'}$, whence $(st)^{-1}ts \in G'$. It follows that $(st)^{-1}ts \in D$, whence $st \equiv ts \pmod{D}$, which shows that G/D is commutative.

It follows immediately from theorem 9 that every subgroup of a commutative group is normal. This applies in particular to the additive group $\underline{Z}$ of integers. We shall now determine the subgroups of $\underline{Z}$.

Theorem 10. *If* G' *is any subgroup of the additive group* $\underline{Z}$ *of integers, there is a uniquely determined integer* $n \geqslant 0$ *such that* $G' = n\underline{Z}$ *consists of all multiples of* n *in* $\underline{Z}$.

The group G' contains at least one integer $m \geqslant 0$; for, if x is an element < 0 of G', then $-x$ is also in G'. Moreover, the argument shows that, if $G' \neq \{0\}$, then G' contains at least one integer which is > 0. If $G' = \{0\}$, then G' consists of all multiples of 0. If not, let n be the smallest integer > 0 belonging to G'. Then G' contains the group generated by n, which is the set of multiples of n. Conversely, let m be any integer in G'. Then it is well known that there exist integers q and r such that $m = nq + r$, $0 \leqslant r < n$. Since m and nq are in G', so is $r = m - nq$; since n is the smallest integer > 0 in G' and $0 \leqslant r < n$, we have $r = 0$, $m = nq$, and $G' = n\underline{Z}$ consists of all multiples of n. If n and n' are integers $\geqslant 0$ such that $n\underline{Z} = n'\underline{Z}$, then each of n, n' is a multiple of the other, and we know that this implies $n = n'$.

For any integer $n \geqslant 0$, the group $\underline{Z}/n\underline{Z}$ is denoted by $\underline{Z}_n$. If m and m' are any integers, and if $m \equiv m' \pmod{n\underline{Z}}$ we also write $m \equiv m' \pmod{n}$, and we say that m and m' are congruent to each other modulo n. The statement that $m \equiv m' \pmod{n}$ is equivalent to the statement that $m' - m$ is divisible by n.

Let G be any group and s any element of G. Then there is a homomorphism f of $\underline{Z}$ into G which maps any integer n upon s^n. Since $\underline{Z}$ is generated by 1, and $f(1) = s$, $f(G)$ is generated by s. The kernel of f is $n\underline{Z}$ for some uniquely determined integer $n \geqslant 0$.

If $n > 0$, then $\underline{Z}_n$ has exactly n elements. For, let m be any integer; writing m in the form $nq + r$, $0 \leqslant r < n$, we have $m \equiv r \pmod{n\underline{Z}}$, and the coset of m modulo $n\underline{Z}$ contains one of the integers $0, 1, \cdots, n-1$. It contains only one of these integers; for, if q, q' are two of these integers, and $q < q'$, then $q' - q < n$, and we can only have $q' \equiv q \pmod{n\underline{Z}}$ if $q = q'$. Thus every coset of $\underline{Z}$ modulo $n\underline{Z}$ contains exactly one of the integers $0, 1, \cdots, n-1$, which shows that $\underline{Z}_n$ has n elements. On the other hand, $\underline{Z}_0$, which is isomorphic to $\underline{Z}$, has infinitely many elements; thus, if n and n' are distinct integers $\geqslant 0$, then $\underline{Z}_n$ and $\underline{Z}_{n'}$ are not isomorphic. In any case, $f(\underline{Z})$ is isomorphic to $\underline{Z}_n$; if $n = 0$, then $f(\underline{Z})$ is isomorphic to $\underline{Z}$. We have therefore proved

Theorem 11. *If G is a cyclic group, there is a uniquely determined integer $n \geqslant 0$ such that G is isomorphic to $\underline{Z}_n$. If $n = 0$, then G is isomorphic to $\underline{Z}$ and has infinitely many elements. If $n > 0$, then G has n elements.*

Theorem 12. *Let K_1 and K_2 be normal subgroups of a group G such that $K_1 \subset K_2$; let π_i be the natural homomorphism of G onto G/K_i $(i = 1, 2)$. Then there is a uniquely determined mapping ρ of G/K_1 into G/K_2 such that $\pi_2 = \rho \circ \pi_1$; ρ is an epimorphism; K_1 is normal in K_2, and the kernel of ρ is K_2/K_1.*

Any coset $q_1 = K_1 s$ modulo K_1 is contained in a uniquely determined coset q_2 modulo K_2, namely, in $K_2 s$; we set $q_2 = \rho(q_1)$, and define in this manner a mapping ρ of G/K_1 into G/K_2. It is clear that $\pi_2 = \rho \circ \pi_1$. If ρ' is any mapping of G/K_1 into G/K_2 such that $\pi_2 = \rho' \circ \pi_1$, then, if $q_1 = K_1 s$, we have $\pi_1(s) = q_1$, whence $\rho'(q_1) = \pi_2(s) = K_2 s = \rho(q_1)$, which shows that ρ is uniquely determined. Let $q_1 = K_1 s$ and $q_1' = K_1 s'$ be elements of G/K_1. Then $q_1 = \pi_1(s)$, $q_1' = \pi_1(s')$, $q_1 q_1' = \pi_1(ss')$, whence

$$\rho(q_1 q_1') = \pi_2(ss') = \pi_2(s)\pi_2(s') = \rho(q_1)\rho(q_1'),$$

and ρ is a homomorphism. It is clear that ρ is an epimorphism. If s is any element of K_2, then we have $K_1 s = sK_1$, which shows that K_1 is normal in K_2. If $q_1 = \pi_1(s_1)$ is any element of G/K_1, a necessary and sufficient condition for $\rho(q_1)$ to be the neutral element is that $\pi_2(s_1)$ be the neutral element, i. e. that s be in K_2, which is equivalent to $q_1 = K_1 s \subset K_2$. Thus the kernel of ρ is the set of cosets modulo K_1 which are contained in K_2, i. e., it is K_2/K_1. Theorem 12 is thereby proved.

It follows from theorem 12 that K_2/K_1 is a normal subgroup of G/K_1, and that $(G/K_1)/(K_2/K_1)$ is isomorphic to G/K_2. More precisely, there is a uniquely determined isomorphism ω of $(G/K_1)/(K_2/K_1)$ with G/K_2 such that the mapping ρ of theorem 12 is equal to $\omega \circ \pi_3$, where π_3 is the natural homomorphism of G/K_1 onto $(G/K_1)/(K_2/K_1)$; ω is called the *natural isomorphism* of $(G/K_1)/(K_2/K_1)$ with G/K_2, and $\overset{-1}{\omega}$ the natural isomorphism of G/K_2 with $(G/K_1)/(K_2/K_1)$.

Theorem 13. *Let f and f' be homomorphisms of a group G into groups H, H' and let K, K' be their respective kernels. Assume that $K' \subset K$. Then there is a unique homomorphism g of $f'(G)$ into H such that $f = g \circ f'$, whence $g(f'(G)) = f(G)$, and the kernel of g is $f'(K)$.*

We may write $f = \varphi \circ \pi$ ($f' = \varphi' \circ \pi'$), where φ (resp. : φ') is an isomorphism of G/K (resp.: G/K') with $f(G)$ (resp.: $f'(G)$) and π (resp.: π') is the natural homomorphism of G on G/K (resp.: on G/K'). We may write $\pi = \rho \circ \pi'$, where ρ is the natural homomorphism of G/K' on G/K; whence

$$f = \varphi \circ \rho \circ \pi' = \varphi \circ \rho \circ \overset{-1}{\varphi'} \circ f',$$

and $\varphi \circ \rho \circ \overset{-1}{\varphi'} = g$ is a homomorphism of $f'(G)$ into H. Let g' be any homomorphism of $f'(G)$ into H such that $f = g' \circ f'$. If s is any element of G, then $g'(f'(s)) = f(s) = g(f'(s))$, whence $g = g'$. If $s \in K$, then $g(f'(s))$ is the unit element e of H; conversely, if $g(f'(s))$ is the unit element, then $f(s) = e$, whence $s \in K$, and the kernel of g is $f'(K)$. It is clear that $g(f'(G)) = f(G)$.

Theorem 14. *Let G be a group, K a normal subgroup of G and L any subgroup of G; let π be the natural homomorphism of G onto G/K. Then* *the subgroup $\overset{-1}{\pi}(\pi(L))$ of G is the set of all products st, for $s \in L$, $t \in K$; it is also the set of all products ts, for $t \in K$, $s \in L$. If π_L is the restriction of π to L, then π_L is an epimorphism of L on $\pi(L)$ whose kernel is $K \cap L$. A necessary and sufficient condition for K to be contained in L is that $L = \overset{-1}{\pi}(\pi(L))$; the mapping $L \to \pi(L)$ establishes a bijection of the set of all subgroups of G containing K on the set of all subgroups of G/K.*

We know that $\pi(L)$ is a subgroup of G/K, and therefore that $\overset{-1}{\pi}(\pi(L))$ is a subgroup of G. If $s' \in \overset{-1}{\pi}(\pi(L))$, then $\pi(s') \in \pi(L)$ and there is an element $s \in L$ such that $\pi(s) = \pi(s')$. This means that $\pi(s^{-1}s')$ is the neutral element, i. e. that $s^{-1}s' = t \in K$ and $s' = st$. Conversely, if $s \in L$, $t \in K$, then $\pi(st) = \pi(s)\pi(t) = \pi(s)$, whence $st \in \overset{-1}{\pi}(\pi(L))$, and so $\overset{-1}{\pi}(\pi(L))$ is the set of products st, $s \in L$, $t \in K$. We can see in the same way that it is the set of products ts, $t \in K$, $s \in L$. It is clear that π_L is an epimorphism of L on $\pi(L)$ whose kernel is $K \cap L$. If $L = \overset{-1}{\pi}(\pi(L))$, then any $t \in K$ belongs to $\overset{-1}{\pi}(\pi(L))$ (since $\pi(t)$ is the neutral element of G/K) and therefore to L. Conversely, if $K \subset L$, any product of an element of L by an element of K is in L, whence $\overset{-1}{\pi}(\pi(L)) = L$. If L_1, L_2 are subgroups containing K such that $\pi(L_1) = \pi(L_2)$, then $L_1 = \overset{-1}{\pi}(\pi(L_1)) = \overset{-1}{\pi}(\pi(L_2)) = L_2$. On the other hand, if M is any subgroup of G/K, then $\overset{-1}{\pi}(M) = L$ is a subgroup of G, and $\pi(L) = \pi(\overset{-1}{\pi}(M)) = M$, whence $L = \overset{-1}{\pi}(\pi(L))$ and $K \subset L$; this proves the last assertion of theorem 14.

Let K be a normal subgroup of G and L a subgroup of G. In view of the results of theorem 14, the group $\overset{-1}{\pi}(\pi(L))$ is denoted by either one of the notations KL or LK. The mapping π_L may be factored in the form $\omega \circ \pi'$, where π' is the natural homomorphism of L on $L/(K \cap L)$ and ω an isomorphism of $L/(K \cap L)$ with $\pi(L)$. Moreover, $\pi(L)$ is the set of cosets of LK modulo K, which shows that K is normal in LK, and that $\pi(L) = LK/K$. Thus, $L/(L \cap K)$ is isomorphic to LK/K; ω is called the *natural isomorphism* of $L/(L \cap K)$ with LK/K, and $\overset{-1}{\omega}$ the natural isomorphism of LK/K with $L/(L \cap K)$.

4. Groups operating on a set

Let G be a group, and E any set. Then the set P of all bijections of E on itself (i. e., of all permutations of E) is a group under the law of composition $\circ$. Assume that we are given a homomorphism φ of G into the group P; then we say that φ makes G *operate* on the set E, and we say that E, together with the mapping φ, constitutes a G-set.

EXAMPLES: *a*) Let Q^* be the group, under multiplication, of all rational numbers $\neq 0$, and Q the set of all rational numbers. For any $x \in Q^*$, denote by $\varphi(x)$ the mapping $q \to xq$ of Q into itself. Then $\varphi(1)$ is the identity mapping of Q, and, if x, y are in Q^*, we have $(xy)q = x(yq)$, whence $\varphi(xy) = \varphi(x) \circ \varphi(y)$; thus, φ makes Q^* operate on Q.

b) Let G be any group. If $s \in G$, the mapping $L(s)$ which assigns to every $t \in G$ the element st of G is called the *left translation* produced by s (or the *left translation* by s). It is easily seen that the mapping which to every $s \in G$ assigns the left translation by s is a homomorphism of G into the group of permutations of G, which makes G operate on G. Similarly, the mapping $t \to ts$ of G into itself is called the *right translation* produced by s (or the *right translation* by s), and the mapping which assigns to every $s \in G$ the right translation by s^{-1} makes G operate on G.

c) If we assign to every $s \in G$ the inner automorphism of G produced by s, we obtain a third method of making G operate on G.

d) Assume that a group G operates on a set E by means of a homomorphism φ of G into the group of permutations of E. Let $\mathfrak{E}$ be the set of all subsets of E. If A is any subset of E and s any element of G, denote by $(\Phi(s))(A)$ the set composed of all elements $(\varphi(s))(a)$, for $a \in A$; then $\Phi(s)$ is a mapping of $\mathfrak{E}$ into itself. Let s and t be in G; then, for any subset A of E, the set $(\Phi(st))(A)$ is the set of all elements $(\varphi(st))(a) = \varphi(s)((\varphi(t))(a))$ for all $a \in A$; it is therefore identical with $\Phi(s)((\Phi(t))(A))$. Moreover, if e is the unit element, then $(\Phi(e))(A) = A$, for every set $A \subset E$. Thus, the mapping $\Phi : s \to \Phi(s)$ is a homomorphism of G into the group of permutations of $\mathfrak{E}$; i. e., it makes G operate on $\mathfrak{E}$.

Let E be any set on which G operates by means of a homomorphism φ of G into the group of permutations of E. If $s \in G$ and $x \in E$, the element $(\varphi(s))(x)$ will be denoted by $s\ x$ in order to simplify the notation. Thus, we have $e \cdot x = x$ if e is the unit element, and $s \cdot (t \cdot x) = st \cdot x$ if s, $t \in G$.

Let F be any subset of E. Then the set of all elements $s \cdot x$, for $s \in G$ and $x \in F$, is called the *orbit* of F under G. If F consists of a single point x, then the orbit of F is also called the *orbit* of x.

A subset F of E is called *stable* (under G) if it is its own orbit, i. e. if we have $s \cdot x \in F$ whenever $s \in G$, $x \in F$. Similarly, a point x is said to be stable (under G), or a *fixed point* of G, if we have $s \cdot x = x$ for all $s \in G$. The orbit Ω of any set F is stable under G; for, if $x \in F$, $s \in G$, then we have, for any $t \in G$, $t \cdot (s \cdot x) = ts \cdot x \in \Omega$.

Let F be any stable subset of E. Then, if we assign to every $s \in G$ the restriction to F of the mapping $x \to s \cdot x$, we clearly obtain a homomorphism of G into the group of permutations of F, i. e. G operates on F.

We say that G operates *transitively* (or is transitive) on the set E if, given any two points x, y of E, there always exists an element s of G such that $s \cdot x = y$. We then say also that E is a *homogeneous G-set.* An equivalent formulation is that the orbit of any point of E should be the whole of E; or again, that the only stable subsets of E be the empty set and the whole of E. In order for the condition to be satisfied, it is sufficient that there should exist at least one point x_0 of E whose orbit is E. For, let then $x = s \cdot x_0$ and $y = t \cdot y_0$ be points of E; then we have

$$(ts^{-1}) \cdot x = ts^{-1} \cdot (s \cdot x_0) = t \cdot x_0 = y.$$

For instance, if we consider the group P of all permutations of E as operating on E (by means of the identity mapping of P into P), then P operates transitively. For, let x and y be any elements of E, and E_x (resp.: E_y) the set of elements $\neq x$ (resp.: $\neq y$) in E. Then it is well known that E_x and E_y are equipotent. If p' is a bijection of E_x on E_y, we may extend p' to a permutation p of E which maps x upon y.

On the other hand, any group G operates transitively upon itself by means of either left or right translations.

If G operates on a set E (not necessarily transitively), and x is any point of E, then it follows from what we have just said that G operates transitively on the orbit Ω_x of x under G. On the other hand, if x' is any point of G and if $\Omega_x \cap \Omega_{x'} \neq \emptyset$, then we have $\Omega_x = \Omega_x$. For, $\Omega_x \cap \Omega_{x'}$, which is the intersection of two sets which are stable under G, is itself stable under G; since G is transitive on Ω_x and $\Omega_{x'}$, we have $\Omega_x \cap \Omega_{x'} = \Omega_x = \Omega_{x'}$. Since every point x belongs to its orbit, we see that the orbits of the points of E form a quotient set of the set E.

Let E and E' be G-sets, on which G operates by means of homomorphisms φ and φ' of G into the permutation groups of E and E'. We then say that E and E' are isomorphic G-sets if there is a bijection J of E on E' such that $\varphi'(s) = \varphi(s) \circ J$ for any $s \in G$, from which it follows that $\varphi(s) = \varphi'(s) \circ \overset{-1}{J}$; J is then called an isomorphism of E with E'. We shall now see that the homogeneous G-sets may be entirely classified (up to isomorphisms) by means of the subgroups of G.

If x is any point of a G-set E, then the set G' of all elements $s \in G$ such that $s \cdot x = x$ is a subgroup of G. For, it is obvious that the unit element e of G is in G' and that, if s and t are in G', then st is in G'; we therefore have only to check that $s^{-1} \in G'$ whenever $s \in G'$. This is true because $s^{-1} \cdot x = s^{-1} \cdot (s\ x) = (s^{-1}s) \cdot x = x$. The group G' is called the *stability group* of x.

Now, let G be any group, and let G' be any subgroup of G. Assign to every $s \in G'$ the left translation by s in G; in this manner, we make G' operate on the set G. If s is any element of G, then the orbit of s is obviously $G's$; the set $G's$ is called the *right coset* of s modulo G'; any set which is the right coset of some element modulo G' is called a right coset modulo G'. Thus we see that the right cosets modulo G' form a quotient set of G. The image of a right coset modulo G' by any right translation of G is again a right coset; for, the image of the right coset $G's$ by the right translation produced by t is the right coset $G'(st)$. Moreover, every right coset $G's$ is the transform of the right coset $G'e = G'$ by a right translation, namely by the right translation produced by s. Making G operate on itself by right translation, we may also make G operate on the set of subsets of G, and we see that the set Q_r of right cosets modulo G' is stable under G and that G operates transitively on this set. In other words, Q_r is a homogeneous G-set, called the homogeneous set of right cosets modulo G'.

Similarly, if we make G' operate on G by right translation, then the orbit of an element s of G is sG'; for, the set of all elements st^{-1}, $t \in G'$, is the same as the set of elements st, $t \in G'$. The set sG' is called the *left coset* of s modulo G'; any set which is the left coset of some element is called a left coset of G modulo G'. Making use of the operation of G on G by left translations, we see that the set Q_l of left cosets modulo G' is a quotient set of G and has the structure of a homogeneous G-set; it is called the homogeneous set of left cosets.

Considering G' itself as a right coset, its stability group is G' itself. For, the transform of G' by an element s of G is $G's^{-1}$. If $s \in G'$, then $G's^{-1}$ has the unit element ss^{-1} in common with G', and therefore coincides with G' since Q_r is a quotient set of G. Conversely, if $G' = G's^{-1}$, then $s^{-1} = es^{-1} \in G'$, whence $s \in G'$. We see in the same way that the stability group of G' considered as a left coset is G'.

Theorem 15. *Let G be a group and E a non empty homogeneous G-set. Let x be any point of E and G' its stability group. Let Q_r and Q_l be the homogeneous sets of right and left cosets modulo G'. Then E, Q_r and Q_l are isomorphic G-sets.*

If $y \in E$, let $J(y)$ be the set of elements $s \in G$ such that $s \cdot x = y$. This set is not empty, since G operates transitively on E, and we have $J(x) = G'$. Let s be any element of $J(y)$; if $t \in G'$, we have $st \cdot x = s(t \cdot x) = s \cdot x = y$, whence $st \in J(y)$, or $sG' \subset J(y)$. Conversely, let s' be any element of $J(y)$; then $s^{-1}s' \cdot x = s^{-1} \cdot y = s^{-1} \cdot (s \cdot x) = x$, whence $s^{-1}s' \in G'$, $s' \in sG'$. It follows that $J(y) = sG'$, and that $J: y \to J(y)$ is a mapping of E into Q_l. Since $s \in J(s \cdot x)$ for any $s \in G$, J is a surjection; since $s \cdot x = y$ for any $s \in J(y)$, J is a bijection of E on Q_l. Let t be in G and $y = s \cdot x$ in E; then $J(t \cdot y) = J(ts \cdot x) = tsG'$; but tsG' is also the transform of sG' by the left translation produced by t; J is therefore a G-set isomorphism of E with Q_l. Applying this to the case where $E = Q_r$, $x = G'$, we see that Q_r is isomorphic to Q_l; theorem 15 is thereby proved.

In particular, we see that the sets Q_l and Q_r are equipotent. If one of them is finite, then so is the other, and they have the same number of elements ν; in that case, we say that G' is of finite index in G, and ν is called the *index* of G' in G.

Theorem 16. *Let G be a finite group of order n and G' a subgroup of G of order n'; if ν is the index of G' in G, then we have $n = n'\nu$.*

The left cosets of G modulo G', being the transforms of G' by left translations of G, are all equipotent, and each has n' elements. They form a quotient set of G, and there are ν of them, which proves theorem 16.

Corollary 1. *If G is a finite group, the order of any subgroup of G divides the order of G.*

Corollary 2. *If G is a finite group, the order of any element of G divides the order of G.*

For the order of an element s of G is the order of the group generated by s.

We shall apply the preceding considerations to the determination of the order $N(E)$ of the group $P(E)$ of all permutations of a set E with n elements. If E is empty, then, obviously, $N(E) = 1$. Assume now that $n > 0$. Let x be any element of E, E' the set of elements $\neq x$ of E and H the stability group of x. If $s \in H$, then the restriction $\rho(s)$ of s to E' is obviously a permutation of the set E'. Conversely, if p is any permutation of E', then the mapping of E into itself which coincides with p on E' and which maps x upon itself is a permutation of E and belongs to H; thus we see that ρ is a bijection of H on $P(E')$. We know that P operates transitively on E; thus, the index of H in G, which is the number of elements in the orbit of x under G, is n, and it follows that $N(E) = n \cdot N(E')$. Proceeding by induction on n, we deduce immediately from this that

$$N(E) = n!$$

where $n!$ (factorial n) is defined to be $\prod_{i=1}^{n} i$.

5. Products of groups

Theorem 17. *Let $(G_i)_{i \in I}$ be a family of groups. Then the product $\prod_{i \in I} G_i$ and the weak product $\prod_{i \in I}^{w} G_i$ are groups.*

Let $s = (s_i)_{i \in I}$ be an element of the product. Let $s' = (s_i^{-1})_{i \in I}$; then it is clear that ss' and $s's$ are both equal to the unit element of the product, which proves that $\prod_{i \in I} G_i$ is a group. If s belongs to the weak product $\prod_{i \in I}^{w} G_i$, then, for all i except a finite number, s_i is the unit element e_i of G_i, whence $s_i^{-1} = e_i$ for these values of i, and $s' \in \prod_{i \in I}^{w} G_i$, which shows that the weak product is a group.

6. Free groups

Let S be any set. We say that a group F, together with a mapping ψ of S into F, constitutes a *free group* on S if the following condition is satisfied: if φ is any mapping of S into a group H, there exists a unique homomorphism f of F into H such that $f \circ \psi = \varphi$.

Exactly as in the case of monoids, we see that this implies that $\psi(S)$ is a set of generators of F, and we establish

Theorem 18. *Let* (F, ψ) and (F', ψ') *be free groups on the set S. Then there exists a unique isomorphism J of F with F' such that* $J \circ \psi = \psi'$.

We shall now prove the existence of a free group on any given set S. Let S' be any set equipotent with S such that $S \cap S' = \emptyset$, and let j be a bijection of S on S'; in order to simplify the notation, we denote by $\bar{a}$ the element $j(a)$, for $a \in S$. Let (M, ψ_0) be a free monoid on $S \cup S'$. If Q is any quotient monoid of M, let π_Q be the natural homomorphism of M on Q. We consider the set Σ of all quotient monoids Q of M with the property that, for any $a \in S$, $\pi_Q(\psi_0(\bar{a}))$ is the inverse of $\pi_Q(\psi_0(a))$ in Q. This implies that $\pi_Q(\psi_0(a))$ is the inverse of $\pi_Q(\psi_0(\bar{a}))$, and, since $\psi_0(S \cup S')$ generates M as a monoid, Q is a group (theorem 4, Sect. 2). Let P be the product $\prod_{Q \in \Sigma} Q$; then P is a group (theorem 17, Sect. 5). For each $Q \in \Sigma$, let ω_Q be the projection of P on Q. Then there exists a homomorphism g of the monoid M into P such that $\omega_Q \circ g = \pi_Q$ for every $Q \in \Sigma$. Let $F = g(M)$ and denote by ψ the restriction of $g \circ \psi_0$ to the subset S of $S \cup S'$. If $a \in S$, then $g(\psi_0(\bar{a}))$ is inverse to $g(\psi_0(a))$ in F; for, if Q is any element of Σ, then $\omega_Q(g(\psi_0(\bar{a}))) = \pi_Q(\psi_0(\bar{a}))$ is inverse to $\omega_Q(g(\psi_0(a))) = \pi_Q(\psi_0(a))$, from which our assertion follows immediately. Since F is generated as a monoid by $g(\psi_0(S \cup S'))$, F is a group (theorem 4, Sect. 2). Let φ be any mapping of S into a group H; then, since S and S' are disjoint from each other, we may extend φ to a mapping φ_0 of $S \cup S'$ into H such that

$$\varphi_0(\bar{a}) = (\varphi_0(a))^{-1} = (\varphi(a))^{-1}$$

for any $a \in S$. Since (M, ψ_0) is a free monoid on $S \cup S'$, there exists a homomorphism h of M into H such that $h \circ \psi_0 = \varphi_0$. Let Q be the quotient monoid associated with h. Then Q is isomorphic to the submonoid $h(M)$ of H. For any $a \in S$, $\varphi_0(\bar{a})$ is the inverse of $\varphi_0(a)$; it follows that $\pi_Q(\psi_0(\bar{a}))$ is the inverse of $\pi_Q(\psi_0(a))$ in Q, whence $Q \in \Sigma$. Let $\bar{h}$ be the isomorphism of Q with $h(M)$ such that $h = \bar{h} \circ \pi_Q$; then $f = \bar{h} \circ \omega_Q$ is a homomorphism of F into H. The mapping $f \circ \psi$ is the restriction to S of $f \circ g \circ \psi_0$; $f \circ \psi$ is the restriction to S of $\bar{h} \circ \omega_Q \circ g \circ \psi_0$, i. e. of $\bar{h} \circ \pi_Q \circ \psi_0 = h \circ \psi_0 = \varphi_0$, whence $f \circ \psi = \varphi$. Since F is generated as a monoid by $g(\psi_0(S \cup S'))$, it is generated as a group by $g(\psi_0(S)) = \psi(S)$, and there can be only one homomorphism f of F into H such that $f \circ \psi = \varphi$. Thus, (F, ψ) is a free group on S.

Theorem 19. *If (F, ψ) is a free group on S, ψ is an injection of S into F.*

Let a and a' be distinct elements of S. Denote by $\underline{Z}$ the group of integers and by φ the mapping of S into $\underline{Z}$ which maps a upon 1 and every other element (including a') upon 0. Let f be the homomorphism of F into $\underline{Z}$ such that $f \circ \psi = \varphi$. Then we have $f(\psi(a)) = 1$, $f(\psi(a')) = 0$, whence $\psi(a) \neq \psi(a')$.

Theorem 20. *Let M be a monoid. Then there exist a group A and a homomorphism θ of M into A with the following property: if ρ is any homomorphism of M into a group B, then there exists a unique homomorphism f of A into B such that $f \circ \theta = \rho$.*

Let (F, ψ) be a free group on the set of elements of M. Let H be the intersection of all normal subgroups of F which contain all elements of the form $\psi(xy)(\psi(y))^{-1}(\psi(x))^{-1}$ for x and y in M; denote by A the group F/H and by π the natural homomorphism of F onto A; set $\theta = \pi \circ \psi$. We shall see that θ is a homomorphism of M into A. If x, y are in M, then $\theta(xy) = \pi(\psi(xy))$; but we have $\psi(xy)(\psi(y))^{-1}(\psi(x))^{-1} \in H$, whence $\psi(xy) \equiv \psi(x)\psi(y) \pmod{H}$ and therefore

$$\theta(xy) = \pi(\psi(x)\psi(y)) = \pi(\psi(x))\pi(\psi(y)) = \theta(x)\theta(y).$$

Denote by e_M and e_A the unit elements of M and A. We have $\theta(e_M) = \theta(e_M^2) = \theta(e_M)\theta(e_M)$, whence $\theta(e_M) = e_A$ since A is a group; θ is therefore a homomorphism. Let ρ be a homomorphism of M into a group B. Then there is a homomorphism g of F into B such that $g \circ \psi = \rho$. If x, y are in M, then $g(\psi(xy)) = \rho(xy) = \rho(x)\rho(y) = g(\psi(x)\psi(y))$; it follows that $\psi(xy)(\psi(y))^{-1}(\psi(x))^{-1}$ belongs to the kernel of g. This kernel, being a normal subgroup, contains H, and there exists a homomorphism f of $A = F/H$ into B such that $g = f \circ \pi$, whence $f \circ \theta = g \circ \psi = \rho$. If f' is any homomorphism of A into B such that $f' \circ \theta = \rho$, then $g' = f' \circ \pi$ is a homomorphism of F into B and $g' \circ \psi = f' \circ \theta = \rho$, whence $g' = g$; it follows that $f' = f$ (theorem 13, Sect. 3).

The notation being as in theorem 20, the set $\theta(M)$ is a set of generators of A. Moreover, if A' and θ' are any group and any homomorphism of M into A' with the same property as A and θ, then there is a unique isomorphism J of A with A' such that $J \circ \theta = \theta'$. These statements are established exactly in the same manner as the corresponding statements for free monoids (or groups).

The homomorphism θ of theorem 20 is in general not a monomorphism. We can easily find a necessary condition for this to be the case. Let a, b, c

be elements of M such that $ac = bc$. Then we have $\theta(a)\theta(c) = \theta(b)\theta(c)$, whence $\theta(a) = \theta(b)$ since A is a group. Thus, if θ is a monomorphism, we must have $a = b$. Similarly, if a', b', c' are elements of M and $c'a' = c'b'$, then we must have $a' = b'$.

We shall say that the *cancellation law* holds in M if the following conditions are satisfied: if a, b, c are any elements of M such that $ac = bc$, then we have $a = b$; if a', b', c' are any elements of M such that $c'a' = c'b'$, then we have $a' = b'$.

Thus, a necessary condition for the homomorphism θ to be a monomorphism is that the cancellation law should hold in M. We shall see that this condition is also sufficient in the case where M is commutative.

Let M be a commutative monoid in which the cancellation law holds. For any $(a, b) \in M \times M$, let $\gamma(a, b)$ be the set of elements $(a', b') \in M \times M$ such that $ab' = a'b$. If $(a', b') \in \gamma(a, b)$, we have $\gamma(a', b') = \gamma(a, b)$. For, let (a'', b'') be in $\gamma(a', b')$; then $a'b'' = a''b'$, whence $ba'b'' = ba''b'$; but we have $ab' = a'b$ by assumption, so that $b'ab'' = ba''b'$, and therefore $ab'' = a''b$ by the cancellation law, which shows that $\gamma(a', b') \subset \gamma(a, b)$. On the other hand, we have also $(a, b) \in \gamma(a', b')$, whence $\gamma(a, b) \subset \gamma(a', b')$ and $\gamma(a, b) = \gamma(a', b')$. Thus, if the sets $\gamma(a, b)$ and $\gamma(a_1, b_1)$ have an element (a', b') in common, these sets are equal, which shows that the sets $\gamma(a, b)$, for all $(a, b) \in M \times M$, are mutually disjoint. Since $(a, b) \in \gamma(a, b)$, the sets $\gamma(a, b)$ are not empty, and their union is the whole of $M \times M$; thus, they form a quotient set Q of $M \times M$. If (a, b) and (a', b') are any two elements of $M \times M$, then the product $(a_1a'_1, b_1b'_1)$ of any element (a_1, b_1) of $\gamma(a, b)$ by any element (a'_1, b'_1) of $\gamma(a', b')$ lies in $\gamma(aa', bb')$. For we have $ab_1 = a_1b$, $a'b'_1 = a'_1b'$, whence, by multiplication, $aa'b_1b'_1 = a_1a'_1bb'$, which proves our assertion. It follows that Q is a quotient monoid of $M \times M$. Its neutral element is $\gamma(e, e)$, if e is the neutral element of M. Now, we have $\gamma(a, b)\gamma(b, a) = \gamma(ab, ab) = \gamma(e, e)$ since $abe = eab$. Since Q is commutative, this means that $\gamma(b, a)$ is inverse to $\gamma(a, b)$ in Q, and therefore that Q is a group. If $a \in M$, set $\rho(a) = \gamma(a, e)$; then we have, for any a, $b \in M$, $\rho(ab) = \gamma(ab, e) = \gamma(a, e)\gamma(b, e)$; since $\rho(e) = \gamma(e, e)$, ρ is a homomorphism of M into Q. Let a, a' be elements of M such that $\rho(a) = \rho(a')$; then we have $\gamma(a, e) = \gamma(a', e)$, whence $ae = ea'$, $a = a'$, and ρ is a monomorphism. Now, in the notation of theorem 20, we have $\rho = f \circ \theta$, where f is a homomorphism of A into Q. Since ρ is a monomorphism, the same is obviously true of θ; and our assertion is proved.

Still assuming that M is commutative and that the cancellation law holds in M, we observe that every element of the group A of theorem 20 commutes with every other element of A, since A is generated by $\theta(M)$. Moreover, taking into account the corollary to theorem 4, Sect. 2, together with the commutativity of A, we see that every element of A may be written in the form $\theta(x_1) \cdots \theta(x_p)(\theta(y_1))^{-1} \cdots (\theta(y_q))^{-1}$, where $x_1, \cdots, x_p$, $y_1, \cdots, y_q$ are in M; but this is also $\theta(x_1 \cdots x_q)(\theta(y_1 \cdots y_q))^{-1}$. Thus we have proved:

Theorem 21. *Let M be a commutative monoid in which the cancellation law holds. Then there exist a group A and a monomorphism θ of M into A which have the following properties:*

If ρ is any homomorphism of M into a group B, there is a unique homomorphism f of A into B such that $\rho = f \circ \theta$;

Every element of A may be written in the form $\theta(x)(\theta(y))^{-1}$, with x, y in M.

Corollary. *If $a_1, \cdots, a_p$ are any elements of A, there exist elements $x_1, \cdots, x_p, y$ of M such that $a_i = \theta(x_i)(\theta(y))^{-1}$ $(1 \leqslant i \leqslant p)$.*

For, set $a_i = \theta(x_i')(\theta(y_i))^{-1}$, with $x_i', y_i \in M$. Then we may take

$$x_i = x_i' \prod_{j \neq i} y_j, \quad y = \prod_{i=1}^{p} y_i.$$

Exercises on Chapter II

1. Let A be a monoid and e its neutral element. An element x of A is called left-invertible of there eixsts an element y of A such that $yx = e$; y is then called a left-inverse to x. Show that, if y is a left-inverse to x and is left-invertible, then x and y are invertible and inverse to each other. Conclude that, if every element of a monoid is left-invertible, then the monoid is a group.
   Let M be the monoid of all mappings of a set E into itself (under the law of composition $\circ$); show that the left-invertible elements of M are the injections of E into E. Use this to show that an element of a monoid may have several distinct left-inverses; show that, in a finite monoid, every left-invertible element is invertible.
2. Let E be a finite set with n elements and f a permutation of E such that $f \circ f$ is the identity mapping. Let r be the number of elements x of E such that $f(x) = x$; show that $n - r$ is even. Let G be a finite group of even order; show that there exists an element of order 2 in G [make use of the mapping $x \rightarrow x^{-1}$ of G into itself].
3. Let G be a group such that every element of G is of order either 1 or 2; show that G is commutative.
4. Show that the mapping $x \rightarrow -x$ of the additive group $\underline{Z}$ of integers into itself is an automorphism, but not an inner automorphism; show that it is the only automorphism of $\underline{Z}$ distinct from the identity mapping.
5. Show that every subgroup of index 2 of a group G is normal in G.

6. Let P be the group of permutations of a set with 3 elements; show that P is not commutative, and that P has exactly 6 subgroups, of which 3 are normal and 3 are not.

7. Show that, if S is a subset of a finite group G, then the submonoid of G generated by S is a group. Show by an example that the conclusion is not true in general when G is not assumed to be finite.

8. Let S be a subset of a group G which is mapped into itself by every inner automorphism of G; show that the subgroup of G generated by S is normal.

9. Let P be an operation which assigns to every subgroup H of any group G some subgroup $P(H)$ of G; assume that P satisfies the following condition: if J is an isomorphism of G with some group G' and H a subgroup of G, then $P(J(H)) = J(P(H))$. Show that, if H is a normal subgroup of G, then $P(H)$ is likewise normal.

10. Show that the centralizer of a normal subgroup of a group G is a normal subgroup of G [either apply ex. 9 or prove directly].

11. Let H be a subgroup of a group G. Show that the elements s of G such that the mapping $t \to sts^{-1}$ of G into itself map H into itself form a subgroup N of G, of which H is a normal subgroup; show that every subgroup of G containing H and in which H is normal is contained in N.

12. Show that the derived group of a group G is generated by the elements of the form $sts^{-1}t^{-1}$, for all s and t in G.

13. Let H and K be normal subgroups of a group G, and L the group generated by all elements of the form $sts^{-1}t^{-1}$ where $s \in H$, $t \in K$. Show that L is normal; prove that it is the intersection of the kernels of those homomorphisms f of G which have the property that every element of $f(H)$ commutes with every element of $f(K)$.

14. Let G be a group. Define inductively a sequence (D_n) of subgroups of G as follows: $D_0 = G$; D_{n+1} is the derived group of D_n. Show that the groups D_n are all normal subgroups of G, and that, for every n, any automorphism of G maps D_n into itself. If there exists an index n such that D_n consists of the unit element only, then G is called solvable. Show that any subgroup or quotient group of a solvable group is solvable. Show that, if a finite group is not solvable, then it has a normal subgroup of order > 1 which is its own derived group. Show that a solvable group of order > 1 has a commutative normal subgroup of order > 1. Show that, if a group G has a normal subgroup H such that H and G/H are solvable, then G is solvable. Show that a necessary and sufficient condition for a group G to be solvable is that there should exist a finite sequence $(H_0, \cdots, H_n)$ of subgroups of G with the following properties: $H_0 = G$; if $1 < i < n$, H_i is a normal subgroup of H_{i-1} and H_{i-1}/H_i is Abelian; H_n consists of the unit element only. Show that the group of permutations of a set with 3 elements is solvable [use ex. 6].

15. Let G be a group. Define inductively a sequence (N_n) of subgroups of G as follows: $N_0 = G$; N_{n+1} is the group generated by all elements of the form $sts^{-1}t^{-1}$ where $s \in G$ and $t \in N_n$. Show that, for every n, any automorphism of G maps N_n into itself; conclude that the groups N_n are normal in G. Show that N_{n-1}/N_n is in the center of G/N_n. If there exists an index n such that N_n consists of the unit element only, G is called nilpotent. Show that every subgroup or quotient group of a nilpotent group is nilpotent. Show that a necessary and sufficient condition for a group G to be nilpotent is that there should exist a finite sequence $(Z_0, \cdots, Z_n)$ of subgroups of G with the following properties: Z_0 consists of the unit element only; if $1 \leqslant i \leqslant n$, Z_{i-1} is a normal subgroup of G contained in Z_i and Z_i/Z_{i-1} is in the center of G/Z_{i-1}; Z_n is G. Show that every nilpotent group is solvable [cf. ex. 14]; show that the group of permutations of a set with 3 elements is not nilpotent. Conclude that a group G which has a nilpotent normal subgroup N such that G/N is nilpotent is not necessarily nilpotent.

16. Let E be a set and G a group operating on E. The group G then also operates on the set of subsets of E, and consequently also on the set of subsets of the set of subsets of E. Show that the set of quotient sets of E is stable under G. Assume now that E has 4 elements, and that G is the group of permutations of E. Let Q be the set of quotient sets of E consisting of two mutually disjoint subsets of E with 2 elements each. Show that Q has 3 elements and is stable under G. Show that every permutation of the set Q is produced by the action of some element of G. Conclude that there is an epimorphism of G on the group of permutations of a set with 3 elements. Using the fact that every group of order 4 is commutative (and therefore solvable), and the results of ex. 14, prove that G is solvable.

17. Let s be a permutation of a set E and F_s the set of elements x of E such that $s(x) = x$. Show that, if t is a permutation of E and $s' = tst^{-1}$, then $F_{s'} = t(F_s)$. Conclude that, if F_s is neither $\emptyset$ nor E, then s cannot belong to any normal commutative subgroup of the group of permutations of E. Assume now that E has 5 elements, and let P be the group of permutations of E. Show that, if s is an element of P of order > 1 and $\neq 5$, then there is an integer k such that s^k is distinct from the identity and leaves at least one element of E fixed. Show that if s is of order 5 and t an operation of E which commutes with s, then, if t is distinct from the identity, t cannot leave any element of E fixed; applying this to $s^k t$ (where k is any integer) instead of t, show that t must be a power of s. Show that P has no commutative normal subgroup of order > 1, and conclude that P is not solvable [cf. ex. 14]. Show that the group of permutations of a set containing at least 5 elements is never solvable.

18. Show that every subgroup of a cyclic group G is cyclic; show that, if G is cyclic of finite order n, then, for every divisor d of n, G contains exactly one subgroup of order d.

19. Let G be a finite group of order n such that two distinct subgroups of G always have different orders. Show that every subgroup of G is normal. Show that G is cyclic [proceed by induction on n; among all subgroups H of G such that G/H is cyclic, let H_0 be one of smallest order, and let a be an element of G such that aH_0 generates G/H_0; show that H_0 is cyclic and that, if $b \in H_0$, bab^{-1} is in the group generated by a and is $\equiv a \pmod{H_0}$; conclude that $ab = ba$; show that the orders of a and b are relatively prime to each other, and conclude that G is cyclic].

See below.

20. Let E and R be sets; if n is an integer > 0, let E^n be the product of n sets identical to E and M the set of mappings of E^n into R. Let G be a group which operates on E; if $f \in M$, $s \in G$, denote by $s \cdot f$ the mapping $(x_1, \cdots, x_n) \to f(s^{-1} \cdot x_1, \cdots, s^{-1} \cdot x_n)$. Show that the mapping $(s, f) \to s \cdot f$ makes G operate on M. If a mapping $f \in M$ is such that $s \cdot f = f$, then f is called an invariant of s; if f is an invariant of s for all $s \in G$, then f is called an invariant of G. Prove that, for any subset N of M, the set of elements $s \in G$ of which the elements of N are all invariants is a subgroup H of G; if N is stable under G, then H is a normal subgroup.

21. Let P be a 2-dimensional plane. A permutation of P is called isometric if it admits as invariant the mapping of $P \times P$ into the set of real numbers which assigns to every pair $(x, y) \in P \times P$ the distance from x to y (cf. ex. 20). Show that the translations of P form a normal subgroup T of the group G of all isometric permutations of P. Show that G/T has a normal subgroup of index 2 isomorphic to the group of rotations of P around some fixed point. Conclude that G is solvable (cf. ex. 14).

22. Let E be the set of vertices of a cube in 3-space. Define the notion of isometric permutation of E as in ex. 21. Determine the order of the group of isometric permutations of E.

23. Make a group G operate on itself by the formula $s \cdot t = sts^{-1}$. The orbits under G of the elements of G are then called the conjugate classes of G. Assuming that G is finite, show that the number of elements in a conjugate class of G divides the order of G. Assume now that the order of G is a power of a prime number. Using the fact that the set consisting of the unit element alone is a conjugate class, show that, if the order of G is > 1, there is at least one conjugate class consisting of a single element distinct from the unit element; conclude that the order of the center of G is > 1. Deduce from this that any finite group whose order is a power of a prime number is nilpotent [cf. ex. 15].

24. Let E be the set $\{1, \cdots, n\}$, where n is an integer > 0, and let P be the group of permutations of E. Set $N = \prod_{1 \leqslant i < j \leqslant n}(j - i)$. Show that, if $p \in P$, then $\prod_{1 \leqslant i < j \leqslant n}(p(j) - p(i)) = \theta(p)N$, where $\theta(p)$ is either 1 or -1; show that θ is a homomorphism of P into the multiplicative group $\{-1, 1\}$ and that θ is an epimorphism if $n > 1$.

25. Let H and K be subgroups of a group G, both distinct from G and both containing at least two elements. Show that there exists an element of G which is neither in H nor in K.

26. Let E be a set of the form $S \cup S'$, where S and S' are equipotent disjoint sets, and let j be a bijection of S on S'. Let J be the permutation of E which coincides with j on S and with $\overset{-1}{j}$ on S'. Let M be the monoid of finite sequences of elements of E, with the law of composition τ defined in Chap. I, Sect. 6. Define a mapping ρ of M into itself in the following manner: if $x = (a_1, \cdots, a_n)$ $(a_i \in E, 1 \leqslant i \leqslant n)$ and $a_{i+1} \neq J(a_i)$ for every i, then $\rho(x) = x$; if there exists at least one i such that $a_{i+1} = J(a_i)$, let k be the smallest index with this property; then $\rho(x) = (b_1, \cdots, b_{n-2})$, with $b_i = a_i$ if $i < k$, $b_i = a_{i+2}$ if $i \geqslant k$. Define inductively a sequence (ρ_n) of mappings of M into itself by $\rho_1 = \rho$, $\rho_{n+1} = \rho \circ \rho_n$. Show that, for any $x \in$ M, there is an integer ν such that $\rho_n(x) = \rho_\nu(x)$ for all $n \geqslant \nu$; ν being the smallest integer satisfying this condition, set $\rho_\nu(x) = \sigma(x)$. Show that σ is a surjection of M on the set R of elements x such that $\rho(x) = x$. Prove that, if x, y are in M and $\rho(x) \neq x$, then

$$\rho(x \tau y) = \rho(\rho(x) \tau y),$$

and that, for any two elements x, y of M, $\sigma(x \tau y) = \sigma(\sigma(x) \tau y)$. Show that, if $a \in E$, then $\sigma(x \tau a \tau J(a)) = \sigma(x)$, and conclude first that $\sigma(x \tau \rho(y)) = \sigma(x \tau y)$ and then that $\sigma(x \tau y) = \sigma(\sigma(x) \tau \sigma(y))$ for any x, y in M. Define a multiplication in R by the formula $xy = \sigma(x \tau y)$ $(x, y \in R)$; show that R becomes a group under this multiplication. If $a \in S$, let $\psi(a)$ be the sequence (a) with a single term a; show that $\psi(S) \subset R$ and that (R, ψ) is a free group on S.

(19.) An argument from Sylow's theorem (on the existence of p-power subgroups of a finite group) may be given:

let $n = \prod_{i=1}^{s} p_i^{e_i}$. The Sylow subgroups, S_{p_i}, of G will be normal, and clearly $G = \bigotimes_{i=1}^{s} S_{p_i}$.

Since $(|S_{p_i}|, |S_{p_j}|) = 1$, for $i \neq j$, to prove the theorem it suffices to establish the result for the special case: $n = p^m$.

The argument is from induction: When $m = 1$, the result follows immediately. Suppose the theorem is true for $m = k$, and let $n = p^{k+1}$. Sylow's thm. guarantees a subgroup, G', of G, with $|G'| = p^k$, and every proper subgroup of G will be contained in G'. Thus, for $a \in G - G'$, $|a| = p^{k+1}$, else the subgroup generated by a (and thus a itself) would be in G', and G is cyclic.

We have then that a finite group whose lattice of subgroups is linearly ordered by inclusion, must be cyclic; of prime power order.

CHAPTER III

Rings and Modules

1. Rings

By a *ring* we mean a set R with two laws of composition, one denoted additively and the other multiplicatively, which satisfy the following conditions:

1. The elements of R form a commutative group under addition;
2. The elements of R form a monoid under multiplication;
3. If a, b, c are elements of R, we have

$$a(b + c) = ab + ac, \quad (a + b)c = ac + bc.$$

Let R be a ring. If a, b, c are any elements of R, we have $(a - b)c = ac - bc$, $a(b - c) = ab - ac$. For, we have $ac = ((a - b) + b)c = (a - b)c + bc$, whence $(a - b)c = ac - bc$; the second formula is proved in the same way. It follows that $0c = (0 - 0)c = 0c - 0c = 0$, and we see in the same way that $c0 = 0$. The unit element for the multiplication of a ring R is always denoted by 1. If $1 = 0$, then $R = \{0\}$, for we then have, for any $a \in R$, $a = 1a = 0a = 0$. If $1 \neq 0$, then 0 cannot have an inverse with respect to multiplication, since $0a = 0$ can never be 1. A ring in which every element $a \neq 0$ is invertible (relative to multiplication) and which contains at least two elements is called a *sfield*. A ring R is called commutative if its multiplication is commutative. A commutative sfield is called a *field*.

EXAMPLES: *a*) The set of integers constitutes a ring relative to the usual operations of addition and multiplication. The set of rational numbers constitutes a field relative to the usual operations of addition and multiplication.

b) Let A be any commutative additive group, and R the set of endomorphisms of A. If φ and φ' are in R, we denote by $\varphi + \varphi'$ the mapping $a \to \varphi(a) + \varphi'(a)$ of A into itself. This is again an endomorphism. For, it is clear that $(\varphi + \varphi')(0) = 0$, and we have, for a, b in A,

$$\begin{aligned}(\varphi + \varphi')(a + b) &= \varphi(a + b) + \varphi'(a + b) = \varphi(a) + \varphi(b) + \varphi'(a) + \varphi'(b) \\ &= \varphi(a) + \varphi'(a) + \varphi(b) + \varphi'(b) = (\varphi + \varphi')(a) + (\varphi + \varphi')(b).\end{aligned}$$

We thus have an additive law of composition in R. This law admits a zero element, which is the endomorphism which maps every element of A upon 0. If $\varphi, \varphi', \varphi''$ are in R, then, for any $a \in A$,

$$((\varphi + \varphi') + \varphi'')(a) = (\varphi + \varphi')(a) + \varphi''(a) = \varphi(a) + \varphi'(a) + \varphi''(a)$$
$$= \varphi(a) + (\varphi' + \varphi'')(a) = (\varphi + (\varphi' + \varphi''))(a),$$

which shows that our addition is associative. We see in an analogous manner that it is commutative. The mapping ω defined by $\omega(a) = -a$ ($a \in A$) is in R since A is commutative; if $\varphi \in R$, then we have $\varphi + \varphi \circ \omega = 0$, which shows that R is an additive group. Now, if φ, φ' are in R, so is $\varphi \circ \varphi'$; we define a multiplication in R by $\varphi\varphi' = \varphi \circ \varphi'$. This multiplication is associative and admits as unit element, the identity mapping of R into itself. Let $\varphi, \varphi', \varphi''$ be any elements of R; then we have, for $a \in A$,

$$((\varphi + \varphi')\varphi'')(a) = (\varphi + \varphi')(\varphi''(a)) = \varphi(\varphi''(a)) + \varphi'(\varphi''(a)) = (\varphi\varphi'' + \varphi'\varphi'')(a),$$

whence $(\varphi + \varphi')\varphi'' = \varphi\varphi'' + \varphi'\varphi''$. We would see in the same way that $\varphi(\varphi' + \varphi'') = \varphi\varphi' + \varphi\varphi''$. Thus R constitutes a ring.

Let A, B and C be commutative groups. A mapping β of $A \times B$ into C is called bi-additive if the following conditions are satisfied:

1. For any $b \in B$, the mapping $a \to \beta(a, b)$ is a homomorphism of A into C;
2. For any $a \in A$, the mapping $b \to \beta(a, b)$ is a homomorphism of B into C.

For instance, the multiplication in a ring R is a bi-additive mapping of $R \times R$ into R.

Theorem 1. *Let A, B, C be commutative additive groups and β a bi-additive mapping of $A \times B$ into C. Let $(a_i)_{i \in I}$ and $(b_j)_{j \in J}$ be families of elements of A and B respectively. If the sums $\sum_{i \in I} a_i$, $\sum_{j \in J} b_j$ are defined, then the sum $\sum_{(i,j) \in I \times J} \beta(a_i, b_j)$ is defined and we have*

$$\beta(\textstyle\sum_{i \in I} a_i, \sum_{j \in J} b_j) = \sum_{(i,j) \in I \times J} \beta(a_i, b_j).$$

Since β is bi-additive, we have $\beta(0, b) = \beta(a, 0) = 0$ for any $a \in A$, $b \in B$. Let I' (resp.: J') be the set of indices $i \in I$ (resp.: $j \in J$) such that $a_i \neq 0$ (resp.: $b_j \neq 0$). If (i, j) is not in the finite set $I' \times J'$, then $\beta(a_i, b_j) = 0$, which shows that the sum $\sum_{(i,j) \in I \times J} \beta(a_i, b_j)$ is defined.

This being said, we consider first the case where J consists of a single index j, and we set $b_j = b$. In this case, we first prove our formula in the case where I is finite, and, in that case, we proceed by induction on the number, n, of elements of I. If $n = 0$, then I and $I \times J$ are empty, and both sides of the formula to be proved are 0. Assume that $n > 0$ and that the formula is true for $n - 1$. Let i_0 be any element of I and I' the set of elements $\neq i_0$ in I. Then

$$\beta(\textstyle\sum_{i \in I} a_i, b) = \beta(a_{i_0} + \sum_{i \in I'} a_i, b) = \beta(a_{i_0}, b) + \sum_{i \in I'} \beta(a_i, b),$$

since I' has $n-1$ elements; this proves our formula for n. If I is infinite, let I' be a finite subset of I such that $a_i = 0$ for $i \notin I'$. Then

$$\beta(\Sigma_{i \in I} a_i, b) = \beta(\Sigma_{i \in I'} a_i, b) = \Sigma_{i \in I'} \beta(a_i, b) = \Sigma_{i \in I} \beta(a_i, b),$$

since $\beta(a_i, b) = 0$ if $i \notin I'$. Thus, our formula is proved whenever J consists of a single element. Applying this to the bi-additive mapping β' of $B \times A$ into C defined by $\beta'(b, a) = \beta(a, b)$, we see immediately that

$$\beta(\Sigma_{i \in I} a_i, \Sigma_{j \in J} b_j) = \Sigma_{j \in J} \beta(\Sigma_{i \in I} a_i, b_j) = \Sigma_{j \in J}(\Sigma_{i \in I} \beta(a_i, b_j)),$$

and this is equal to $\Sigma_{(i,j) \in I \times J} \beta(a_i, b_j)$ since the sets $I \times \{j\}$, $j \in J$, form a partition of $I \times J$.

The formula of theorem 1 may be generalized as follows. Let $A_1, \cdots, A_n$ be commutative additive groups. A mapping β of $A_1 \times \cdots \times A_n$ into a commutative additive group C is called n-additive if the following condition is satisfied: for any k between 1 and n and for any given elements a_i $(i \neq k)$ of the groups A_i, let $\delta(x)$, for any $x \in A_k$, be the element of $A_1 \times \cdots \times A_n$ whose k-coordinate is x and whose i-coordinate is a_i whenever $i \neq k$; then we require that, for any choices of k and of the elements a_i $(i \neq k)$, $\beta \circ \delta$ should be a homomorphism of A_k into C. This being said, let there be given for each k $(1 \leqslant k \leqslant n)$ a family $(a_{k;i})_{i \in I_k}$ of elements of A_k such that $\Sigma_{i \in I_k} a_{k;i}$ is defined. Then

$$\Sigma_{(i_1, \cdots, i_n) \in I_1 \times \cdots \times I_n} \beta(a_{1;i_1}, \cdots, a_{n;i_n})$$

is defined, and we have

$$\beta(\Sigma_{i \in I_1} a_{1;i_1}, \cdots, \Sigma_{i \in I_n} a_{n;i_n}) = \Sigma_{(i_1, \cdots, i_n) \in I_1 \times \cdots \times I_n} \beta(a_{i_1}, \cdots, a_{i_n}).$$

This can be proved easily by induction on n. We leave the proof to the reader.

If we apply theorem 1 to the multiplication in a ring, which is bi-additive, we obtain the formula

$$(\Sigma_{i \in I} a_i)(\Sigma_{j \in J} b_j) = \Sigma_{(i,j) \in I \times J} a_i b_j,$$

where $(a_i)_{i \in I}$, $(b_j)_{j \in J}$ are families of elements of a ring such that the sums $\Sigma_{i \in I} a_i$, $\Sigma_{j \in J} b_j$ are defined.

Let R be a ring. Then the mapping $n \rightarrow n \cdot 1$ is a homomorphism of the additive group $\underline{Z}$ of integers into the additive group of R. The kernel of this homomorphism consists of all multiples of some integer $p \geqslant 0$; the number p is called the *characteristic* of the ring.

If x, y are any elements of R, then we have $n \cdot xy = (nx) \cdot y$ for any $n \in \underline{Z}$, which follows immediately from the fact that the mapping $x \rightarrow xy$ is an endomorphism of the additive group of R into itself. Similarly, we have $x(n \cdot y) = n \cdot xy$. In particular we have $n \cdot x = (n \cdot 1)x$; thus, if p is the characteristic of the ring, then we have $p \cdot x = 0$ for every element x in the ring.

2. Field of quotients

A mapping f of a ring R into a ring R' is called a *homomorphism* if it is a homomorphism of the additive group of R and of the multiplicative monoid of R. The notions of monomorphism, isomorphism, etc., of a ring are defined analogously to the corresponding notions for monoids.

If K is a sfield, and a an element $\neq 0$ of K, then, for any $b \in K$, there is a unique element $x \in K$ such that $ax = b$. For, $x = a^{-1}b$ is a solution of this equation; and, conversely, if $ax = b$, then $x = 1 \cdot x = a^{-1}ax = a^{-1}b$. It follows that the only element $x \in K$ such that $ax = 0$ is $x = 0$.

If R is a ring, an element $a \in R$ is called a *zero divisor* if there exists an element $x \neq 0$ of R such that $ax = 0$.

Theorem 2. *If a ring R has at least two elements and has no zero divisor $\neq 0$, then its characteristic is either 0 or a prime number.*

For, let p be the characteristic of R, which we assume to be $\neq 0$. If m and n are integers such that $p = mn$, then

$$0 = mn \cdot 1 = m \cdot (n \cdot 1) = m \cdot ((n \cdot 1)1) = (n \cdot 1)(m \cdot 1);$$

this implies that one of $n \cdot 1$, $m \cdot 1$ is 0, and therefore that one of m, n is divisible by p. We have $p \neq 1$ since R has at least two elements. Thus p is a prime number.

A sfield has no zero divisor other than 0; it follows immediately that, if a ring R has a monomorphism into a sfield, then the only zero divisor in R is 0. It is not true in general that a ring R in which there is no zero divisor $\neq 0$ admits a monomorphism into a sfield; however, we shall prove that this is the case if R is furthermore assumed to be commutative.

A commutative ring R in which there is no zero divisor $\neq 0$ is called a *domain of integrity*.

If R is a domain of integrity with at least two elements, and R^* the multiplicative monoid of elements $\neq 0$ in R, then the cancellation law holds in R^*. For, if a, b, c are elements of R^* such that $ac = bc$, then we have $(a - b)c = 0$, whence $a - b = 0$ since $c \neq 0$, and therefore $a = b$.

Theorem 3. *Let R be a domain of integrity with at least two elements. Then there exist a field K and a monomorphism ψ of R into K which satisfy the following condition: if φ is any monomorphism of R into a sfield L, there exists a unique homomorphism f of K into L such that $f \circ \psi = \varphi$.*

We denote by R^* the multiplicative monoid of elements $\neq 0$ in R. Then we know by theorem 21, Chapter II, Sect. 6, that there exists a monomorphism ψ_0 of R^* into a multiplicative group K^* such that every element of K^* may be written in the form $\psi_0(a)(\psi_0(b))^{-1}$, where $a, b \in R^*$;

moreover, if ρ is any homomorphism of R^* into a group L^*, there is a uniquely determined homomorphism f of K^* into L^* such that $\rho = f \circ \psi_0$. Let us form a set K which is the union of K^* and of an element not belonging to K^*, which we shall denote by 0. We extend the multiplication of K^* to a multiplication in K by defining $0 \cdot u$ and $u \cdot 0$ to be 0 whenever $u \in K$; it is easy to verify that K becomes a monoid under this law of composition, and that K^* is a submonoid of K. We extend ψ_0 to a mapping ψ of R into K^* by setting $\psi(0) = 0$; ψ is clearly a monomorphism of the multiplicative monoid M into the multiplicative monoid K. We shall now define an addition in K. If u, v are in K, there are elements a, b, c of R, with $c \in R^*$, such that $u = \psi(a)(\psi(c))^{-1}$, $v = \psi(b)(\psi(c))^{-1}$ (as follows from the corollary to theorem 21, Chapter II, Sect. 6). Although a, b and c are not uniquely determined by u, v, we shall see that $(\psi(a) + \psi(b))(\psi(c))^{-1}$ depends only on u and v. For, assume that $u = \psi(a')(\psi(c'))^{-1}$, $v = \psi(b')(\psi(c'))^{-1}$, with a', b' in R, $c' \in R^*$. Then we have $\psi(a'c) = \psi(a')\psi(c) = \psi(a)\psi(c') = \psi(ac')$, whence $ac' = a'c$; we see in the same way that $bc' = b'c$; thus, we have

$$(a + b)c' = (a' + b')c, \qquad \psi(a + b)\psi(c') = \psi(a' + b')\psi(c)$$

and

$$\psi(a + b)(\psi(c))^{-1} = \psi(a' + b')(\psi(c'))^{-1},$$

which proves our assertion. We set

$$u + v = \psi(a + b)(\psi(c))^{-1},$$

and define in this manner an addition in the set K. We shall see that K becomes a commutative group under our addition. Since $\psi(a + b) = \psi(b + a)$, the addition in K is commutative. Let u, v, w be elements of K; then there exist elements a, b, c of R and d of R^* such that

$$u = \psi(a)(\psi(d))^{-1} \qquad v = \psi(b)(\psi(d))^{-1} \qquad w = \psi(c)(\psi(d))^{-1}$$

(corollary to theorem 21, Chapter II, Sect. 6). It follows that

$$u + v = \psi(a + b)(\psi(d))^{-1},$$

whence $(u + v) + w = \psi(a + b + c)(\psi(d))^{-1}$, and we see in the same way that $u + (v + w) = \psi(a + b + c)(\psi(d))^{-1}$, which proves that the addition in K is associative. If $u = \psi(a)(\psi(c))^{-1} = 0$ with $a \in R$, $c \in R^*$, then $a = 0$; for, were $a \neq 0$, then u would be in K^*, and therefore $\neq 0$. It follows that 0 is a zero element for our addition. If $u = \psi(a)(\psi(c))^{-1}$, with $a \in R$, $c \in R^*$, then $u + \psi(-a)(\psi(c))^{-1} = 0$, which shows that every element of K is invertible with respect to addition.

Let u, v, w be elements of K, $u = \psi(a)(\psi(d))^{-1}$, $v = \psi(b)(\psi(d))^{-1}$, $w = \psi(c)(\psi(e))^{-1}$, with $a, b, c \in R$, $d, e \in R^*$. Then we have

$$\begin{aligned}(u + v)w &= \psi(a + b)\psi(c)(\psi(d)\psi(e))^{-1} \\ &= \psi((a + b)c)(\psi(de))^{-1} = \psi(ac + bc)(\psi(de))^{-1}\end{aligned}$$

$$uw = \psi(ac)(\psi(de))^{-1} \qquad vw = \psi(bc)(\psi(de))^{-1},$$

whence $(u + v)w = uw + vw$. Since the multiplication in K is commutative, we see that K is a commutative ring. The multiplicative monoid of elements $\neq 0$ in K is a group, and K is therefore a field.

If $a \in R$, then we have $\psi(a) = \psi(a)(\psi(1))^{-1}$; it follows that

$$\psi(a) + \psi(b) = \psi(a + b)$$

if $a, b \in R$; ψ is therefore a monomorphism of the ring R into K.

Let φ be a monomorphism of R into a sfield L, and let L^* be the multiplicative group of elements $\neq 0$ in L. Then there exists a unique homomorphism f_0 of the monoid K^* into L^* such that $f_0 \circ \psi_0 = \varphi_0$, where φ_0 is the restriction of φ to R^*. If we extend f_0 to a mapping f of K into L by setting $f(0) = 0$, then f is a homomorphism of the multiplicative monoid K into the multiplicative monoid L, and $f \circ \psi = \varphi$. Let $u = \psi(a)(\psi(c))^{-1}$, $v = \psi(b)(\psi(c))^{-1}$ be elements of K, with $a, b \in R$, $c \in R^*$. We have $f(\psi(c)) = \varphi_0(c) \neq 0$ since φ is a monomorphism. It follows that

$$f(u) = f(\psi(a))f((\psi(c))^{-1}) = \varphi(a)(\varphi(c))^{-1}$$

and similarly $f(v) = \varphi(b)(\varphi(c))^{-1}$, $f(u + v) = \varphi(a + b)(\varphi(c))^{-1}$. Since $\varphi(a + b) = \varphi(a) + \varphi(b)$, we have $f(u + v) = f(u) + f(v)$, and f is a homomorphism of K into L such that $f \circ \psi = \varphi$. If f' is any homomorphism of K into L such that $f' \circ \psi = \varphi$, then we have $f'(0) = 0$, and the restriction f'_0 of f' to K^* maps K^* into L^*, for $f'(K^*)$ is a subgroup of the multiplicative monoid L and can therefore not contain 0. Since $f'_0 \circ \psi_0 = \varphi_0$, we have $f'_0 = f_0$, whence $f' = f$. Theorem 3 is thereby proved.

A field K, given together with a monomorphism ψ of R into K such that the condition of theorem 3 is satisfied, is called a *field of quotients* of R. If (K, ψ) and (K', ψ') are fields of quotients of R, then there is a unique isomorphism J of K with K' such that $J \circ \psi = \psi'$; this is established in the same way as the corresponding statement for free monoids.

In questions where a field of quotients (K, ψ) of a ring R is made use of, one very often adopts the convention of denoting the image $\psi(a)$ of an element a of R by a instead of $\psi(a)$; while this is an incorrect notation, it is much less cumbersome than the correct one, $\psi(a)$.

3. Modules

Let R be a ring. Assume that we are given a commutative additive group M together with a mapping: $(\alpha, x) \to \mu(\alpha, x)$ of $R \times M$ into M which satisfy the following conditions:

a) μ is a bi-additive mapping, i. e., $\mu(\alpha + \beta, x) = \mu(\alpha, x) + \mu(\beta, x)$, $\mu(\alpha, x + y) = \mu(\alpha, x) + \mu(\alpha, y)$ for any α, β in R, x, y in M;

b) $\mu(\alpha, \mu(\beta, x)) = \mu(\alpha\beta, x)$ for any $\alpha, \beta \in R$, $x \in M$;

c) $\mu(1, x) = x$ for any $x \in M$, where 1 is the unit element of R.

Then we say that M is a *module* over R, or *R-module*; the mapping $(\alpha, x) \rightarrow \mu(\alpha, x)$ is called the *scalar multiplication*, and $\mu(\alpha, x)$ is called the *scalar product* of x by α.

EXAMPLES: *a*) Let M be any commutative additive group, and $\underline{Z}$ the ring of integers. We have defined a mapping $(n, x) \rightarrow nx$ of $\underline{Z} \times M$ into M (cf. Chapter II, Sect. 1). If we set $\mu(n, x) = nx$, then μ has the properties *a*), *b*), *c*) above. Thus any commutative group may be considered as a module over the ring of integers.

b) Let R be any ring; set $\mu(\alpha, x) = \alpha x$ when $\alpha, x \in R$. Then this mapping μ has the properties *a*), *b*), *c*) above. Thus, any ring may be considered as a module over itself.

c) Let R be a ring, E a set and M the additive group of all mappings of E into R, where addition is defined in M by $(f + g)(u) = f(u) + g(u)$ for any $f, g \in M$. If $f \in M$ and $\alpha \in R$, denote by $\mu(\alpha, f)$ the mapping $u \rightarrow \alpha f(u)$ of E into R; then the mapping μ has the properties *a*), *b*), *c*) above and defines a module structure over R on the group M.

The modules we have just defined are also called *left modules*. One also considers *right modules* over a ring R. A right module is a commutative additive group M together with a mapping μ of $R \times M$ into M which satisfy conditions *a*), *c*) above but which satisfies, instead of *b*), the condition

b')
$$\mu(\alpha, \mu(\beta, x)) = \mu(\beta\alpha, x).$$

The mapping μ is still called the scalar multiplication of M, and $\mu(\alpha, x)$ the scalar product of x by α.

If R is a commutative ring, then the notions of left and right module over R coincide with each other.

In general, let (M, μ) be a left module over a ring R. We may construct a new ring R' as follows: the elements of R' are the same as those of R; the addition in R' is the same as the addition in R; but the multiplication τ in R' is defined by

$$\alpha\tau\beta = \beta\alpha \qquad (\alpha, \beta \in R);$$

for, we see immediately that the addition and the new multiplication we have introduced satisfy the conditions 1., 2., 3. of Sect. 1. The unit element of R' is the same as that of R. If an element α is invertible in R, then it is invertible in R' and it has the same inverse in R' as in R; in particular, if R is a sfield, so is R'. The ring R' is called the *opposite ring* of R. It is clear that the opposite ring of R' is R; if R is commutative, then $R' = R$. This being said, if M is a left module (resp.: a right module) over R, it is clear that M, with the same scalar multiplication, is a right module (resp.: a left module) over R'. This remark permits us to derive the properties of right modules from those of left modules; in the following, we shall study mostly left modules, leaving it to the reader to translate the results we shall obtain into results on right modules.

If M is a left module over the ring R, the scalar product $\mu(\alpha, x)$ of an $x \in M$ by an $\alpha \in R$ is usually denoted by αx, while, if M is a right module over R, then $\mu(\alpha, x)$ is usually denoted by $x\alpha$. We shall adhere to these conventions in the remainder of this chapter.

With these conventions, conditions *a*), *b*), *c*) for left modules take the following forms:

a) $(\alpha + \beta)x = \alpha x + \beta x \qquad \alpha(x + y) = \alpha x + \alpha y \qquad (\alpha, \beta \in R, \quad x, y \in M)$

b) $\alpha(\beta x) = (\alpha\beta)x \qquad (\alpha, \beta \in R, \quad x \in M)$

c) $1x = x \qquad (x \in M)$

while conditions *a*), *b'*), *c*) for right modules take the following forms:

a) $x(\alpha + \beta) = x\alpha + x\beta \qquad (x + y)\alpha = x\alpha + y\alpha \qquad (\alpha, \beta \in R, \quad x, y \in M)$

b') $(x\alpha)\beta = x(\alpha\beta) \qquad (\alpha, \beta \in R, \quad x \in M)$

c) $x1 = x \qquad (x \in M).$

Let M be a module over R. Then, for any fixed $\alpha \in R$, the mapping $x \to \alpha x$ is an endomorphism of the additive group of M; it follows that we have

$$\alpha 0 = 0 \qquad \alpha(x - y) = \alpha x - \alpha y \qquad (\alpha \in R, \quad x, y \in M),$$

The mapping $x \to \alpha x$ is called the *dilation* of ratio α. If we denote this dilation by D_α, then condition *b*) means that $D_{\alpha\beta} = D_\alpha \circ D_\beta$.

If x is any fixed element of M, the mapping $\alpha \to \alpha x$ is a homomorphism of the additive group of R into the additive group of M. It follows that

$$0x = 0 \qquad (\alpha - \beta)x = \alpha x - \beta x \qquad (\alpha, \beta \in R, \quad x \in M).$$

Moreover, if n is any integer, then we have

$$n(\alpha x) = (n\alpha)x;$$

in particular we have $-x = (-1)x$. If p is the characteristic of R, then we have $p \cdot x = 0$ for every $x \in M$.

4. Submodules

Let M be a module over a ring R. Let N be an additive subgroup of M such that we have $\alpha x \in N$ whenever $\alpha \in R$, $x \in N$. Then the restriction to $R \times N$ of the scalar multiplication of M defines on N a module structure over R. A module obtained in this manner is called a *submodule* of M.

If N is any subset of M such that $\alpha x \in N$ whenever $\alpha \in R$, $x \in N$, then N is said to be *stable under scalar multiplication*. Since $(-1)x = -x$, we see that $x \in N$ implies $-x \in N$. Thus, to check that a subset N of M is a submodule, it is sufficient to check that N is stable under scalar multiplication and that the sum of any two elements of N lies in N.

Theorem 4. *Any intersection of submodules of M is a submodule.*

This follows directly from the definitions.

It follows that, given any subset S of M, there exists a smallest submodule N of M containing S, viz. the intersection of all submodules of M containing S. We say that N is the submodule of M *generated by* S.

Let $(x_i)_{i \in I}$ be any family of elements of M. An element x of M is said to be a *linear combination* of the elements x_i if there exists a family $(\alpha_i)_{i \in I}$ of elements of R, with the same set I of indices as the given family $(x_i)_{i \in I}$, such that $\alpha_i = 0$ for almost all indices i and $x = \sum_{i \in I} \alpha_i x_i$; we also say that this formula expresses x as a linear combination of the elements x_i with the coefficients α_i. If E is a subset of R and if the family $(\alpha_i)_{i \in I}$ above may be selected in such a way that $\alpha_i \in E$ for every i, then we say that x is a *linear combination of the x_i's with coefficients in E*. If S is a subset of M and if there exists a family $(x_i)_{i \in I}$ of elements of S such that x is a linear combination of the elements x_i, then we say that x is a *linear combination of elements of S*; if the family $(x_i)_{i \in I}$ of elements of S may be selected in such a way that x is a linear combination of the elements x_i with coefficients in E, then we say that x is a *linear combination of elements of S with coefficients in E.*

Theorem 5. *Let S be a subset of a module M. In order for an element $x \in M$ to belong to the submodule N generated by S, it is necessary and sufficient that x be a linear combination of elements of S.*

In order to prove this, we first establish two lemmas.

Lemma 1. *Let S be any subset of M, and T the set of all elements αx, for $\alpha \in R$, $x \in S$. Then T is stable under scalar multiplication.*

For, if β is any element of R, we have $\beta(\alpha x) = (\beta\alpha)x$, and this element belongs to T if $\alpha \in R$, $x \in S$.

Lemma 2. *If T is a subset of M which is stable under multiplication, then the additive monoid N generated by T is a submodule of M.*

Let α be in R; then the dilation D_α of ratio α of M maps N upon the additive submonoid αN of M generated by $D_\alpha(T)$ (theorem 6, Chapter I, Sect. 3). We have by assumption $D_\alpha(T) \subset T$, whence $D_\alpha(T) \subset N$; since N is an additive monoid, it follows that $\alpha N \subset N$, i. e., that N is stable under multiplication. By a remark made earlier, it follows that N is a submodule.

This being said, we can now prove theorem 5. If $x = \sum_{i \in I} \alpha_i x_i$, with

$\alpha_i \in R$, $x_i \in S$ and $\alpha_i = 0$ for almost all i, then we have $\alpha_i x_i \in N$ for all i, whence $x \in N$. To prove the converse, let T be defined as in lemma 1; then N is the additive submonoid generated by T (lemma 2). Thus every element $x \in N$ may be written in the form $\Sigma_{i \in I} y_i$, where $(y_i)_{i \in I}$ is a finite family of elements of T (theorem 15*a*, Chapter I, Sect. 6). For each i, we may write $y_i = \alpha_i x_i$, with $\alpha_i \in R$, $x_i \in S$, which shows that x is a linear combination of elements of S.

Theorem 6. *Let $(N_i)_{i \in I}$ be a family of submodules of M. Then the submodule N generated by the set $\bigcup_{i \in I} N_i$ is the set of all elements x which may be represented in the form $\Sigma_{i \in I} x_i$, where $(x_i)_{i \in I}$ is a family of elements of M such that $x_i = 0$ for almost all i and $x_i \in N_i$ for every i.*

It is clear that $\bigcup_{i \in I} N_i$ is stable under scalar multiplication; therefore, N is the additive monoid generated by $\bigcup_{i \in I} N_i$. Let N^* be the weak product of the additive monoids N_i, and θ_i the natural injection of N_i into N^*; then there exists a homomorphism θ of N^* into M such that $(\theta \circ \theta_i)(x_i) = x_i$ for all i and all $x_i \in N_i$ (theorem 13, Chapter I, Sect. 5). We have $N_i = \theta(\theta_i(N_i)) \subset \theta(N^*)$ for every $i \in I$, whence $N \subset \theta(N^*)$. Since every element of N^* is the sum of its components, N^* is generated by $\bigcup_{i \in I} \theta_i(N_i)$, which shows that $\theta(N^*)$ is generated by $\bigcup_{i \in I} N_i$, whence $\theta(N^*) = N$, and the elements of N are the sums $\Sigma_{i \in I} x_i$, where $x_i \in N_i$ for all i and $x_i = 0$ for almost all i. Theorem 6 is thereby proved.

The notation being as in theorem 6, the submodule N is denoted by $\Sigma_{i \in I} N_i$. Similarly, if $A, B, \cdots, C$ are submodules of M, then the submodule generated by $A \cup B \cup \cdots \cup C$ is denoted by $A + B + \cdots + C$.

Lemma 3. *Assume that M is the sum of two submodules A and B. If N is a submodule of M containing A, we have $N = A + (B \cap N)$.*

Let x be any element of N; write $x = a + b$, with $a \in A$, $b \in B$; then $b = x - a$ lies in N, since both x and a are in N; thus, $b \in B \cap N$ which proves lemma 3.

Let $(N_i)_{i \in I}$ be a family of submodules of M. Let $(J_k)_{k \in K}$ be a family of subsets of I such that $\bigcup_{k \in K} J_k = I$. Then we have

$$\Sigma_{i \in I} N_i = \Sigma_{k \in K}(\Sigma_{i \in J_k} N_i). \tag{1}$$

In fact, the right-hand side of this formula represents a submodule N' of M. If $i \in I$, there is a $k \in K$ such that $i \in J_k$, whence $N_i \subset \Sigma_{i \in J_k} N_i \subset N'$; since $\bigcup_{i \in I} N_i \subset N'$, we have $\Sigma_{i \in I} N_i \subset N'$. Conversely, if $k \in K$, we have $N_i \subset \Sigma_{i \in I} N_i$ for every $i \in J_k$; it follows that $\Sigma_{i \in J_k} N_i \subset \Sigma_{i \in I} N_i$. This being true for every $k \in K$, we have $N' \subset \Sigma_{i \in I} N_i$.

It should be observed that, in formula (1), it is not required that the sets J_k be mutually disjoint. In particular, we have $A + A = A$ for any submodule A.

On the other hand, it follows from our definition that the sum of the empty family of submodules of M is the submodule $\{0\}$ consisting of 0 alone. We have $A + \{0\} = A$ for every submodule A.

Let $(N_i)_{i \in I}$ be a family of submodules of M. Then we say that the sum of these submodules is *direct* if the following condition is satisfied: given any $x \in \sum_{i \in I} N_i$, there exists only one family $(x_i)_{i \in I}$ such that $x_i \in N_i$ for all i, $x_i = 0$ for almost all i and $x = \sum_{i \in I} x_i$. This means that the homomorphism θ of the additive group $N^* = \prod^w_{i \in I} N_i$ into $N = \sum_{i \in I} N_i$ defined by $\theta((x_i)_{i \in I}) = \sum_{i \in I} x_i$ for all $(x_i)_{i \in I} \in N^*$ is a monomorphism, i. e., that the kernel of θ is $\{0\}$. Thus we obtain

Theorem 7. *Let $(N_i)_{i \in I}$ be a family of submodules of M. In order for the sum $\sum_{i \in I} N_i$ to be direct, it is necessary and sufficient that the following condition be satisfied: if $(x_i)_{i \in I}$ is a family of elements such that $x_i \in N_i$ for all i, $x_i = 0$ for almost all i and $\sum_{i \in I} x_i = 0$, then we have $x_i = 0$ for all i.*

If a sum $\sum_{i \in I} N_i$ is direct, one often states this fact by writing

$$\sum_{i \in I} N_i \quad \text{(direct)}.$$

Theorem 8. *Let $(N_i)_{i \in I}$ be a family of submodules of M, and let $(J_k)_{k \in K}$ be a family of mutually disjoint subsets of I such that $\bigcup_{k \in K} J_k = I$. In order for the sum $\sum_{i \in I} N_i$ to be direct, it is necessary and sufficient that the following conditions be satisfied:*

a) For each k, the sum $P_k = \sum_{i \in J_k} N_i$ is direct;

b) The sum $\sum_{k \in K} P_k$ is direct.

Suppose that the sum $\sum_{i \in I} N_i$ is direct. Let $(x_i)_{i \in J_k}$ be a family indexed by J_k such that $x_i \in N_i$ for all $i \in J_k$ and such that the sum $\sum_{i \in J_k} x_i$ is defined and has the value 0. Then we may extend this family to a family $(x_i)_{i \in I}$ defined on I by setting $x_i = 0$ for all i not in J_k. We then have $\sum_{i \in I} x_i = \sum_{i \in J_k} x_i = 0$, whence $x_i = 0$ for all i, and, in particular, for $i \in J_k$. This shows that the sum $\sum_{i \in J_k} N_i$ is direct. Let $(y_k)_{k \in K}$ be a family of elements such that $y_k \in P_k$ for all k and such that the sum $\sum_{k \in K} y_k$ is defined and has the value 0. For each k, we may write $y_k = \sum_{i \in J_k} x_{ki}$, $x_{ki} \in N_i$, almost all x_{ki} being 0. For any $i \in I$, there exists exactly one index k, say $k(i)$, such that $i \in J_k$; set $x_i = x_{k(i),i}$. Then the sum $\sum_{i \in I} x_i$ is defined. For, let K' be the set of indices k such that $y_k \neq 0$; if k is not in K', then we have $x_i = 0$ for all $i \in J_k$ because the sum $\sum_{i \in J_k} N_i$ is direct. If $k \in K'$, let J'_k be the set of indices $i \in J_k$ such that $x_i \neq 0$. Then $I' = \bigcup_{k \in K'} J'_k$ is a finite set, and we have $x_i = 0$ for all i not in I', which proves our assertion. It follows that $\sum_{i \in I} x_i = \sum_{k \in K}(\sum_{i \in J_k} x_i) = \sum_{k \in K} y_k = 0$ and therefore that $x_i = 0$ for every $i \in I$. This clearly implies $y_k = 0$ for every $k \in K$, which shows that the sum $\sum_{k \in K} P_k$ is direct.

Now, assume that the conditions are satisfied. Let $(x_i)_{i \in I}$ be a family of elements such that $x_i \in N_i$, $x_i = 0$ for almost all i and $\sum_{i \in I} x_i = 0$. Then we know that the sums $y_k = \sum_{i \in J_k} x_i$ are defined and that $\sum_{k \in K} y_k = \sum_{i \in I} x_i = 0$. By condition *b*), this implies $y_k = 0$ for every k, and therefore, by condition *a*), $x_i = 0$ for all $i \in J_k$. Since every $i \in I$ belongs to some set J_k, all elements x_i are 0 and the sum $\sum_{i \in I} N_i$ is direct.

Theorem 9. *Let A and B be submodules of M. In order for the sum $A + B$ to be direct, it is necessary and sufficient that $A \cap B = \{0\}$.*

Assume that the sum $A + B$ is direct. If $x \in A \cap B$, we have $x + (-x) = 0$, $x \in A$, $-x \in B$, whence $x = 0$. Assume conversely that the condition is satisfied. If $x \in A$, $y \in B$, $x + y = 0$, then $y = -x \in A$, whence $y \in A \cap B$ and therefore $y = 0$, which implies $x = 0$; thus, the sum $A + B$ is direct.

Corollary. *Let $(N_i)_{i \in I}$ be a family of submodules of M. In order for $\sum_{i \in I} N_i$ to be a direct sum, it is necessary and sufficient that the following condition be satisfied: for any $i \in I$, we have $N_i \cap \sum_{j \neq i} N_i = \{0\}$.*

The condition is necessary by theorems 8 and 9. Assume that it is satisfied, and let $(x_i)_{i \in I}$ be a family such that $x_i \in N_i$ for all i, $x_i = 0$ for almost all i and $\sum_{i \in I} x_i = 0$. Let i be any index in I; then we have $x_i + \sum_{j \neq i} x_j = 0$; the sum $N_i + (\sum_{j \neq i} N_j)$ being direct (theorem 9), we have $x_i = 0$. Thus, the sum $\sum_{i \in I} N_i$ is direct.

For instance, if A, B, C are submodules of M, in order for $A + B + C$ to be a direct sum, it is necessary and sufficient that the following conditions be satisfied: $A \cap (B + C) = \{0\}$, $B \cap (C + A) = \{0\}$, $C \cap (A + B) = \{0\}$.

A submodule N of M is called a *direct summand* in M if there exists a submodule P such that $M = N + P$ (direct); this being the case, P is called a *supplementary module to* N; in general, P is not uniquelydetermined.

A module M is called *semi-simple* if every submodule of M is a direct summand.

A module M is called *simple* if $M \neq \{0\}$ and if the only submodules of M are $\{0\}$ and M.

Theorem 10. *Any submodule of a semi-simple module is semi-simple.*

Let M be a semi-simple module, N a submodule of M and P a submodule of N. Let Q be a submodule of M supplementary to P and $Q' = Q \cap N$. Then it is clear that $P \cap Q' = \{0\}$, and we have $N = Q + Q'$ by lemma 3. Thus Q' is supplementary to P in N.

Theorem 11. *The following conditions are all equivalent to each other:*

1) *M is semi-simple;*
2) *M is the direct sum of a family of simple submodules of M;*
3) *M is the sum of a family of simple submodules of M.*

If M is the sum of a family $(N_i)_{i \in I}$ of simple submodules and if P is any submodule of M, then P has a supplementary submodule Q such that $Q = \sum_{i \in J} N_i$, J being a subset of I, and the sum $\sum_{i \in J} N_i$ is direct.

Let $(N_i)_{i \in I}$ be a family of simple submodules of M. Let P be a submodule of $\sum_{i \in I} N_i$; consider those subsets T of I which have the following two properties: *a*) the sum $\sum_{i \in T} N_i$ is direct; *b*) $P \cap \sum_{i \in T} N_i = \{0\}$. We denote by $\mathfrak{F}$ the set of subsets T of I which have these properties. We shall see that $\mathfrak{F}$ is inductive. Let $\mathfrak{F}_0$ be a subset of $\mathfrak{F}$ such that, whenever T and T' are in $\mathfrak{F}_0$, then either $T \subset T'$ or $T' \subset T$. Let T^* be the union of all sets belonging to $\mathfrak{F}_0$; we shall prove that $T^* \in \mathfrak{F}$. Let $(x_i)_{i \in T^*}$ be a family of elements such that $x_i \in N_i$ for all $i \in T^*$ and $x_i = 0$ for almost all $i \in T^*$. Let $T_1 = \{i_1, \cdots, i_r\}$ be the finite set of elements $i \in T^*$ such that $x_i \neq 0$. Since T^* is the union of the sets in $\mathfrak{F}_0$, each i_k belongs to some $T_k \in \mathfrak{F}_0$. Given any two indices k, k' one of the sets T_k, $T_{k'}$, is contained in the other. It follows immediately that there is an index h such that $T_k \subset T_h$ for all k $(1 \leqslant k \leqslant r)$. Since $T_h \in \mathfrak{F}$, the sum $\sum_{i \in T_h} N_i$ is direct, and

$$P \cap \textstyle\sum_{i \in T_h} N_i = \{0\}.$$

It follows that the sum $N_{i_1} + \cdots + N_{i_r}$ is direct and that

$$P \cap (N_{i_1} + \cdots + N_{i_r}) = \{0\}.$$

If $\sum_{i \in T^*} x_i \in P$, then $x_{i_1} + \cdots + x_{i_r} \in P$; this implies that $x_{i_1} + \cdots + x_{i_r} = 0$, whence $x_{i_k} = 0$ for $k = 1, 2, \cdots, r$, and therefore $x_i = 0$ for all $i \in T^*$. Since $0 \in P$, this implies that $\sum_{i \in T^*} N_i$ is direct; and furthermore, we have $P \cap \sum_{i \in T^*} N_i = \{0\}$. Thus T^* belongs to $\mathfrak{F}$, and consequently $\mathfrak{F}$ is inductive. It follows that $\mathfrak{F}$ contains a maximal element T_1.

Now let i_0 be any index $i \in I$. We shall see that $N_{i_0} \subset P + \sum_{i \in T_1} N_i$. Assume for a moment that this is not the case. Then $N_{i_0} \cap (P + \sum_{i \in T_1} N_i)$ is a submodule $\neq N_{i_0}$ of N_{i_0}; since N_{i_0} is simple, this submodule is $\{0\}$, and the sum $N_{i_0} + (P + \sum_{i \in T_1} N_i)$ is direct. Since $P + \sum_{i \in T_1} N_i$ is direct by our construction of T_1, the sums $N_{i_0} + P + \sum_{i \in T_1} N_i$, $N_{i_0} + \sum_{i \in T_1} N_i$, and $P + (N_{i_0} + \sum_{i\in T_1} N_i)$ are direct (theorem 8). Let $T'_1 = T_1 \cup \{i_0\}$; then, the sum $\sum_{i\in T_1} N_i$ being direct, the sum $\sum_{i\in T'_1} N_i$ is direct (theorem 8), and $P \cap \sum_{i\in T'_1} N_i = \{0\}$ (theorem 9). It follows that $T'_1 \in \mathfrak{F}$. Since $T_1 \subset T'_1$ and T_1 is a maximal element of $\mathfrak{F}$, we have $T_1 = T'_1$. This means that $i_0 \in T_1$, whence $N_{i_0} \subset \sum_{i\in T_1} N_i$, contradicting our former result that the sum $N_{i_0} + \sum_{i\in T_1} N_i$ is direct (for $N_{i_0} \neq \{0\}$). Thus we have proved that all modules N_i are contained in $P + \sum_{i\in T_1} N_i$, whence $\sum_{i\in I} N_i = P + \sum_{i\in T_1} N_i$ (direct). Considering the case where $\sum_{i\in I} N_i = M$, this proves the last assertion of theorem 11; therefore it proves also that condition 3) implies 1) and (considering the special case where $P = \{0\}$) that 3) implies 2).

Obviously 2) implies 3).

Now, assume that 1) is satisfied. We shall first prove that every submodule $A \neq \{0\}$ of M contains a simple submodule. It will obviously be sufficient to prove this in the case where A is generated by some element $x \neq 0$. To establish our assertion in that case, we first prove

Lemma 4. *Let $\mathfrak{p}$ be a set of submodules of an arbitrary module M. Assume that, if P, P' are in $\mathfrak{p}$, one of the modules P, P' is contained in the other. Then $\bigcup_{P\in\mathfrak{p}} P$ is a submodule of M.*

The set $\bigcup_{P\in\mathfrak{p}} P$ is obviously stable under scalar multiplica ion. Let x and x' be in it. Then there are modules P, P' belonging to $\mathfrak{p}$ such that $x \in P$, $x' \in P'$. If $P' \subset P$, then x, x' are both in P, whence $x + x' \in P$; if $P \subset P'$, then $x + x' \in P'$. In either case, $x + x'$ belongs to $\bigcup_{P\in\mathfrak{p}} P$, which proves lemma 4.

This being said, let $\mathfrak{A}$ be the set of those submodules of A which do not contain x; $\mathfrak{A}$ is not empty since $\{0\} \in \mathfrak{A}$. Let $\mathfrak{p}$ be a subset of $\mathfrak{A}$ such that, whenever P, P' belong to $\mathfrak{p}$, one of P, P' is contained in the other. Then the union $\bigcup_{P\in\mathfrak{p}} P$ is a submodule of A (lemma 4) and obviously does not contain x; it therefore belongs to $\mathfrak{A}$. We conclude that $\mathfrak{A}$ has at least one maximal element P. It follows from theorem 10 that A is the direct sum of P and of some submodule N; we have $N \neq \{0\}$ since $x \in A$, $x \notin P$. Let N' be a submodule $\neq \{0\}$ of N. Then $P + N'$ contains P and is $\neq P$, because $N \cap P = \{0\}$, whence $N' \cap P = \{0\}$; since P is maximal in $\mathfrak{A}$, we have $x \in P + N'$, whence $P + N' = A$ since x generates A. We have $N = N' + (N \cap P)$ by lemma 3, whence $N = N'$ since $N \cap P = \{0\}$. Thus N is a simple module contained in A, which proves our assertion.

Now, let S be the sum of all simple modules contained in M. Since M is semi-simple, M is the direct sum of S and of a submodule T; since $S \cap T = \{0\}$, T cannot contain any simple submodule. Therefore $T = \{0\}$, and $M = S$, which proves that 1) implies 3).

5. Linear mappings

Let M and N be modules over a ring R. By a *homomorphism*, or *linear mapping*, of M into N is meant a homomorphism f of the additive group of M into the additive group of N such that

$$f(\alpha x) = \alpha f(x)$$

for any $\alpha \in R$ and $x \in M$.

If f is a linear mapping of M into N and g a linear mapping of N into an R-module P, then $g \circ f$ is a linear mapping of M into P.

The notions of monomorphism, epimorphism, isomorphism, endomorphism, automorphism are defined for modules in the same way they have been for monoids. The reciprocal mapping of an isomorphism of a module M with a module N is an isomorphism of N with M.

Let f be a linear mapping of a module M over a ring R into a module N. Let $(x_i)_{i \in I}$ be a family of elements of M and $(\alpha_i)_{i \in I}$ a family of elements of R such that $\alpha_i = 0$ for almost all i; then we have

$$f(\Sigma_{i \in I}\alpha_i x_i) = \Sigma_{i \in I}\alpha_i f(x_i);$$

this follows immediately from the definitions.

Theorem 12. *Let f be a linear mapping of a module M into a module N. If M' is a submodule of M, then $f(M')$ is a submodule of N; if N' is a submodule of N, then $\overset{-1}{f}(N')$ is a submodule of M; in particular the kernel $\overset{-1}{f}(0)$ of f is a submodule of M.*

We know already that $f(M')$ is a subgroup of N and $\overset{-1}{f}(N')$ a subgroup of M. If $x \in M'$, $\alpha \in R$, then $\alpha f(x) = f(\alpha x) \in f(M')$, which proves that $f(M')$ is a submodule of N. If $x \in M$ is such that $f(x) \in N'$, then $f(\alpha x) = \alpha f(x) \in N'$, whence $\alpha x \in \overset{-1}{f}(N')$, which proves that $\overset{-1}{f}(N')$ is a submodule of M.

Theorem 13. (Schur's lemma). *Let f be a linear mapping of a simple module M into a module N; then, if $f(M) \neq \{0\}$, f is a monomorphism, and $f(M)$ is a simple submodule of N. If N is simple and $f(M) \neq \{0\}$, then f is an isomorphism.*

The kernel K of f, which is a submodule of M, can only be $\{0\}$ or M; if $f(M) \neq \{0\}$, then $K = \{0\}$, and f is a monomorphism. Since $f(M)$ is then isomorphic to M, it is simple. If N is simple and $f(M) \neq \{0\}$, then $f(M) = N$, since $f(M)$ is a submodule of N.

We shall now see that every submodule K of a module M is the kernel of some linear mapping of M. Since K is a subgroup of the additive group of M, which is commutative, we may construct the quotient group M/K. We shall see that it is possible in one and only one way to define a scalar multiplication on M/K such that M/K becomes a module and that the natural homomorphism π of the additive group M on M/K becomes a linear mapping. Let q be any coset of M modulo K and α any element of R; then the scalar products αx, where α remains fixed and x runs over the elements of q, all lie in the same coset q' modulo K. For, if x, y are elements of q, then $x - y$ belongs to K, whence $\alpha x - \alpha y = \alpha(x - y) \in K$, since K is a submodule; this shows that αx and αy lie in the same coset. We may therefore define a mapping $(\alpha, q) \to \alpha q$ of $R \times (M/K)$ into M/K by calling αq the coset which contains all elements αx, $x \in q$. It is then clear that $\pi(\alpha x) = \alpha\pi(x)$ for any $x \in M$. Let α, α' be elements of R and q, q' elements of M/K; let x, x' be elements of M such that $\pi(x) = q$, $\pi(x') = q'$; then we have

$$(\alpha + \alpha')q = \pi((\alpha + \alpha')x) = \pi(\alpha x + \alpha' x) = \pi(\alpha x) + \pi(\alpha' x) = \alpha q + \alpha' q,$$

and

$$\alpha(q + q') = \alpha(\pi(x) + \pi(x')) = \alpha\pi(x + x') = \pi(\alpha(x + x')) = \pi(\alpha x + \alpha x') = \pi(\alpha x) + \pi(\alpha x') = \alpha q + \alpha q';$$

moreover

$$\alpha\alpha' \cdot q = \pi((\alpha\alpha')x) = \pi(\alpha \cdot (\alpha' x)) = \alpha\pi(\alpha' x) = \alpha \cdot (\alpha' \cdot q),$$

and, finally

$$1 \cdot q = \pi(1 \cdot x) = \pi(x) = q.$$

This proves that our scalar multiplication defines on M/K a module structure over R relative to which π is a linear mapping. Moreover, this structure is unique; for, if we must have $\alpha\pi(x) = \pi(\alpha x)$ for any $x \in M$, then, for any $q \in M/K$, we must have $\alpha x \in \alpha q$ whenever $x \in q$. The module M/K we have just defined is called the *quotient module* of M by K.

The theorems on normal subgroups generalize immediately to the case of quotient modules.

Theorem 14. *Let f and f' be linear mappings of a module M into modules N, N', and let K, K' be their respective kernels. Assume that $K' \subset K$. Then there is a unique linear mapping g of $f'(M)$ into N such that $f = g \circ f'$; we have $g(f'(M)) = f(M)$, and the kernel of g is $f'(K)$.*

There is a unique homomorphism g of the additive group $f'(M)$ into $f(M)$ such that $f = g \circ f'$, and this mapping has the last two properties stated in theorem 14. If $x \in M$ and $\alpha \in R$, we have

$$g(\alpha f'(x)) = g(f'(\alpha x)) = f(\alpha x) = \alpha f(x) = \alpha g(f'(x)),$$

which proves that g is linear.

Corollary. Let f and f' be linear mappings of a module M onto modules N, N' and let their respective kernels be equal. Then N and N' are isomorphic.

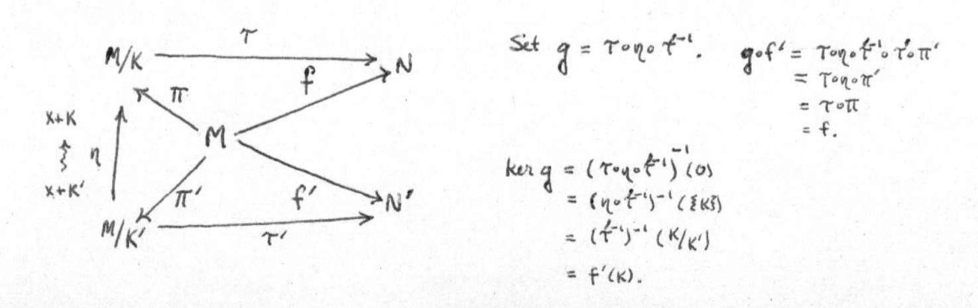

By theorem 14 there is a unique linear mapping g (resp.: g') of $f'(M) = N'$ into N (resp.: $f(M) = N$ into N') such that $f = g \circ f'$ (resp.: $f' = g' \circ f$). We shall show that g is an isomorphism of N' with N. Since f is onto the equation $f = g \circ f'$ shows that g is onto. Suppose $g(x') = 0$ for some $x' \in N'$. Let $f'(y) = x'$, $y \in M$, then $x' = f'(y) = g'(f(y)) = g'(g(f'(y))) = g'(g(x)) = 0$.

Let K be a submodule of a module M and L a submodule of M; then the natural isomorphism of the additive group $L/(L \cap K)$ with $(L + K)/K$ is also an isomorphism of modules, as follows immediately from the definitions. Moreover, theorem 14, Chapter II, Sect. 3, givers the following result:

Theorem 15. *Let K be a submodule of a module M, and π the natural mapping of M on M/K. Let L be a submodule of M. In order that $\pi(L) = M/K$ it is necessary and sufficient that $M = L + K$; in order for the restriction of π to L to be an isomorphism with M/K, it is necessary and sufficient for M to be the direct sum of L and K. Any submodule of M/K may be written in one and only one way in the form N/K, where N is a submodule of M containing K.*

We know that $\overset{-1}{\pi}(\pi(L)) = L + K$. A necessary and sufficient condition for $\pi(L)$ to be M/K is that $\overset{-1}{\pi}(\pi(L))$ be the whole of M, which proves the first assertion. The second assertion follows from the first and from the fact that the kernel of the restriction of π to L is $L \cap K$. The third assertion is contained in theorem 14, Chapter II, Sect. 3.

Theorem 16. *Let M and N be two modules over a ring R. If f and g are linear mappings of M into N, then the mapping $f + g$ defined by $(f + g)(x) = f(x) + g(x)$ is also linear. The addition we have just defined on the set L of linear mappings of M into N defines on L the structure of a commutative additive group.*

If x, y are elements of M, we have

$$\begin{aligned}(f + g)(x + y) &= f(x + y) + g(x + y) = f(x) + f(y) + g(x) + g(y) \\ &= f(x) + g(x) + f(y) + g(y) = (f + g)(x) + (f + g)(y),\end{aligned}$$

and if $\alpha \in R$,

$$\begin{aligned}(f + g)(\alpha x) &= f(\alpha x) + g(\alpha x) = \alpha f(x) + \alpha g(x) \\ &= \alpha(f(x) + g(x)) = \alpha((f + g)(x));\end{aligned}$$

this shows that $f + g$ is linear. Is is clear that $f + g = g + f$ for any f, g in L. If f, g, h are elements of L, then, for any $x \in M$,

$$((f + g) + h)(x) = f(x) + g(x) + h(x) = (f + (g + h))(x),$$

which shows that the addition in L is associative. It has a zero element, for if f_0 is the constant mapping of value 0 of M into N, then $f + f_0 = f_0 + f$ for any $f \in L$. If $f \in L$, then the mapping $f' : x \rightarrow -f(x)$ is linear, as can be immediately verified; since $f + f' = f' + f = f_0$, we see that L, with our addition, becomes a commutative group.

The notation being as in theorem 16, the additive group of linear mappings of M into N is denoted by

$$\text{Hom}\,(M, N).$$

Let P be a third module over R. Then the mapping $(f, g) \to g \circ f$ of $\text{Hom}\,(M, N) \times \text{Hom}\,(N, P)$ into $\text{Hom}\,(M, P)$ is bi-additive. For, if f, f' are in $\text{Hom}\,(M, N)$ and g in $\text{Hom}\,(N, P)$, we have, for any $x \in M$,

$$(g \circ (f + f'))(x) = g(f(x) + f'(x)) = g(f(x)) + g(f'(x)),$$

whence $g \circ (f + f') = g \circ f + g \circ f'$, and we would see in the same way that $(g + g') \circ f = g \circ f + g' \circ f$ if $f \in \text{Hom}\,(M, N)$, $g, g' \in \text{Hom}\,(N, P)$.

Let N be a module over the ring R, and let S be some other ring. Assume that N has also the structure of a right module over S, and that the following conditions are satisfied: 1) the addition in the right module structure of N over S is the same as the addition in the left module structure of N over R; 2) if $\alpha \in R$, $y \in N$, $\gamma \in S$, then we have $(\alpha x)\gamma = \alpha(x\gamma)$. Then we say that N is an *(R, S)-module*. It follows immediately from conditions 1), 2) that, for any $\gamma \in S$, the mapping $d_\gamma: y \to y\gamma$ is an endomorphism of the module structure of M over R.

Theorem 17. *Let M be a module over R and N an (R, S)-module. If $f \in$ Hom (M, N) and $\gamma \in S$, denote by $f\gamma$ the mapping $x \to f(x)\gamma$ of M into N. Then $f\gamma$ belongs to* Hom (M, N), *and the mapping $(\gamma, f) \to f\gamma$ is the scalar multiplication of a right module structure over S on* Hom (M, N).

The mapping d_γ being defined as above, we have $f\gamma = d_\gamma \circ f$, whence $f\gamma \in \text{Hom}\,(M, N)$. If γ, γ' are in S, then $d_{\gamma+\gamma'} = d_\gamma + d_{\gamma'}$; it follows that $(\gamma, f) \to f\gamma$ is a bi-additive mapping of $S \times \text{Hom}\,(M, N)$ into $\text{Hom}\,(M, N)$. Moreover, it is clear that $f(\gamma\gamma') = (f\gamma)\gamma'$ and that $f1_S = f$, if 1_S is the unit element of S. Theorem 17 is thereby proved.

Theorem 17a. *Let M be an (R, S)–module and N an R-module. If $f \in$ Hom (M, N) and $\gamma \in S$, denote by γf the mapping $x \to f(x\gamma)$ of M into N. Then γf belongs to* Hom (M, N) *and the mapping $(\gamma, f) \to \gamma f$ is the scalar multiplication of a module structure over S on* Hom (M, N).

If d_γ is the mapping $x \to x\gamma$ of M into itself, then $\gamma f = f \circ d_\gamma$, whence $\gamma f \in \text{Hom}\,(M, N)$. We see in the same manner as in the proof of theorem 17 that $(\gamma, f) \to \gamma f$ is a bi-additive mapping. If $\gamma, \gamma' \in S$, $f \in \text{Hom}\,(M, N)$, $x \in M$, we have $(\gamma(\gamma' f))(x) = (\gamma' f)(x\gamma) = f((x\gamma)\gamma') = f(x(\gamma\gamma'))$, which shows that $\gamma(\gamma' f) = (\gamma\gamma')f$. Finally, it is clear that $1_S f = f$ if 1_S is the unit element of S; theorem 17 *a* is thereby proved.

By a *double module* over a ring R is meant an (R, R)-module. If R is a commutative ring, then every module M over R has an (R, R)-module structure: we define $x\alpha$ to be αx if $\alpha \in R$, $x \in M$, and it is then clear that

$\alpha(x\beta) = (\alpha x)\beta$ for any α, β in R and x in M. Assuming that R is commutative, and that M and N are modules over R, the results of theorems 17 and 17 *a* give us a way to define right module structures and left module structures on Hom (M, N). If $f \in$ Hom (M, N), $\alpha \in R$, we have $f\alpha = \alpha f$; for, if $x \in M$, $(f\alpha)(x) = (f(x))\alpha = \alpha f(x) = (\alpha f)(x)$. Thus, *if M and N are modules over a commutative ring R, we may consider* Hom (M, N) *as a module over R.*

On the other hand, any ring R (commutative or not) may be considered either as a left module or as a right module over itself. The associativity of the multiplication in R implies that R is an (R, R)-module. Let M be any module over R; then Hom (M, R) is a right module over R; this module is called the *dual module* of M; its elements, which are the linear mappings of M into R, are also called the *linear forms on M*.

We can define in a similar manner the notions of linear mapping of a right module into a right module and of linear form on a right module. The set of linear forms on a right module M has the structure of a left module over R; this module is called the *dual module* of M.

Let M be a left module over R and M^* its dual module. Since M^* is a right module, it has a dual module $(M^*)^* = M^{**}$, which is a left module over R; M^{**} is called the *bidual* of M.

Let x be a fixed element of M. Let φ_x be the mapping of M^* into R defined by

$$\varphi_x(f) = f(x) \qquad (f \in M^*).$$

Then φ_x is a linear form on M^*. For, let f and g be elements of M^*. Then $\varphi_x(f + g) = (f + g)(x) = f(x) + g(x) = \varphi_x(f) + \varphi_x(g)$. Now, let α be in R. Then $\varphi_x(f\alpha) = (f\alpha)(x) = f(x)\alpha = (\varphi_x(f))\alpha$; thus φ_x is linear, and is therefore an element of M^{**}. The mapping $x \to \varphi_x$ is called the *natural mapping* of M into M^{**}.

Theorem 18. *Let M be a module over the ring R. Then the natural mapping of M into its bidual M^{**} is linear.*

We use the same notation as above. Let x, y be elements of M; then we have, for any $f \in M^*$, $\varphi_{x+y}(f) = f(x + y) = f(x) + f(y) = \varphi_x(f) + \varphi_y(f)$, whence $\varphi_{x+y} = \varphi_x + \varphi_y$. Now, let α be an element of R. Then

$$\varphi_{\alpha x}(f) = f(\alpha x) = \alpha f(x) = \alpha\varphi_x(f) = (\alpha\varphi_x)(f),$$

whence $\varphi_{\alpha x} = \alpha\varphi_x$. This proves theorem 18.

EXAMPLES *a*) Take for M the ring R itself, considered as a left module. Let f be a linear form on R, and suppose $f(1) = \lambda$. Then we have, for any $\alpha \in R$, $f(\alpha) = f(\alpha \cdot 1) = \alpha f(1) = \alpha\lambda$, and we see that f is the mapping $\alpha \to \alpha\lambda$,

i. e., the right multiplication by λ. Conversely, if λ is any element of R, the mapping $\alpha \to \alpha\lambda$ is a linear form on R; for we have, for $\alpha, \beta \in R$,

$$(\alpha + \beta)\lambda = \alpha\lambda + \beta\lambda \quad \text{and} \quad (\alpha\beta)\lambda = \alpha(\beta\lambda).$$

It is therefore clear that the mapping $f \to f(1)$ is a bijection of the dual R^* of R on R. This mapping is also an isomorphism of right modules if we give to R the structure of a right module over itself; for, if $f, g \in R^*$, we have $(f + g)(1) = f(1) + g(1)$, and, if $\mu \in R$, $(f\mu)(1) = f(1)\mu$. Thus we see that R^* is isomorphic to R itself, considered as a right module over itself. We see in the same way that the dual module of R with its right module structure is isomorphic to R, considered as a left module. It follows that the bidual of R, considered as a left module, is isomorphic to R. If $\alpha \in R$, $f \in R^*$, then $f(\alpha) = \alpha \cdot f(1)$; it follows that the natural mapping of R into R^{**} is in that case an isomorphism.

b) Take R to be the ring $\underline{Z}$ of integers and M to be $\underline{Z}_n$, where n is an integer > 0. Let f be a linear form on $\underline{Z}_n$. If x is any element of $\underline{Z}_n$, then $nx = 0$ in $\underline{Z}_n$, whence $nf(x) = f(nx) = 0$. Since $n > 0$ and $f(x) \in \underline{Z}$, this implies $f(x) = 0$. It follows that $(\underline{Z}_n)^* = \{0\}$, and therefore also $(\underline{Z}_n)^{**} = \{0\}$. In that case, the natural mapping of M into M^{**} is the zero mapping; it is a surjection but not an injection if $n > 1$. There are also cases in which the natural mapping of M into M^{**} is neither an injection nor a surjection.

Let M and N be modules over a ring R, and M^* and N^* their dual modules. Let f be a linear mapping of M into N. If $v \in N^*$, then $v \circ f$ is a linear form on M, and therefore an element of M^*. The mapping $v \to v \circ f$ of N^* into M^* is linear; for, firstly, it is clear that $(v + v') \circ f = v \circ f + v' \circ f$ if v, v' are in N^*; secondly, if $\alpha \in R$, we have, for any $x \in M$,

$$(v\alpha \circ f)(x) = (v\alpha)(f(x)) = (v(f(x)))\alpha = ((v \circ f)\alpha)(x).$$

The linear mapping $v \to v \circ f$ is called the *transpose mapping* of f and is denoted by ${}^tf$.

It follows immediately from the definition that the mapping $f \to {}^tf$ of Hom (M, N) into Hom (N^*, M^*) is a group homomorphism. Let M, N and P be modules over R, f a linear mapping of M into N and g a linear mapping of N into P; then we have

$${}^t(g \circ f) = {}^tf \circ {}^tg.$$

For, let w be in the dual of P; then

$$({}^t(g \circ f))(w) = (g \circ f) \circ w = g \circ (f \circ w) = g \circ ({}^tf(w)) = {}^tg({}^tf(w)),$$

which proves our formula.

If R is a commutative ring, then the mapping $f \to {}^tf$ of Hom (M, N) into Hom (N^*, M^*) is linear. For, let α be in R and v in N^*; then $({}^t(\alpha f))(v) = (\alpha f) \circ v$; the image of an element x of M under this mapping is $v((\alpha f)(x)) = v(\alpha f(x)) = \alpha v(f(x))$, whence $(\alpha f) \circ v = \alpha(f \circ v)$ and ${}^t(\alpha f) = \alpha {}^tf$.

Wrong again.
For each $v \in N^*$ and for each $x \in M$, $(({}^t(\alpha f))(v))(x) = (v \circ \alpha f)(x) = v(\alpha f(x)) = v(\alpha(f(x)))$
$= \alpha(v(f(x))) = (\alpha(v \circ f))(x) = (\alpha({}^tf(v)))(x) = ((\alpha {}^tf)(v))(x)$,
so $({}^t(\alpha f))(v) = (\alpha {}^tf)(v)$, and ${}^t(\alpha f) = \alpha {}^tf$.

No. $({}^t(g \circ f))(w) = w \circ (g \circ f) = (w \circ g) \circ f$
$= ({}^tg(w)) \circ f = {}^tf({}^tg(w)) = ({}^tf \circ {}^tg)(w)$,
so ${}^t(g \circ f) = {}^tf \circ {}^tg$.

6. Products

Let $(M_i)_{i\in I}$ be a family of modules over a ring R. Then $\prod_{i\in I}M_i$ is an additive group. Let π_i be its projection on M_i. Then we can define on $\prod_{i\in I}M_i$ a module structure over R such that, for each i, π_i is a linear mapping. In fact, define a scalar multiplication on $\prod_{i\in I}M_i$ by the formula

$$\alpha(x_i)_{i\in I} = (\alpha x_i)_{i\in I}$$

for $(x_i)_{i\in I} \in \prod_{i\in I}M_i$. If α, $\beta \in R$ and $(x_i)_{i\in I}$, $(y_i)_{i\in I}$ are elements of $\prod_{i\in I}M_i$, then we have

$$\begin{aligned}
(\alpha + \beta)(x_i)_{i\in I} &= ((\alpha + \beta)x_i)_{i\in I} = (\alpha x_i + \beta x_i)_{i\in I} \\
&= (\alpha x_i)_{i\in I} + (\beta x_i)_{i\in I} = \alpha(x_i)_{i\in I} + \beta(x_i)_{i\in I} \\
(\alpha\beta)(x_i)_{i\in I} &= ((\alpha\beta)x_i)_{i\in I} = (\alpha(\beta x_i))_{i\in I} = \alpha(\beta x_i)_{i\in I} = \alpha(\beta(x_i)_{i\in I}) \\
\alpha((x_i)_{i\in I} + (y_i)_{i\in I}) &= \alpha(x_i + y_i)_{i\in I} = (\alpha(x_i + y_i))_{i\in I} \\
&= (\alpha x_i + \alpha y_i)_{i\in I} = (\alpha x_i)_{i\in I} + (\alpha y_i)_{i\in I} \\
&= \alpha(x_i)_{i\in I} + \alpha(y_i)_{i\in I} \\
1\cdot(x_i)_{i\in I} &= (1\cdot x_i)_{i\in I} = (x_i)_{i\in I}.
\end{aligned}$$

This shows that our scalar multiplication defines on $\prod_{i\in I}M_i$ a module structure; this module is called the *product of the modules* M_i. It is clear that, for each i, π_i is a linear mapping of $\prod_{i\in I}M_i$ into M_i.

Theorem 19. *Let M and M_i $(i \in I)$ be modules over a ring R; let π_i be the projection of $\prod_{i\in I}M_i$ on M_i. A necessary and sufficient condition for a mapping f of M into $\prod_{i\in I}M_i$ to be linear is that, for each i, $\pi_i \circ f$ should be a linear mapping of M into M_i.*

The condition is obviously necessary. If it is satisfied, then we know that f is a homomorphism of the additive group M into the additive group $\prod_{i\in I}M_i$ (theorem 12, Chapter I, Sect. 5). Let α be in R and x in M; set $f(x) = (y_i)_{i\in I}$, $f(\alpha x) = (z_i)_{i\in I}$. Then, for each i, we have $(\pi_i \circ f)(x) = y_i$, $(\pi_i \circ f)(\alpha x) = z_i$, whence $z_i = \alpha y_i$ since $\pi_i \circ f$ is linear. It follows that $f(\alpha x) = \alpha f(x)$; f is therefore linear.

It follows immediately from the definitions that $\prod^w_{i\in I}M_i$ is a submodule of $\prod_{i\in I}M_i$. The natural injection ψ_i of M_i into $\prod^w_{i\in I}M_i$ is linear. For, we know already that this mapping is a homomorphism of the additive group of M_i. If $\alpha \in R$ and $x \in M_i$, then we have $\pi_j(\psi_i(\alpha x)) = 0 = \alpha\pi_j(\psi_i(x))$ if $j \neq i$, and $\pi_i(\psi_i(\alpha x)) = \alpha x = \alpha\pi_i(\psi_i(x))$; thus each $\pi_j \circ \psi_i$ is linear, and our assertion follows from theorem 19.

Theorem 20. *Let M_i ($i \in I$) and N be modules over a ring R; denote by ψ_i the natural injection of M_i into $\prod^w_{i \in I} M_i$. Let there be given, for each $i \in I$, a linear mapping θ_i of M_i into N. Then there exists a unique linear mapping θ of $\prod^w_{i \in I} M_i$ into N such that $\theta \circ \psi_i = \theta_i$ for every $i \in I$.*

We know that there exists a unique homomorphism θ of the additive group of $\prod^w_{i \in I} M_i$ into N such that $\theta \circ \psi_i = \theta_i$ for every $i \in I$ (theorem 13, Chapter I, Sect. 5). Let α be an element of R. Then the mappings $\theta' : x \to \theta(\alpha x)$ and $\theta'' : x \to \alpha\theta(x)$ are obviously homomorphisms of the additive group $\prod^w_{i \in I} M_i$ into N; we have, for any $i \in I$, and for any $y \in M_i$, $(\theta' \circ \psi_i)(y) = \theta(\alpha\psi_i(y)) = (\theta \circ \psi_i)(\alpha y) = \alpha((\theta \circ \psi_i)(y)) = (\theta'' \circ \psi_i)(y)$; it follows that $\theta' = \theta''$ (by the result quoted just above). This proves that θ is linear.

Corollary 1. *Let $(M_i)_{i \in I}$ be a family of submodules of a module M. Then the formula $\lambda((x_i)_{i \in I}) = \sum_{i \in I} x_i$ (for any $(x_i)_{i \in I} \in \prod^w_{i \in I} M_i$) defines a linear mapping of $\prod^w_{i \in I} M_i$ into M. A necessary and sufficient condition for λ to be a monomorphism is that the sum $\sum_{i \in I} M_i$ be direct.*

Let the notation be as in theorem 20. If λ' is the linear mapping of $\prod^w_{i \in I} M_i$ into M such that $\lambda' \circ \psi_i$ is the identity mapping for any $i \in I$, then we have $\lambda' = \lambda$ (theorem 13, Chapter I, Sect. 5), which shows that λ is linear. In order for an element $(x_i)_{i \in I} \in \prod^w_{i \in I} M_i$ to belong to the kernel of λ, it is necessary and sufficient that $\sum_{i \in I} x_i = 0$, which proves the second assertion.

Corollary 2. *Assume that a module M over a ring R is the direct sum of a family $(M_i)_{i \in I}$ of submodules. Let N be a module over R; let there be given for each $i \in I$ a linear mapping f_i of M_i into N. Then there exists a unique linear mapping f of M into N which extends all the mappings f_i. The group* Hom (M, N) *is isomorphic to $\prod_{i \in I}$* Hom (M_i, N); *if N has a double module structure over R, then the right module* Hom (M, N) *is isomorphic to $\prod_{i \in I}$* Hom (M_i, N).

Let the notation be as in corollary 1; in this case, λ is an isomorphism of $\prod^w_{i \in I} M_i$ with M. Let ψ_i be the natural injection of M_i into $\prod^w_{i \in I} M_i$. Then there exists a unique linear mapping θ of $\prod^w_{i \in I} M_i$ into N such that $\theta \circ \psi_i = f_i$ for every i. If we set $f = \theta \circ \overset{-1}{\lambda}$, then f is the unique linear mapping of M into N which extends all mappings f_i. For any linear mapping f of M into N, let $\rho_i(f)$ be the restriction of f to M_i; then it follows from the first part of the corollary that the mapping $\rho : f \to (\rho_i(f))_{i \in I}$ is a bijection of the set Hom (M, N) on $\prod_{i \in I}$ Hom (M_i, N). If ω_i is the i-th projection of $\prod_{i \in I}$ Hom (M_i, N), then $\omega_i \circ \rho = \rho_i$, and ρ_i is clearly a homomorphism of the additive group Hom (M, N). It follows that ρ is an isomorphism. If N

A converse may be proven. Let $(p_i)_{i \in I}$ be a family of projectors of M. Set $M_i = p_i(M)$, for each $i \in I$. Suppose $p_i(M_j) = \{0\}$, when $i \neq j$. Suppose that for each $x \in M$, $I_x = \{i \in I \mid p_i(x) \neq 0\}$ is finite and $x = \sum_{i \in I_x} p_i(x)$. Then M is the direct sum of $(M_i)_{i \in I}$.

has a structure of a double module, then each ρ_i is clearly linear, which proves that ρ is then linear.

By a *projector* of a module M is meant an endomorphism p of M such that $p \circ p = p$.

Theorem 21. *Let M be a module which is the direct sum of a family $(M_i)_{i \in I}$ of submodules. Then there exists a unique family $(p_i)_{i \in I}$ of projectors of M such that $p_i(M) = M_i$, $p_i(M_j) = \{0\}$ if $i \neq j$; if $x \in M$, then the sum $\Sigma_{i \in I} p_i(x)$ is defined and we have $x = \Sigma_{i \in I} p_i(x)$.*

Let the isomorphism λ of $\Pi^w_{i \in I} M_i$ with M be defined as in corollary 1 to theorem 20. Denote by π_i the i-th projection of $\Pi_{i \in I} M_i$, and set $p_i = \pi_i \circ \overset{-1}{\lambda}$. Then p_i is a linear mapping of M into M_i. For each j, the restriction of $\overset{-1}{\lambda}$ to M_j is the natural injection ψ_j of M_j into $\Pi^w_{i \in I} M_i$. Since $\pi_i \circ \psi_i$ is the identity mapping of M_i, and $\pi_i \circ \psi_j = 0$ if $i \neq j$, we have $p_i(M_i) = M_i$, $p_i(M_j) = \{0\}$ if $j \neq i$; more precisely, we have $p_i(x) = x$ if $x \in M_i$, whence $p_i(p_i(x)) = p_i(x)$ for any $x \in M$ since $p_i(x) \in M_i$; this shows that each p_i is a projector. Conversely, if p_i' is a projector such that $p_i'(M) = M_i$, $p_i'(M_j) = \{0\}$ for $j \neq i$, then we have, for $x \in M$, $p_i'(p_i'(x)) = p_i'(x)$, whence $p_i'(x_i) = x_i$ if $x_i \in M_i$; it follows that $p_i' = p_i$. Let $x = \Sigma_{j \in I} x_j$ be any element of M (with $x_j \in M_j$ for all j). Then

$$p_i(x) = \Sigma_{j \in I} p_i(x_j) = x_i \quad \text{and} \quad x = \Sigma_{i \in I} p_i(x).$$

The notation being as in theorem 21,we say that $(p_i)_{i \in I}$ is the *family of projectors* associated with the direct sum decomposition $M = \Sigma_{i \in I} M_i$.

Theorem 22. *Let M be a module and M' a submodule of M. In order for M' to be a direct summand in M, it is necessary and sufficient that there should exist a projector p of M such that $p(M) = M'$.*

The condition is necessary in view of theorem 21. Assume that it is satisfied, and let M'' be the kernel of p. If $x \in M$, then we have $x - p(x) \in M''$ for $p(x - p(x)) = p(x) - (p \circ p)(x) = 0$; the formula $x = p(x) + (x - p(x))$; then shows that $M = M' + M''$. Let x be in $M' \cap M''$; then we may write $x = p(y)$ for some $y \in M$, whence $x = p(p(y)) = p(x) = 0$ since $x \in M''$; this shows that the sum $M' + M''$ is direct.

7. Uniqueness theorems for semi-simple modules

Let M be a semi-simple module. For every simple submodule N of M, let S_N be the sum of all those submodules of M which are isomorphic to N. The submodules S_N of M are called the *isotypic submodules* of M. Assume that we are given any representation $M = \sum_{i \in I} M_i$ of M as a direct sum of simple submodules. Let $I(N)$ be the set of indices i such that $M_i \cong N$; then we shall see that $S_N = \sum_{i \in I(N)} M_i$. It is obvious that $\sum_{i \in I(N)} M_i \subset S_N$; it will therefore be sufficient to prove that any submodule N' of M which is isomorphic to N is contained in $\sum_{i \in I(N)} M_i$. Let $(p_i)_{i \in I}$ be the family of projectors associated with the direct sum decomposition $M = \sum_{i \in I} M_i$. For any i, p_i induces a linear mapping of N' into M_i; since N' and M_i are simple, this linear mapping is either 0 or an isomorphism (theorem 13, Sect. 5); the second case can only occur if $i \in I(N)$. If $x \in N'$, we have $x = \sum_{i \in I} p_i(x) = \sum_{i \in I(N)} p_i(x) \in \sum_{i \in I(N)} M_i$, which proves our assertion.

Theorem 23. *Let M be a semi-simple module. Let $(N_\alpha)_{\alpha \in A}$ be a family of simple submodules of M with the following property: for each simple submodule N of M, there exists one and only one index α such that $N \cong N_\alpha$. Let S_α be the sum of the submodules of M isomorphic to N_α. Then M is the direct sum of the modules S_α.*

Let $M = \sum_{i \in I} M_i$ be a representation of M as a direct sum of simple submodules. For each $\alpha \in A$, let $I(\alpha)$ be the set of indices i such that $M_i \cong N_\alpha$; then we have seen that $S_\alpha = \sum_{i \in I(\alpha)} M_i$. On the other hand, it is clear that $(I(\alpha))_{\alpha \in A}$ is a partition of I. Theorem 23 therefore follows from theorem 8, Sect. 4.

Theorem 23 may be expressed by saying that any semi-simple module is the direct sum of its isotypic submodules.

A module is said to be isotypic if it is one of its own isotypic submodules, i. e., if all its simple submodules are isomorphic to each other. Two isotypic modules M and M' are said to be of the *same type* if any simple submodule of M is isomorphic to any simple submodule of M'.

Theorem 24. *Let M and M' be isotypic modules of the same type; assume that $M = \sum_{i \in I} M_i$, $M' = \sum_{i' \in I'} M'_{i'}$, are representations of M and M' as direct sums of simple submodules. A necessary and sufficient condition for M and M' to be isomorphic is that I and I' should be equipotent sets.*

We first prove that the condition is sufficient. Let λ be a bijection of I on I'. For each $i \in I$, let f_i be an isomorphism of M_i with $M'_{\lambda(i)}$. Then there exists a linear mapping f of M into M' which extends all mappings f_i (corollary 2 to theorem 20, Sect. 6). Since $f(M_i) = M'_{\lambda(i)}$, we have $M'_{i'} \subset f(M)$ for every $i' \in I'$, whence $f(M) = M'$. Let $x = \sum_{i \in I} x_i$ ($x_i \in M_i$) be an element of the kernel of f; then $f(x) = \sum_{i \in I} f_i(x_i) = 0$ and $f_i(x_i) \in M'_{\lambda(i)}$; since λ is an injection, we have $f_i(x_i) = 0$ for every $i \in I$, whence $x_i = 0$, $x = 0$. This shows that f is an isomorphism.

Assume now that φ is an isomorphism of M and M'. We first prove by induction on ν that, if I is a finite set with ν elements, then so is I'. This is obvious if $\nu = 0$; assume that it is true for $\nu - 1$, ν being > 0. Let a' be any index in I' and set $N' = \Sigma_{i \neq a'} M'_i$; denote by π' the natural mapping of M' on $M'/M'_{a'}$. The module M' is the direct sum of $M'_{a'}$ and N' (theorem 8, Sect. 4); M'/N' is therefore isomorphic to $M'_{a'}$, and consequently simple. $\overset{-1}{\varphi}(M'_{a'})$ is isomorphic to $M'_{a'}$ and thus is a simple submodule of M. By theorem 11, Sect. 4, there is a subset J of I such that $M = \overset{-1}{\varphi}(M'_{a'}) + N$ (direct) where $N = \Sigma_{i \in J} M_i$; denote by π the natural mapping of M on $M/\overset{-1}{\varphi}(M'_{a'})$; again M/N is isomorphic to $\overset{-1}{\varphi}(M'_{a'})$, and therefore simple. Let ρ be the natural mapping of M on M/N. We have $M/N = \rho(M) = \Sigma_{i \in I} \rho(M_i)$; thus, there exists an index $a \in I$ such that $\rho(M_a) \neq \{0\}$. The restriction of ρ to M_a is an isomorphism of M_a with M/N (theorem 13, Sect. 5), which shows that $M = M_a + N$ (direct). But $M = M_a + \Sigma_{i \neq a} M_i$ (direct); thus both N and $\Sigma_{i \neq a} M_i$ are isomorphic to M/M_a; since the set of elements $\neq a$ in I has $\nu - 1$ elements, by the induction assumption J must have $\nu - 1$ elements. Now $\pi' \circ \varphi$ and π are epimorphisms of the module M into $M'/M'_{a'}$ and $M/\overset{-1}{\varphi}(M'_{a'})$, respectively, both with kernel $\overset{-1}{\varphi}(M'_{a'})$; by the corollary to theorem 14, Sect. 5, $M'/M'_{a'}$ and $M/\overset{-1}{\varphi}(M'_{a'})$ are isomorphic. But $M'/M'_{a'}$ is isomorphic to N' and $M/\overset{-1}{\varphi}(M'_{a'})$ is isomorphic to N (since the sums $M' = M'_{a'} + N'$ and $M = \overset{-1}{\varphi}(M'_{a'}) + N$ are direct), and thus N and N' are isomorphic; applying the induction assumption, the set of elements $\neq a'$ in I' also has $\nu - 1$ elements, and I' has ν elements, which proves the assertion for ν.

It follows that, if either I or I' is finite, then they both are, and they have the same number of elements.

Assume now that I is infinite. For each $i \in I$, let x_i be an element $\neq 0$ in M_i; then we can find a finite subset $F'(i)$ of I' such that $\varphi(x_i) \in \Sigma_{j \in F'(i)} M'_j$. We then have $\varphi(M_i) \cap \Sigma_{j \in F'(i)} M'_j \neq \{0\}$, for $\varphi(x_i) \neq 0$, whence $\varphi(M_i) \subset \Sigma_{j \in F'(i)} M'_j$ since $\varphi(M_i)$ is simple. Let $I'' = \bigcup_{i \in I} F'(i)$; then we have $\varphi(M_i) \subset \Sigma_{i \in I''} M'_i$ for all i, whence $M' = \varphi(M) = \Sigma_{i \in I} \varphi(M_i) \subset \Sigma_{i \in I''} M'_i$. The sum $\Sigma_{i \in I'} M'_i$ being direct, it follows that $I'' = I'$. Each of the sets $F'(i)$ being finite and I infinite, it follows that card $I' \leqslant$ card I. In the same way we can prove that card $I \leqslant$ card I'. Theorem 24 is thereby proved.

Theorem 25. *Let M be a semi-simple module; let $M = \Sigma_{i \in I} M_i$ be a representation of M as a direct sum of simple modules. Assume that I is finite. Then, if $M = \Sigma_{i' \in I'} M'_{i'}$ is any decomposition of M into a direct sum of simple modules, I' is finite and has the same number of elements as I.*

Select a family $(N_\alpha)_{\alpha\in A}$ of simple submodules of M with the property stated in theorem 23, and define S_α as in that theorem. Let $I(\alpha)$ (resp.: $I'(\alpha)$) be the set of elements i of I (resp.: i' of I') such that $M_i \simeq N_\alpha$ (resp.: $M'_{i'} \simeq N_\alpha$). Then we have seen above that $S_\alpha = \sum_{i\in I(\alpha)} M_i = \sum_{i\in I'(\alpha)} M'_i$; making use of theorem 24, we see that, for every α, $I'(\alpha)$ is a finite set with the same number of elements as $I(\alpha)$, which proves theorem 25.

The notation being as in theorem 25, we say that M is of *finite length*, and we call *length of M* the number of elements of I.

Theorem 26. *Let M be a semi-simple module of finite length l. If M' is a submodule of M, then M' is of finite length l', and $l' \leqslant l$; M/M' is of finite length $l - l'$. If $l' = l$, then we have $M' = M$.*

Let $M = \sum_{i\in I} M_i$ and $M' = \sum_{i'\in I'} M'_{i'}$ be representations of M and M' as direct sums of simple modules. We know (by theorem 11, Sect. 4) that there exists a subset J of I such that M is the direct sum of M' and $\sum_{i\in J} M_i$, whence $M = \sum_{i'\in I'} M'_{i'} + \sum_{i\in J} M_i$ (direct). It follows that I' is finite and that l is the sum of the numbers of elements of I' and J. This means that M' is of finite length $l' \leqslant l$ and that J has $l - l'$ elements. Since $M/M' \simeq \sum_{i\in J} M_i$, M/M' is of length $l - l'$. It follows that, if $l' = l$ then $M' = M$.

8. Tensor products of modules

Let R be a ring, M a right module over R and N a left module over R. A mapping β of the set $M \times N$ into a commutative additive group H is called a *balanced map* if it satisfies the following conditions: 1) it is bi-additive; 2) if $x \in M$, $y \in N$, $\alpha \in R$, we have $\beta(x\alpha, y) = \beta(x, \alpha y)$.

Theorem 27. *Let R be a ring, M a right module over R and N a left module over R. Then there exist an additive group T and a balanced map τ of $M \times N$ into T with the following property: if β is any balanced map of $M \times N$ into a commutative additive group H, then there exists a unique homomorphism f of T into H such that $\beta = f \circ \tau$.*

We construct a free commutative group (Φ, λ) on the set $M \times N$ (disregarding completely the additive group structure of this set). If Ω is any subgroup of Φ, we denote by π_Ω the natural homomorphism of Φ on Φ/Ω. Let Σ be the set of subgroups Ω of Φ which have the property that $\pi_\Omega \circ \lambda$ is a balanced map, and let Ω_0 be the intersection of all groups in Σ; set $T = \Phi/\Omega_0$, $\tau = \pi_{\Omega_0} \circ \lambda$. The mapping τ is balanced. For, let x, x' be elements of M, y, y' elements of N and α an element of R. If Ω is any group belonging to Σ, the images under $\pi_\Omega \circ \lambda$ of the elements $(x + x', y) - (x, y) - (x',y)$,

$(x, y + y') - (x, y) - (x, y')$, $(x\alpha, y) - (x, \alpha y)$ are zero, which proves that the images under λ of these elements are in Ω. This being true for every $\Omega \in \Sigma$, the images under λ of these three elements are in Ω_0, and their images under $\tau = \pi_{\Omega_0} \circ \lambda$ are 0, which proves that τ is balanced. Now, let β be any balanced mapping of $M \times N$ into a commutative group H. Then, by definition of a free commutative group there exists a unique homomorphism F of Φ into H such that $\beta = F \circ \lambda$. Let Ω be the kernel of F; then F may be factored in the form $G \circ \pi_\Omega$, where G is an isomorphism of Φ/Ω with $F(\Phi)$. We have $G \circ \pi_\Omega \circ \lambda = F \circ \lambda = \beta$, whence $\pi_\Omega \circ \lambda = \overset{-1}{G} \circ \beta$; it follows immediately from this formula that $\pi_\Omega \circ \lambda$ is balanced, i. e., that $\Omega \in \Sigma$, whence $\Omega_0 \subset \Omega$. Making use of theorem 13, Chapter II, Sect. 3, we may write $F = f \circ \pi_{\Omega_0}$, where f is a unique homomorphism of $T = \Phi/\Omega_0$ into H. We have $f \circ \tau = f \circ \pi_{\Omega_0} \circ \lambda = F \circ \lambda = \beta$. Conversely, let f' be a homomorphism of T into H such that $f' \circ \tau = \beta$; set $F' = f' \circ \pi_{\Omega_0}$. Then we have $F' \circ \lambda = f' \circ \tau = \beta = F \circ \lambda$, whence $F' = F$, in view of the definition of a free commutative group. This implies that $f \circ \pi_{\Omega_0} = f' \circ \pi_{\Omega_0}$ and since f is unique, $f = f'$.

If (T', τ') is any other pair with the same properties, then there exists a unique isomorphism J of T with T' such that $J \circ \tau = \tau'$. In fact, τ' being a balanced map, there is a unique homomorphism J of T into T' such that $J \circ \tau = \tau'$. On the other hand, by the same argument, there is a homomorphism J' of T' into T such that $J' \circ \tau' = \tau$. We have

$$(J \circ J') \circ \tau' = \tau' = I' \circ \tau',$$

where I' is the identity mapping of T', whence $J \circ J' = I'$. We see in the same way that $J' \circ J$ is the identity mapping of T; J is therefore an isomorphism of T with T'. Moreover, $\tau(M \times N)$ is a set of generators of T. For, let T_1 be the submodule of T generated by $\tau(M \times N)$; then there exists a homomorphism f of T into T_1 such that $\tau = f \circ \tau$. We may also consider f as a homomorphism of T into itself; since $\tau = f \circ \tau = I \circ \tau$, where I is the identity mapping of T, we have $f = I$, whence $T_1 = f(T) = T$.

If the pair (T, τ) satisfies the conditions of theorem 27, then we say that T is a *tensor product of* M *and* N and that τ is the *tensor map of* $M \times N$ *into* T. Moreover, T is generally denoted by $M \otimes N$ and $\tau(x, y)$ by $x \otimes y$, when $x \in M$, $y \in N$. (These notations are to be used only in those circumstances where only one tensor product of M and N is considered.) Thus we have.

$$(x + x') \otimes y = x \otimes y + x' \otimes y \qquad (x, x' \in M, \ y \in N)$$
$$x \otimes (y + y') = x \otimes y + x \otimes y' \qquad (x \in M, \ y, y' \in N)$$
$$x\alpha \otimes y = x \otimes \alpha y \qquad (x \in M, y \in N, \alpha \in R).$$

We observe that $-x \otimes y = (-x) \otimes y$. Since T is generated by the set of elements $x \otimes y$, it follows that every element of T may be written in the form $\sum_{i=1}^{m} x_i \otimes y_i$, with $x_i \in M$, $y_i \in N$ $(1 \leqslant i \leqslant m)$.

Let $(x_i)_{i \in I}$ be a family of generators of the module M. Then every element t of $M \otimes N$ may be written in the form $\sum_{i \in I} x_i \otimes y_i$, where $(y_i)_{i \in I}$ is a family of elements of N almost all of which are zero. In fact, consider first the case where $t = x \otimes y$, $x \in M$, $y \in N$. Then we may write $x = \sum_{i \in I} x_i \alpha_i$, $\alpha_i \in R$ with almost all α_i's being 0. We then have

$$t = \sum_{i \in I} x_i \alpha_i \otimes y = \sum_{i \in I} x_i \otimes \alpha_i y$$

which proves our assertion in that case. In the general case, we may write $t = \sum_{k=1}^{m} t_k$ where each t_k is of the form $x'_k \otimes y'_k$, with $x'_k \in M$, $y'_k \in N$; we then have $t_k = \sum_{i \in I} x_i \otimes y_{i,k}$, whence

$$t = \sum_{i \in I} x_i \otimes \left(\sum_{k=1}^{m} y_{i,k}\right).$$

Similarly, if $(y_i)_{i \in I}$ is a set of generators of the module N, then every element of $M \times N$ may be written in the form $\sum_{i \in I} x_i \otimes y_i$, with $x_i \in M$, almost all x_i equal to 0.

Theorem 28. *Let M, M' be right modules and N, N' left modules over a ring R. Let u be a linear mapping of M into M' and v a linear mapping of N into N'; then there exists a unique homomorphism w of $M \otimes N$ into $M' \otimes N'$ such that $w(x \otimes y) = u(x) \otimes v(y)$ for any $(x, y) \in M \times N$.*

It is sufficient to prove that the mapping $(x, y) \to u(x) \otimes v(y)$ is balanced, which follows immediately from the definitions.

The notation being as in theorem 28, the mapping w is denoted by $u \otimes v$.

Furthermore, let u' be a linear mapping of M' into a right module M'' and v' a linear mapping of N' into a left module N''. Then we have

$$(u' \otimes v') \circ (u \otimes v) = (u' \circ u) \otimes (v' \circ v). \tag{1}$$

In fact $(u' \otimes v') \circ (u \otimes v)$ is a homomorphism of $M \otimes N$ into $M'' \otimes N''$, and maps any $(x, y) \in M \times N$ upon $(u' \circ u)(x) \otimes (v' \circ v)(y)$.

We know that the linear mappings of M into M' form an additive group Hom (M, M'). Let u_1, u_2 be two elements of this group, and v a linear mapping of N into N'. Then we have

$$(u_1 + u_2) \otimes v = u_1 \otimes v + u_2 \otimes v \tag{2}$$

where the sum on the right side is to be interpreted by considering $M \otimes N$ and $M' \otimes N'$ as modules over $\underline{Z}$. In order to prove this formula, we observe that both sides of (2) represent homomorphisms of $M \otimes N$ into $M' \otimes N'$ and that

$$((u_1 + u_2) \otimes v)(x \otimes y) = (u_1 + u_2)(x) \otimes v(y) = u_1(x) \otimes v(y) + u_2(x) \otimes v(y)$$
$$= (u_1 \otimes v + u_2 \otimes v)(x \otimes y),$$

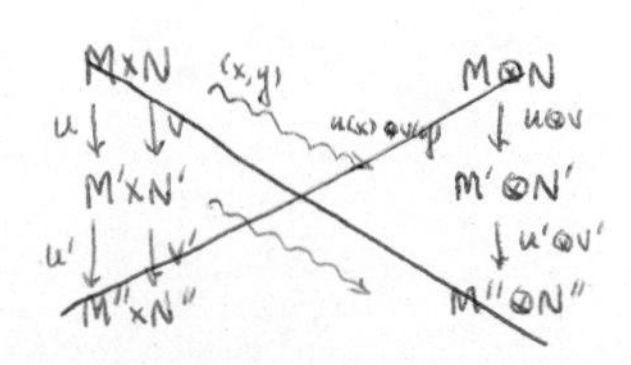

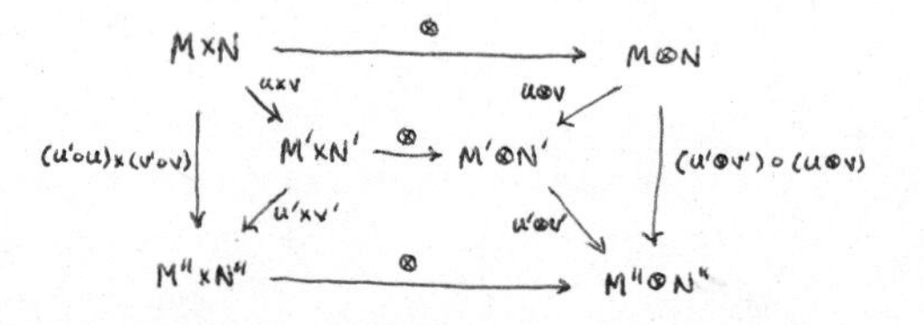

and the equality follows from theorem 28. We see in the same way that, if u is a linear mapping of M into M' and v_1, v_2 are linear mappings of N into N', then

$$(3) \qquad u \otimes (v_1 + v_2) = u \otimes v_1 + u \otimes v_2.$$

Theorem 29. *Let M be a right module over R and N a left module over R. Let u be an epimorphism of M on a module M' and v an epimorphism of N on a module N'; denote by K and L the kernels of u and v respectively. Then the kernel of the mapping $u \otimes v$ of $M \otimes N$ into $M' \otimes N'$ is the additive group H generated by all elements $\xi \otimes y$ and $x \otimes \eta$, where $\xi \in K$ and $\eta \in L$.*

We have $(u \otimes v)(\xi \otimes y) = u(\xi) \otimes v(y) = 0$, $(u \otimes v)(x \otimes \eta) = u(x) \otimes v(\eta) = 0$; this shows that H is contained in the kernel of $u \otimes v$. To prove the converse we shall construct a mapping of $M' \otimes N'$ into $(M \otimes N)/H$. Let φ be the natural homomorphism of $M \otimes N$ on $(M \otimes N)/H$. If $x' \in M'$, $y' \in N'$, select elements $x \in M$, $y \in N$ such that $x' = u(x)$, $y' = v(y)$; then $\varphi(x \otimes y)$ depends only on x', y', not on the choices of x, y. For, let $\bar{x}$ and $\bar{y}$ be any elements such that $x' = u(\bar{x})$, $y' = v(\bar{y})$. Then we have $\xi = \bar{x} - x \in K$ and $\eta = \bar{y} - y \in L$, whence

$$\bar{x} \otimes \bar{y} = x \otimes y + (\xi \otimes y + x \otimes \eta + \xi \otimes \eta) \equiv x \otimes y \pmod{H},$$

and therefore $\varphi(\bar{x} \otimes \bar{y}) = \varphi(x \otimes y)$, which proves our assertion. Let $\varphi(x \otimes y) = \beta(x', y')$; then we shall see that β is a balanced map of $M' \times N'$. Let x_1', x_2' be elements of M', and x_1, x_2 elements of M such that $x_i' = u(x_i)$ $(i = 1, 2)$; let y_1', y_2' be elements of N' and y_1, y_2 elements of N such that $y_i' = v(y_i)$ $(i = 1, 2)$; finally, let α be an element of R. Then

$$\begin{aligned}\beta(x_1' + x_2', y_1') &= \varphi((x_1 + x_2) \otimes y_1) = \varphi(x_1 \otimes y_1) + \varphi(x_2 \otimes y_1) \\ &= \beta(x_1', y_1') + \beta(x_2', y_1'),\end{aligned}$$

and we see in the same way that $\beta(x_1', y_1' + y_2') = \beta(x_1', y_1') + \beta(x_1', y_2)$; finally, we have $\beta(x_1'\alpha, y_1') = \varphi(x_1\alpha \otimes y_1) = \varphi(x_1 \otimes \alpha y_1) = \beta(x_1', \alpha y_1')$, which proves that β is balanced. Thus, there exists a homomorphism λ of $M' \otimes N'$ into $(M \otimes N)/H$ such that $\lambda(x' \otimes y') = \beta(x', y')$ for any $x' \in M'$, $y' \in N'$. It is clear that $\lambda(u(x) \otimes v(y)) = \varphi(x \otimes y)$ for any $x \in M$, $y \in N$, whence $\lambda \circ (u \otimes v) = \varphi$. If z is in the kernel of $u \otimes v$, then we have

$$\varphi(z) = \lambda((u \otimes v)(z)) = \lambda(0) = 0,$$

whence $z \in H$. This proves theorem 29.

It should be observed that the conclusion of theorem 29 would be invalid in general if u and v were not both epimorphisms.

Now let M' be a submodule of M and N' a submodule of N. Denote by $u_{M'}$ the identity mapping of M' into M and by $v_{N'}$ the identity mapping of N' into N. Then $u_{M'} \otimes v_{N'}$ is a homomorphism, which is called the *canon-*

ical homomorphism of $M' \otimes N'$ into $M \otimes N$; but in general it is not a monomorphism. The group $(u_{M'} \otimes v_{N'})(M' \otimes N')$ is obviously the subgroup of $M \otimes N$ generated by all elements of the form $x' \otimes y'$ (where the sign $\otimes$ indicates the tensor map of $M \times N$ into $M \otimes N$). We shall denote this group by $\Theta(M', N')$.

Theorem 30. *Assume that* M *is the sum of a family* $(M_i)_{i \in I}$ *of submodules and* N *the sum of a family* $(N_j)_{j \in J}$ *of submodules; then*

$$M \otimes N = \Sigma_{(i,j) \in I \times J} \Theta(M_i, N_j).$$

If the sums $\Sigma_{i \in I} M_i$, $\Sigma_{j \in J} N_j$ *are direct, then so is the sum* $\Sigma_{(i,j) \in I \times J} \Theta(M_i, N_j)$; *moreover, in that case, the canonical homomorphisms* $M_i \otimes N_j \to \Theta(M_i, N_j)$ *are isomorphisms.*

[In these statements, $M \otimes N$ is considered as a module over the ring $\underline{Z}$ of integers, which accounts for the terms "sum" and "direct sum".]

Let $x = \Sigma_{i \in I} x_i$ $(x_i \in M_i)$ and $y = \Sigma_{j \in J} y_j$ $(y_j \in N_j)$ be any elements of M and N respectively; then we have (by theorem 1, Sect. 1)

$$x \otimes y = \Sigma_{(i,j) \in I \times J} x_i \otimes y_j \in \Sigma_{(i,j) \in I \times J} \Theta(M_i, N_j).$$

Since $\Sigma_{(i,j) \in I \times J} \Theta(M_i, N_j)$ is a group and contains all elements $x \otimes y$, $x \in M$, $y \in N$, it is the whole of $M \otimes N$. Assume now that the given sums are direct. Let $(p_i)_{i \in I}$ and $(q_j)_{j \in J}$ be the families of projectors associated with these sums. Then $p_i \otimes q_j$ is a linear mapping of $M \otimes N$ into $M_i \otimes N_j$. Let u_i and v_j be the identity mappings of M_i and N_j into M and N respectively; then we have $p_i \circ u_{i'} = 0$ if $i \neq i'$, $q_j \circ v_{j'} = 0$ if $j \neq j'$, while $p_i \circ u_i$ is the identity mapping of M_i and $q_j \circ v_j$ the identity mapping of N_j. It follows that $(p_i \otimes q_j)(\Theta(M_{i'}, N_{j'})) = \{0\}$ if $(i', j') \neq (i, j)$ while $(p_i \otimes q_j) \circ (u_i \otimes v_j)$ is the identity mapping of $M_i \otimes N_j$. This being said, let $(t_{ij})_{(i,j) \in I \times J}$ be a family such that $t_{ij} \in \Theta(M_i, N_j)$ and such that the sum $\Sigma_{(i,j)} t_{ij}$ is defined and equal to 0. Then we have

$$0 = (p_i \otimes q_j)(\Sigma_{(i',j')} t_{i'j'}) = (p_i \otimes q_j)(t_{ij});$$

but we may write $t_{ij} = (u_i \otimes v_j)(t'_{ij})$, for some $t'_{ij} \in M_i \otimes N_j$, and then $(p_i \otimes q_j)(t_{ij}) = t'_{ij}$, whence $t'_{ij} = 0$ and $t_{ij} = 0$. This shows that the sum $\Sigma_{(i,j)} \Theta(M_i, N_j)$ is direct. Moreover, $(p_i \otimes q_j) \circ (u_i \otimes v_j)$ being the identity mapping, $u_i \otimes v_j$ is a monomorphism, which completes the proof of theorem 30.

Let M' be a submodule of M which is a *direct summand* in M and N' a submodule of N which is a *direct summand* in N. Denote by τ' the restriction to $M' \times N'$ of the tensor map τ of $M \times N$ into $M \otimes N$; then it follows from theorem 30 that $\Theta(M', N')$ is a tensor product of M' and N', with the tensor map τ'. When no other tensor product of M' and N' has previously been mentioned, we generally denote $\Theta(M', N')$ by $M' \otimes N'$.

We may consider R itself as a right module over R. Let N be any left module over R. We shall see that the additive group of N together with its scalar multiplication σ constitutes a tensor product of R and N. For, the scalar multiplication is obviously a balanced map of $R \times N$ into N. On the other hand, let β be any balanced map of $R \times N$ into an additive group H; if we set $f(x) = \beta(1, x)$, f is a homomorphism of N into H and $f \circ \sigma = \beta$; for $f(\sigma(\alpha, x)) = f(\alpha x) = \beta(1, \alpha x) = \beta(1\,\alpha, x) = \beta(\alpha, x)$ for any $\alpha \in R$, $x \in N$; and it is clear that f is the only homomorphism of N into H such that $f \circ \sigma = \beta$. Thus we may write

$$N = R \otimes N.$$

We would see in the same way that

$$M = M \otimes R$$

if M is a right module over R and R is considered as a left module over itself.

Now, let R and S be rings and let M be an (S, R)-module; let N be a module over R. We shall see that $M \otimes N$ has a structure of a module over S. Let I be the identity mapping of N; if $\gamma \in S$, let d_γ be the dilation of ratio γ in M. Then, if $\gamma \in S$, $d_\gamma \otimes I$ is an endomorphism δ_γ of the group $M \otimes N$. We set $\gamma t = \delta_\gamma(t)$ for any $t \in M \otimes N$. If γ, γ' are elements of S, we have $d_{\gamma+\gamma'} = d_\gamma + d_{\gamma'}$, $d_{\gamma\gamma'} = d_\gamma \circ d_{\gamma'}$; making use of formulas 1), 2), we conclude that $\delta_{\gamma+\gamma'} = \delta_\gamma + \delta_{\gamma'}$, $\delta_{\gamma\gamma'} = \delta_\gamma \circ \delta_{\gamma'}$, whence $(\gamma + \gamma')t = \gamma t + \gamma' t$, $(\gamma\gamma')t = \gamma(\gamma' t)$ if $t \in M \otimes$ N. Moreover, d_1 is the identity mapping of M, from which it follows immediately that $1t = t$ for all $t \in M \otimes N$. This shows that the mapping $(\gamma, t) \rightarrow \gamma t$ defines on $M \otimes N$ a module structure over S.

Theorem 31. *Let M and M' be (S, R)-modules and N, N' modules over R. Let u be a mapping of M into M' which is linear with respect to both the right-module structures of M, M' over R and the left module structures of M, M' over S. Let v be a linear mapping of N into N'. Then $u \otimes v$ is a linear mapping of the module $M \otimes N$ over S into $M' \otimes N'$.*

If $\gamma \in S$, we denote by d_γ and d'_γ the dilations of ratio γ in M and M'; let I and I' be the identity mappings of N and N' respectively. It follows from our assumptions that $u \circ d_\gamma = d'_\gamma \circ u$. Making use of formula 1), we have $(u \otimes v) \circ (d_\gamma \otimes I) = (u \circ d_\gamma) \otimes (v \circ I) = (d'_\gamma \circ u) \otimes (I' \circ v) = (d_\gamma \otimes I') \circ (u \otimes v)$; this means that $(u \otimes v)(\gamma t) = \gamma((u \otimes v)(t))$ for any $t \in M \otimes N$; theorem 31 is thereby proved.

Theorem 32. *Let M be an (S, R)-module and N a module over R. Let P be a module over S and β a mapping of $M \times N$ into P which is balanced (when M*

is considered as an R-module). Assume further that $\beta(\gamma x, y) = \gamma\beta(x, y)$ *if* $\gamma \in S$, $x \in M$, $y \in N$. *Then the homomorphism* f *of* $M \otimes N$ *into* P *such that* $f(x \otimes y) = \beta(x, y)$ *for any* $(x, y) \in M \times N$ *is a linear mapping relative to the module structures over* S *of* $M \otimes N$ *and* P.

Let γ be an element of S. Let f' and f'' be the mappings $t \to f(\gamma t)$ and $t \to \gamma f(t)$ of $M \otimes N$ into P; these mappings are homomorphisms of the additive group $M \otimes N$. Moreover, if $x \in M$, $y \in N$, we have

$$f'(x \otimes y) = f(\gamma(x \otimes y)) = f(\gamma x \otimes y) = \beta(\gamma x, y)$$
$$= \gamma\beta(x, y) = \gamma f(x \otimes y) = f''(x \otimes y).$$

By the definition of a tensor product, we have $f' = f''$. This being true for every $\gamma \in S$, f is linear.

9. Free modules. Bases

Let S be any set and ψ a mapping of S into a module F over a ring R. We say that F, together with ψ, constitutes a *free module on* S *over* R if the following condition is satisfied: if φ is any mapping of S into a module M over R, there exists a unique linear mapping f of F into M such that $f \circ \psi = \varphi$.

If this is the case, then $\psi(S)$ is a set of generators of the module M. Moreover, if (F, ψ) and (F', ψ') are free modules on S over R, then there exists a unique isomorphism J of F with F' such that $J \circ \psi = \psi'$. These statements are established exactly in the same way as the corresponding statements for monoids.

For each $x \in S$, let R_x be identical with R, considered as a module over R. Set $F = \prod^w_{x \in S} R_x$, and denote by ψ_x the natural injection of R_x in F. Set $\psi(x) = \psi_x(1)$; then we shall see that (F, ψ) is a free module on S over R. Let φ be a mapping of S into a module M over R. If $x \in S$, then $\theta_x : \alpha \to \alpha\varphi(x)$ is a linear mapping of R_x into M. For, if α, α' are in R, then

$$\theta_x(\alpha + \alpha') = (\alpha + \alpha')\varphi(x) = \theta_x(\alpha) + \theta_x(\alpha'),$$

and $\theta_x(\alpha\alpha') = (\alpha\alpha')\varphi(x) = \alpha(\alpha'\varphi(x)) = \alpha\theta_x(\alpha')$. There exists a unique linear mapping f of F into M such that $f \circ \psi_x = \theta_x$ for every $x \in S$ (theorem 20, Sect. 6). If $x \in S$, then $f(\psi(x)) = f(\psi_x(1)) = \theta_x(1) = \varphi(x)$, whence $f \circ \psi = \varphi$. Conversely, let f' be a linear mapping of F into M such that $f' \circ \psi = \varphi$. We then have, for $\alpha \in R_x$, $f'(\psi_x(\alpha)) = f'(\alpha\psi_x(1)) = \alpha f'(\psi(x)) = \alpha\varphi(x) = \theta_x(\alpha)$, whence $f' \circ \psi_x = \theta_x$. It follows that $f' = f$ (since f is unique). This shows that (F, ψ) is a free module on S over R.

A family $(x_i)_{i \in I}$ of elements of an R-module M is said to be *linearly independent* if, whenever $(\alpha_i)_{i \in I}$ is a family of elements of R such that $\sum_{i \in I} \alpha_i x_i$ is defined and equal to 0, then $\alpha_i = 0$ for all $i \in I$. We shall say that a family $(u_i)_{i \in I}$ of elements of a module M is a *base* of M if the following condition is satisfied: the elements u_i, $i \in I$, are linearly independent and they form a set of generators of M.

Theorem 33. *Let S be a set and ψ a mapping of S into a module F. In order for (F, ψ) to be a free module on S, it is necessary and sufficient that $(\psi(x))_{x \in S}$ be a base of F.*

Assume first that (F, ψ) is a free module on S. Then it follows from the above construction that there exists an isomorphism J of $\prod^w_{x \in S} R_x$ with F which maps $\psi_x(1)$ upon $\psi(x)$ for every $x \in S$. If $(\alpha_x)_{x \in S} \in \prod^w_{x \in S} R_x$, then $J((\alpha_x)_{x \in S}) = \sum_{x \in S} \alpha_x \psi(x)$. If the right side is 0, then $\alpha_x = 0$ for every $x \in S$, since J is a monomorphism; this shows that the elements $\psi(x)$ are linearly independent. Since J is an epimorphism, the elements $\psi(x)$ generate F; thus they form a base of F. Assume conversely that $(\psi(x))_{x \in S}$ is a base of F. Then we see immediately that the formula written above defines an isomorphism of $\prod^w_{x \in S} R_x$ with F; since $J(\psi_x(1)) = \psi(x)$ for $x \in S$, it follows from the construction given above that (F, ψ) is a free module on S.

Corollary. *Let $(u_i)_{i \in I}$ be a base of a module M over the ring R. Let N be a module over R, and $(a_i)_{i \in I}$ a family of elements of N. Then there exists a unique linear mapping f of M into N such that $f(u_i) = a_i$ for every $i \in I$.*

This follows immediately from theorem 33.

If $(x_i)_{i \in I}$ is a base of a module M, then we have $x_i \neq 0$ for every $i \in I$ and $x_i \neq x_j$ if $i \neq j$; this follows immediately from the fact that the elements x_i are linearly independent.

The notions of being linearly independent or of being a base may be applied not only to families of elements of a module M, but also to subsets of M: a subset S of M is said to be linearly independent (resp.: to be a base) when the family $(y_x)_{x \in S}$, where $y_x = x$ for every $x \in S$, is linearly independent (resp.: is a base). When the word "base" is used, the context will generally indicate whether one means a family of elements or a subset; however, one may make the distinction between the two meanings of the word more precise by using the expressions "basic family" or "basic set" to refer to a base as a family of elements or as a subset respectively. It is clear that, if $(x_i)_{i \in I}$ is a basic family of a module M, then the set of all elements x_i, for $i \in I$, is a basic set.

It is clear that any subset of a linearly independent set is itself linearly independent, and is therefore a base of the submodule it generates.

Theorem 34. *Let M be a module and S a subset of M. In order for S to be linearly independent, it is necessary and sufficient that the following conditions be satisfied:* a) *for every $x \in S$, the mapping $\alpha \to \alpha x$ of R into M is injective;* b) *the sum $\sum_{x \in S} Rx$ is direct.*

Annihilator of {x} is {0}

Assume that S is linearly independent. Assume that $\alpha x = 0$ for some $\alpha \in R$ and $x \in S$; if we set $\alpha_x = \alpha$ and $\alpha_y = 0$ for every $y \neq x$ in S, then $\sum_{z \in S} \alpha_z z = 0$, whence $\alpha_z = 0$ for every $z \in S$, and, in particular $\alpha = 0$; since $\alpha \to \alpha x$ is a group homomorphism, it is an injective mapping. Let $(y_x)_{x \in S}$ be a family of elements of M such that $y_x \in Rx$ for every $x \in S$; assume that the sum $\sum_{x \in S} y_x$ is defined and has the value 0. For each x, let α_x be an element of R such that $y_x = \alpha_x x$. Since $y_x = 0$ for almost all x, it follows from the first part of the proof that $\alpha_x = 0$ for almost all x; since $\sum_{x \in S} \alpha_x x = 0$, we have $\alpha_x = 0$ for all $x \in S$, whence $y_x = 0$, and the sum $\sum_{x \in S} Rx$ is direct. Assume conversely that the conditions are satisfied. Let $(\alpha_x)_{x \in S}$ be a family of elements of R such that $\alpha_x = 0$ for almost all $x \in S$ and $\sum_{x \in S} \alpha_x x = 0$. Then we have $\alpha_x x = 0$ for all $x \in S$ by condition b), whence $\alpha_x = 0$ for all $x \in S$ by condition a); S is therefore linearly independent.

Theorem 35. *Let M be a module, B a subset of M and $B = \bigcup_{i \in I} B_i$ a representation of B as the union of a family of mutually disjoint sets B_i. Let M_i be the submodule generated by B_i. Then the following conditions are equivalent to each other*: a) *B is a base of M*; b) *for each i, B_i is a base of M_i, and M is the direct sum of the modules M_i, $i \in I$.*

If B is a base of M, then B, and therefore also B_i, is a linearly independent set, and B_i is a base of M_i. Since M is the direct sum $\sum_{x \in B} Rx$, $M_i = \sum_{x \in B_i} Rx$, M is the direct sum of the modules M_i (theorem 8, Sect. 4). Conversely, assume that b) is satisfied. It follows immediately from theorem 34 and from theorem 8, Sect. 4, that B is linearly independent. The module M' generated by B contains M_i for every $i \in I$; it follows that $M = \sum_{i \in I} M_i \subset M'$, whence $M = M'$, and B is a base of M.

Theorem 36. *Let f be a linear mapping of a module M into a module N. Let S be a subset of M such that the family $(f(x))_{x \in S}$ is linearly independent in N. Then S is linearly independent, and f induces a monomorphism of the submodule P generated by S. If T is any linearly independent subset of the kernel K of f, then $T \cup S$ is linearly independent. If $(f(x))_{x \in S}$ is a base of N, then $M = P + K$* (direct).

Let $(\alpha_x)_{x \in S}$ be a family of elements of R such that $\alpha_x = 0$ for almost all $x \in S$ and $f(\sum_{x \in S} \alpha_x x) = 0$. Then we have $\sum_{x \in S} \alpha_x f(x) = 0$, whence $\alpha_x = 0$ for all $x \in S$. This shows that S is linearly independent and that $P \cap K = \{0\}$; f therefore induces a monomorphism of P. If Q is the module generated by T, we have $Q \subset K$, which shows that the sum $P + Q$ is direct; by theorem 35, $T \cup S$ is a base of $Q + P$, which shows that this set is linearly independent. Assume that $(f(x))_{x \in S}$ is a base of N. Then, if $y \in M$, $f(y)$ may be represented

Thm. Let M, N be R-modules, and assume N is free. Let α be a linear epimorphism, $\alpha | M \to N$. Then $\ker \alpha$ is a direct summand of M. We may write $M = (\ker \alpha) \oplus P$, where P is free.

in the form $\sum_{x \in S} \alpha_x f(x)$, where $(\alpha_x)_{x \in S}$ is a family of elements of R and $\alpha_x = 0$ for almost all $x \in S$. It follows that $y = \sum_{x \in S} \alpha_x x + z$, with some $z \in K$, and therefore that $y \in P + K$; this shows that $M = P + K$ (direct).

Remark. Let M be a module which has a submodule N which has a base T. Let π be the natural mapping of M on M/N; if S is a subset of M such that $T \cup S$ is linearly independent, then the family $(\pi(x))_{x \in S}$ is linearly independent in M/N.

For, let P be the submodule generated by S; then the sum $N + P$ is direct (theorem 35), which shows that π induces a monomorphism of P. Since S is a base of P, $(\pi(x))_{x \in S}$ is a base of $\pi(P)$, which proves our assertion.

10. Multilinear mappings

In this section, R will denote a *commutative* ring.

Let $(M_i)_{i \in I}$ be a family of modules over R, and let $W = \prod_{i \in I} M_i$ be the product of this family of modules. For each i, we denote by θ_i the natural injection of M_i into W and by π_i the projection of W on M_i.

Let P be any module over R. By a *multilinear mapping* of W into P is meant a mapping φ of W into P which satisfies the following condition: if i is any index in I and $\mathfrak{a}$ an element of W such that $\pi_i(\mathfrak{a}) = 0$, then $x \to \varphi(\theta_i(x) + \mathfrak{a})$ is a linear mapping of M_i into P. A multilinear mapping of W into R (regarded as a module over itself) is called a *multilinear form* on W.

If φ is a multilinear mapping of W into P, it follows immediately from the definition that $\varphi(\mathfrak{x}) = 0$ whenever one of the coordinates of $\mathfrak{x}$ is 0.

The condition of multilinearity may be formulated as follows. Let i be any index in I; let there be given for any $j \neq i$ a fixed element a_j in M_j. If x is any element of M_i, let $\bar{x}$ be the element of W whose j-th coordinate is a_j if $j \neq i$ and whose i-th coordinate is x; then $x \to \varphi(\bar{x})$ must be a linear mapping. In other words, $\varphi((x_i)_{i \in I})$ depends linearly on any one of its arguments when the others are kept fixed.

If I has only two elements a and b, then a bilinear mapping φ of $M_a \times M_b$ is a balanced mapping when M_a is considered as a right module over R. For we have $\varphi(x\alpha, y) = \varphi(\alpha x, y) = \alpha\varphi(x, y) = \varphi(x, \alpha y)$ if $x \in M_a$, $y \in M_b$, $\alpha \in R$.

EXAMPLES: Let M, N and P be modules over R. Then Hom (M, N), Hom (N, P) and Hom (M, P) are modules over R. The mapping $(f, g) \to g \circ f$ of Hom $(M, N) \times$ Hom (N, P) into Hom (M, P) is bilinear.

For, we know already that it is bi-additive. On the other hand, if $\alpha \in R$, $x \in M$, $f \in \operatorname{Hom}(M, N)$, $g \in \operatorname{Hom}(N, P)$, we have

$$(\alpha f \circ g)(x) = (\alpha f)(g(x)) = f(\alpha g(x)) = \alpha f(g(x)),$$

whence $\alpha f \circ g = \alpha(f \circ g)$; and we see in the same way that $f \circ \alpha g = \alpha(f \circ g)$.

Lemma 1. *Let φ be a multilinear mapping of $\prod_{i \in I} M_i$ into P; and let J be a subset of I. Let there be given an element $(a_k)_{k \in I-J}$ of $\prod_{k \in I-J} M_k$. If $\mathfrak{x} \in \prod_{j \in J} M_j$, denote by $\zeta(\mathfrak{x})$ the element of $\prod_{i \in I} M_i$ whose i-th coordinate is the same as that of $\mathfrak{x}$ if $i \in J$, but is a_i if $i \in I$-J. Then $\varphi \circ \zeta$ is a multilinear mapping of $\prod_{j \in J} M_j$ into P.*

If $j \in J$, let θ'_j be the natural injection of M_j into $\prod_{j \in J} M_j$, and let $\mathfrak{a}$ be an element of $\prod_{j \in J} M_j$. Then, if $x \in M_j$, we have

$$\zeta(\theta'_j(x) + \mathfrak{a}) = \theta_j(x) + \zeta(\mathfrak{a}).$$

Moreover, if the j-th coordinate of $\mathfrak{a}$ is 0, then so is the j-th coordinate of $\zeta(\mathfrak{a})$. This proves lemma 1.

Lemma 2. *Let $I = \bigcup_{k \in K} J(k)$ be a partition of the set I into mutually disjoint sets. For each $k \in K$, let N_k be a module over R and ψ_k a multilinear mapping of $\prod_{i \in J(k)} M_i$ into N_k. Furthermore, let φ be a multilinear mapping of $\prod_{k \in K} N_k$ into a module P. If $\mathfrak{x} = (x_i)_{i \in I} \in \prod_{i \in I} M_i$, let $\zeta(x)$ be the element of $\prod_{k \in K} N_k$ whose k-th coordinate is $\psi_k((x_i)_{i \in J(k)})$ for every $k \in K$. Then $\varphi \circ \zeta$ is a multilinear mapping of $\prod_{i \in I} M_i$ into P.*

For each $k \in K$, let ρ_k be the mapping of $\prod_{i \in I} M_i$ into $\prod_{i \in J(k)} M_i$ defined by $\rho_k((x_i)_{i \in I}) = (x_i)_{i \in J(k)}$; ρ_k is obviously linear. Let i_0 be an element of I and k_0 the element of K such that $i_0 \in J(k_0)$. We denote by θ and θ' the natural injections of M_{i_0} into $\prod_{i \in I} M_i$ and $\prod_{i \in J(k_0)} M_i$ respectively, by θ'' the natural injection of N_{k_0} into $\prod_{k \in K} N_k$, and continue to denote by θ_i the natural injection of M_i into $\prod_{i \in I} M_i$. Let $\mathfrak{a}$ be an element of $\prod_{i \in I} M_i$ whose i_0-th coordinate is 0; denote by b_0 the element of $\prod_{k \in K} N_k$ whose k_0-th coordinate if 0 and whose k-th coordinate is $\psi_k(\rho_k(\mathfrak{a}))$ if $k \neq k_0$. We propose to prove that the mapping $x \to \varphi(\zeta(\theta_{i_0}(x) + \mathfrak{a}))$ $(x \in M_{i_0})$ is linear. Set $\mathfrak{a}_0 = \rho_{k_0}(\mathfrak{a})$; then the k_0-th coordinate of $\zeta(\theta_{i_0}(x) + \mathfrak{a})$ is $\psi_{k_0}(\theta_{i_0}(x) + \mathfrak{a}_0)$, while its k-th coordinate is $\psi_k(\rho_k(\mathfrak{a}))$ if $k \neq k_0$. It follows that $\zeta(\theta_{i_0}(x) + \mathfrak{a}) = \theta''(\psi_{k_0}(\theta_{i_0}(x) + \mathfrak{a}_0)) + b_0$. Since the i_0-th coordinate of $\mathfrak{a}_0$ is 0, the mapping $x \to \psi_{k_0}(\theta_{i_0}(x) + \mathfrak{a}_0)$ is linear. Since the k_0-th coordinate of b_0 is 0, the mapping $y \to \varphi(y + b_0)$ of N_{k_0} into P is linear. This proves our assertion.

Lemma 3. *Let φ be a multilinear mapping of $\prod_{i \in I} M_i$ into a module P. For each i, let $(x_{i;j})_{j \in J(i)}$ be a family of elements of M_i and $(\alpha_{i;j})_{i \in J(i)}$ a family of elements of R such that the sum $x_i = \sum_{j \in J(i)} \alpha_{i;j} x_{i;j}$ is defined (i.e., $\alpha_{i;j} x_{i;j} = 0$ for almost all $j \in J(i)$). Assume furthermore that the following condition is satisfied: there exists a finite subset I' of I such that, whenever i is not in I', $J(i)$ has only one element $j(i)$, and $\alpha_{i;j(i)} = 1$. Let $\Phi = \prod_{i \in I} J(i)$; then, for any $f \in \Phi$, the product $\prod_{i \in I} \alpha_{i;f(i)}$ is defined, the sum*

$$\textstyle\sum_{f \in \Phi} \left(\prod_{i \in I} \alpha_{i;f(i)}\right) \varphi((x_{i;f(i)})_{i \in I})$$

is defined and its value is $\varphi((\sum_{j \in J(i)} \alpha_{i;j} x_{i;j})_{i \in I})$.

The first assertion follows from the fact that $\alpha_{i;f(i)} = 1$ if i is not in I'. For each $i \in I$, let $J'(i)$ be the set of elements $j \in J(i)$ such that $\alpha_{i;j} x_{i;j} \neq 0$; this set is finite. If $f \in \Phi$ is such that, for at least one $i_0 \in I$, $f(i_0)$ is not *in* $J'(i_0)$, then $(\prod_{i \in I} \alpha_{i;f(i)}) \varphi((x_{i;f(i)})_{i \in I}) = 0$. For, set $\prod_{i \in I} \alpha_{i;f(i)} = \beta$, $x'_i = x_{i;f(i)}$ if $i \neq i_0$, $x'_{i_0} = \beta x_{i_0;f(i_0)}$; then $\beta\varphi((x_{i;f(i)})_{i \in I}) = \varphi((x'_i)_{i \in I}) = 0$ since $x'_{i_0} = 0$. Now, the set $\prod_{i \in I} J'(i)$ is finite since each $J'(i)$ is finite and $J'(i)$ has either 0 or 1 element if i is not in I'. If $\mathfrak{x}' \in \prod_{i \in I'} M_i$, denote by $\zeta(\mathfrak{x}')$ the element of $\prod_{i \in I} M_i$ whose i-th coordinate is the i-th coordinate of $\mathfrak{x}'$ when $i \in I'$ and is $x_{i;j(i)}$ if i is not in I'; then $\varphi \circ \zeta$ is a multilinear mapping of $\prod_{i \in I'} M_i$ (lemma 1). It will therefore be sufficient to prove lemma 3 in the case where I is a finite set. In that case, we proceed by induction on the number n of elements of I. The lemma is obvious if $n = 0$ or $n = 1$. Assume that $n > 1$ and that the lemma is true for families of $n - 1$ modules. Let i_1 be any element of I and I_1 the set of elements $\neq i_1$ in I. If $u \in M_{i_1}$ and $\mathfrak{y}' \in \prod_{i \in I_1} M_i$, denote by $\rho(u; \mathfrak{y}')$ the element of $\prod_{i \in I} M_i$ whose i_1-th coordinate is u and whose i-th coordinate is the i-th coordinate of $\mathfrak{y}'$ if $i \in I_1$. Let $\mathfrak{x}'$ be the element $(x_i)_{i \in I_1}$ of $\prod_{i \in I_1} M_i$; then $(x_i)_{i \in I} = \rho(x_{i_1}, \mathfrak{x}'))$. Since $u \to \varphi(\rho(u, \mathfrak{x}'))$ is a linear mapping of M_{i_1} into P, we have

$$\varphi((x_i)_{i \in I}) = \textstyle\sum_{j \in J(i_1)} \alpha_{i_1;j} \varphi(\rho(x_{i_1;j}, \mathfrak{x}')).$$

On the other hand, for any fixed index $j \in J(i_1)$, $\mathfrak{y}' \to \varphi(\rho(x_{i_1;j}, \mathfrak{y}'))$ is a multilinear mapping of $\prod_{i \in I_1} M_i$ (lemma 1). Let $\Phi_1 = \prod_{i \in I_1} J(i)$; then, since I_1 has only $n - 1$ elements, we have

$$\varphi(\rho(x_{i_1;j}, \mathfrak{x}')) = \textstyle\sum_{g \in \Phi_1} \left(\prod_{i \in I_1} \alpha_{i;g(i)}\right) \varphi(\rho(x_{i_1;j}, (x_{i;g(i)})_{i \in I_1}).$$

If $j \in J(i_1)$, $g \in \Phi_1$, denote by $[j, g]$ the element $f \in \Phi$ defined by $f(i_1) = j$, $f(i) = g(i)$ if $i \in I_1$. Then we have

$$\alpha_{i_1;j} \textstyle\prod_{i \in I_1} \alpha_{i;g(i)} = \prod_{i \in I} \alpha_{i;[j,g](i)}; \quad \rho(x_{i_1;j}, (x_{i;g(i)})_{i \in I_1}) = (x_{i;[j,g](i)})_{i \in I}.$$

Thus, taking theorem 1, Sect. 1, into account, we have

$$\varphi((x_i)_{i\in I}) = \Sigma_{(j,g)\in J(i_1)\times\Phi_1}(\Pi_{i\in I}\alpha_{i;[j,g](i)})\varphi((x_{i;[j,g](i)})_{i\in I}).$$

The mapping $(j, g) \to [j, g]$ being obviously a bijection of $J(i_1) \times \Phi_1$ on Φ, our formula is proved for the families of n modules.

Considering R as a module over itself, the mapping $(\alpha_1, \cdots, \alpha_n) \to \Pi_{i=1}^n \alpha_i$ is obviously a multilinear mapping of $R \times \cdots \times R$ into R. Applying the preceding lemma, we obtain the formula

$$\Pi_{i=1}^n(\Sigma_{j=1}^r \alpha_{i;j}) = \Sigma_{(f(1),\cdots,f(n))}\alpha_{1;f(1)}\cdots\alpha_{n;f(n)}$$

where the summation is extended to all finite sequences $(f(1), \cdots, f(n))$ of integers such that $1 \leqslant f(i) \leqslant r$ $(1 \leqslant i \leqslant n)$. We apply this in particular to the case where $\alpha_{i;j} = \alpha_j$ for all i, $\alpha_1, \cdots, \alpha_r$ being elements of R. In that case, $\alpha_{1;f(1)} \cdots \alpha_{n;f(n)} = \Pi_{j=1}^r \alpha_j^{e(j)}$ where $e(j)$ is the number of indices i such that $f(i) = j$; it is clear that $\Sigma_{j=1}^r e(j) = n$. Given any integers $e(j) \geqslant 0$ $(1 \leqslant j \leqslant r)$ such that $\Sigma_{j=1}^r e(j) = n$, denote by $\nu(e(1), \cdots, e(r))$ the number of sequences $(f(1), \cdots, f(n))$ such that, for each j, there exist exactly $e(j)$ integers i for which $f(i) = e(j)$. Then we have

$$(\Sigma_{j=1}^r \alpha_j)^n = \Sigma_{(e(1),\cdots,e(r))}\nu(e(1), \cdots, e(r))\alpha_1^{e(1)} \cdots \alpha_r^{e(r)}$$

the sum being extended to all sequences $(e(1), \cdots, e(r))$ with the preceding properties. We shall now compute $\nu(e(1), \cdots, e(r))$. Let F be the set of mappings f of $\{1, \cdots, n\}$ into $\{1, \cdots, r\}$ such that, for each $j \in \{1, \cdots, r\}$, $\overset{-1}{f}(j)$ has exactly $e(j)$ elements. Let ϖ be a permutation of $\{1, \cdots, n\}$; then it is clear that $f \in F$ implies $f \circ \varpi^{-1} \in F$. If we assign to ϖ the permutation $f \to f \circ \varpi^{-1}$ of F, we make the group G of permutations of $\{1, \cdots, n\}$ operate on F. The group G operates transitively on F. For, let f and f' be elements of F; then, for each j, $\overset{-1}{f}(j)$ and $\overset{-1}{f'}(j)$ have the same number of elements, which shows there exists a bijection ϖ_j of $\overset{-1}{f}(j)$ on $\overset{-1}{f'}(j)$. Since the sets $\overset{-1}{f}(j)$ form a partition of $\{1, \cdots, n\}$, there exists a mapping ϖ of $\{1, \cdots, n\}$ into itself which extends all the mappings ϖ_j; and, since the sets $\overset{-1}{f'}(j)$ form a partition of $\{1, \cdots, n\}$, ϖ is a permutation; it is clear that $f' = f \circ \varpi^{-1}$. Thus, if f is any element of F, then $\nu(e(1), \cdots, e(r))$ is equal to the index of the stability group G′ of f. We shall determine the order of G'. If $\varpi \in$ G′, then the restriction ϖ_j of ϖ to $\overset{-1}{f}(j)$ is a permutation of this set; conversely, if we give for each j a permutation ϖ_j of $\overset{-1}{f}(j)$, then there exists a unique $\varpi \in$ G whose restriction to $\overset{-1}{f}(j)$ is ϖ_j for every j; and ϖ belongs to G'. Thus, if we denote by G_j the group of permutations of $\overset{-1}{f}(j)$, $\varpi \to (\varpi_1, \cdots, \varpi_r)$ is a bijection of G' on $\prod_{j=1}^{r} G_j$, which shows that the order of G' is $\prod_{j=1}^{r} e(j)!$ and therefore that $\nu(e(1), \cdots, e(r)) = n!(\prod_{j=1}^{r} e(j)!)^{-1}$. Thus we obtain the formula

$$(\Sigma_{j=1}^{r} \alpha_j)^n = \Sigma_{(e(1), \cdots, e(r))} \frac{n!}{(e(1)!) \cdots (e(r)!)} \alpha_1^{e(1)} \cdots \alpha_r^{e(r)}$$

where the sum is extended to all finite sequences $(e(1), \cdots, e(r))$ such that $e(j) \geqslant 0$ $(1 \leqslant j \leqslant r)$, $\Sigma_{j=0}^{r} e(j) = n$.

Incidentally, we have shown that, if $n = \Sigma_{j=1}^{r} e(j)$ is any representation of n as a sum of integers $\geqslant 0$, then $n!$ is a multiple of $\prod_{j=1}^{r} e(j)!$.

Theorem 37. *Let $(M_i)_{i \in I}$ be a family of modules over R. Then there exist a module T over R and a multilinear mapping τ of $\prod_{i \in I} M_i$ into T which have the following property: if φ is any multilinear mapping of $\prod_{i \in I} M_i$ into a module P, then there exists a unique linear mapping f of T into P such that $f \circ \tau = \varphi$.*

The proof is quite similar to that of theorem 27. Let (Φ, λ) be a free module on the set $\prod_{i \in I} M_i$. If Ω is a submodule of Φ, denote by π_Ω the natural epimorphism of Φ on Φ/Ω. Let Σ be the set of all submodules Ω of Φ such that $\pi_\Omega \circ \lambda$ is a multilinear mapping of $\prod_{i \in I} M_i$ into Φ/Ω. Denote by Θ the intersection of all submodules Ω of the set Σ. We shall prove that $\Theta \in \Sigma$. Let i be any index belonging to I; denote by θ_i the natural injection of M_i into $\prod_{i \in I} M_i$ and by a an element of $\prod_{i \in I} M_i$ whose i-th coordinate is 0. For any $\Omega \in \Sigma$, $x \to (\pi_\Omega \circ \lambda)(\theta_i(x) + a)$ is a linear mapping of M_i into Φ/Ω, whence

$$\lambda(\theta_i(x + y) + a) - (\lambda(\theta_i(x) + a) + \lambda(\theta_i(y) + a)) \in \Omega$$
$$\lambda(\theta_i(\alpha x) + a) - \alpha\lambda(\theta_i(x) + a) \in \Omega$$

if $x, y \in M_i$, $\alpha \in R$. This being true for every Ω, the elements

$$\lambda(\theta_i(x + y) + a) - (\lambda(\theta_i(x) + a) + \lambda(\theta_i(y) + a)),$$
$$\lambda(\theta_i(\alpha x) + a) - \alpha\lambda(\theta_i(x) + a)$$

are in Θ. This being true for every $x, y \in M_i$ and $\alpha \in R$,

$$x \to (\pi_\Theta \circ \lambda)(\theta_i(x) + a)$$

is a linear mapping of M_i into Φ/Θ. This being true for every choice of i and a, $\pi_\Theta \circ \lambda$ is multilinear, whence $\Theta \in \Sigma$. Set $T = \Phi/\Theta$, $\tau = \pi_\Theta \circ \lambda$. Let φ be a multilinear mapping of $\prod_{i \in I} M_i$ into a module P. Then there exists a unique linear mapping F of Φ into P such that $F \circ \lambda = \varphi$; let Ω be its kernel. Then F may be written in the form $F_1 \circ \pi_\Omega$, where F_1 is a monomorphism of Φ/Ω into P; we have $\pi_\Omega \circ \lambda = \overset{-1}{F}_1 \circ \varphi$, from which it follows that $\pi_\Omega \circ \lambda$ is a multilinear mapping, whence $\Omega \in \Sigma$ and therefore $\Theta \subset \Omega$. Thus, F may be factored in the form $f \circ \pi_\Theta$, where f is a linear mapping of T into P. We have $f \circ \tau = f \circ \pi_\Theta \circ \lambda = F \circ \lambda = \varphi$. Conversely, let f' be any linear mapping of T into P such that $f' \circ \tau = \varphi$. Then $F' = f' \circ \pi_\Theta$ is a linear mapping of Φ into P and $F' \circ \lambda = f' \circ \tau = \varphi$; since (Φ, λ) is a free module on $\prod_{i \in I} M_i$, we have $F' = F$; it follows that $f' = f$ by virtue of theorem 14, Sect. 5.

Moreover, if (T', τ') is any other pair which satisfies the same conditions as the pair (T, τ) of theorem 34, there is a unique isomorphism J of T with T' such that $J \circ \tau = \tau'$. For there exist unique linear mappings J of T into T' and J' of T' into T such that $J \circ \tau = \tau'$, $J' \circ \tau' = \tau$; $J \circ J' \circ \tau'$ is then equal to τ', which shows that $J \circ J'$ is the identity mapping of T', and, similarly, $J' \circ J$ is the identity mapping of T; J is therefore an isomorphism.

Let us consider the cases where I has either 0, 1 or 2 elements. If $I = \emptyset$, then $\prod_{i \in I} M_i$ is a set with a single element ρ; any mapping of this set into a module P is multilinear. If we set $T = R$ and if we denote by τ the mapping of $\prod_{i \in I} M_i$ into R defined by $\tau(\rho) = 1$, the conditions of theorem 34 are satisfied; for, if φ is any mapping of $\{\rho\}$ into a module P, then the mapping $\alpha \to \alpha\varphi(\rho)$ of R into P is linear.

If I has one element a, then we may take $T = M_a$, τ being the identity mapping.

Assume that I is a set with two elements a, b. We may consider M_a as a right module over R, since R is commutative; construct a tensor product $M_a \otimes M_b$ of M_a and M_b. Then we know that $M_a \otimes M_b$ has a module structure over R and that, for any bilinear mapping β of $M_a \times M_b$ into a module P, there is a unique linear mapping f of $M_a \otimes M_b$ into P such that $f(x \otimes y) = \beta(x, y)$ for any $(x, y) \in M_a \times M_b$. Thus, in this case, T is isomorphic to $M_a \otimes M_b$.

In the general case, if (T, τ) is a pair which satisfies the conditions of theorem 37, we shall say that T is a *tensor product* of the modules M_i; and, if we have only one tensor product of these modules to consider, we shall denote it by $\bigotimes_{i \in I} M_i$; if $(x_i)_{i \in I}$ is any element of $\prod_{i \in I} M_i$, we denote its image under τ by $\bigotimes_{i \in I} x_i$.

If φ is any multilinear mapping of $\prod_{i \in I} M_i$ into a module P, the linear mapping f of $\bigotimes_{i \in I} M_i$ into P such that

$$f(\bigotimes_{i \in I} x_i) = \varphi((x_i)_{i \in I})$$

is called the *linearization* of the multilinear mapping φ.

Conversely, if f is any linear mapping of $\bigotimes_{i \in I} M_i$ into P, then the mapping $(x_i)_{i \in I} \to f(\bigotimes_{i \in I} x_i)$ is obviously multilinear, which shows that f is the linearization of a unique multilinear mapping of $\prod_{i \in I} M_i$ into P.

We know that the linear mappings of $\bigotimes_{i\in I}M_i$ into P form a module over R. The same is therefore true of the multilinear mappings of $\prod_{i\in I}M_i$ into P; the operations in the module $\mathfrak{M}$ of multilinear mappings of $\prod_{i\in I}M_i$ into P are defined by the formulas

$$(\varphi + \varphi')((x_i)_{i\in I}) = \varphi((x_i)_{i\in I}) + \varphi'((x_i)_{i\in I})$$
$$(\alpha\varphi)((x_i)_{i\in I}) = \alpha\varphi((x_i)_{i\in I})$$

where φ, φ' are any elements of $\mathfrak{M}$, $(x_i)_{i\in I}$ any element of $\prod_{i\in I}M_i$ and α any element of R.

Theorem 38. *Let $(M_i)_{i\in I}$ and $(M'_i)_{i\in I}$ be families of modules over the same ring R. For each i, let u_i be a linear mapping of M_i into M'_i. Then there exists a unique linear mapping u of $\bigotimes_{i\in I}M_i$ into $\bigotimes_{i\in I}M'_i$ such that $u(\bigotimes_{i\in I}x_i) = \bigotimes_{i\in I}u_i(x_i)$ for every $(x_i)_{i\in I}$ in $\prod_{i\in I}M_i$.*

The mapping $(x_i)_{i\in I} \rightarrow \bigotimes_{i\in I}u_i(x_i)$ of $\prod_{i\in I}M_i$ into $\bigotimes_{i\in I}M'_i$ is multilinear (lemma 2, with $K = I$, $J_k = \{k\}$ for every $k \in I$); theorem 38 therefore follows from the definitions.

In particular, if M'_i is a submodule of M_i, and u_i the identity mapping of M'_i into M_i, u is a linear mapping of $\bigotimes_{i\in I}M'_i$ into $\bigotimes_{i\in I}M_i$; it is called the *canonical homomorphism* of $\bigotimes_{i\in I}M'_i$ into $\bigotimes_{i\in I}M_i$. In general, u is not a monomorphism.

The mapping u of theorem 38 is usually denoted by $\bigotimes_{i\in I}u_i$. However, this notation may be confusing, since $\bigotimes_{i\in I}u_i$ is also used to denote a certain element of the tensor product of the modules Hom (M_i, M'_i). If there is a danger of confusion, we shall denote the mapping u by $\bigotimes^m_{i\in I}u_i$.

If we are given two pairs of modules (M, M') and (N, N'), a linear mapping u of M into M' and a linear mapping v of N into N', the linear mapping w of $M \otimes N$ into $M' \otimes N'$ such that $w(x \otimes y) = u(x) \otimes v(y)$ whenever $x \in M$, $y \in N$, is denoted by $u \otimes v$ (or by $u \otimes^m v$, if there is a danger of confusion with the element $u \otimes v$ of the module

$$\text{Hom}(M, M') \otimes \text{Hom}(N, N')).$$

If $M_1, \cdots, M_n, M'_1, \cdots, M'_n$ are modules over R, and, for each i $(i = 1, \cdots, n)$, u_i is a linear mapping of M_i into M'_i, then $\bigotimes_{1\leqslant i\leqslant n}u_i$ is also denoted by $u_1 \otimes \ldots \otimes u_n$.

Let $(M_i)_{i\in I}$ and $(M'_i)_{i\in I}$ be families of modules over the ring R. Set $T = \bigotimes_{i\in I}M_i$, $T' = \bigotimes_{i\in I}M'_i$. Then the mapping

$$(u_i)_{i\in I} \rightarrow \bigotimes^m_{i\in I}u_i$$

of $\prod_{i\in I}$ Hom (M_i, M'_i) into Hom (T, T') is multilinear. For, let $(u_i)_{i\in I}$ be an element of $\prod_{i\in I}$ Hom (M_i, M'_i), let k be an index in I and let u'_k be an element of Hom (M_k, M'_k). Set $u'_i = u_i$ and $v_i = u_i$ for $i \neq k$, $v_k = u_k + u'_k$. Then the multilinear mapping $(x_i)_{i\in I} \to \bigotimes_{i\in I} v_i(x_i)$ is the sum of the multilinear mappings $(x_i)_{i\in I} \to \bigotimes_{i\in I} u_i(x_i)$ and $(x_i)_{i\in I} \to \bigotimes_{i\in I} u'_i(x_i)$, and its linearization $\bigotimes^m_{i\in I} v_i$ is the sum of $\bigotimes^m_{i\in I} u_i$ and $\bigotimes^m_{i\in I} u'_i$. On the other hand, let α be an element of R; set $w_i = u_i$ if $i \neq k$, $w_k = \alpha u_k$. Then we have $\bigotimes_{i\in I} w_i(x_i) = \alpha \bigotimes_{i\in I} u_i(x_i)$ for every $(x_i)_{i\in I} \in \prod_{i\in I} M_i$, which proves that $\bigotimes^m_{i\in I} w_i = \alpha(\bigotimes^m_{i\in I} u_i)$; this establishes the multilinearity of the mapping $(u_i)_{i\in I} \to \bigotimes^m_{i\in I} u_i$. There is associated to this mapping a linear mapping Λ of $\bigotimes_{i\in I}$ Hom (M_i, M'_i) into Hom (T, T'), which maps $\bigotimes_{i\in I} u_i$ upon $\bigotimes^m_{i\in I} u_i$ for any $(u_i)_{i\in I} \in \prod_{i\in I}$ Hom (M_i, M'_i). This mapping is in general not an isomorphism.

Now, let $(M''_i)_{i\in I}$ be a new family of modules over R, with the same set of indices I, and let u'_i be a linear mapping of M'_i into M''_i. Then we have

$$\bigotimes^m_{i\in I}(u'_i \circ u_i) = (\bigotimes^m_{i\in I} u'_i) \circ (\bigotimes^m_{i\in I} u_i).$$

For, let $\mathfrak{x} = (x_i)_{i\in I}$ be an element of $\prod_{i\in I} M_i$; set $x'_i = u_i(x_i)$, $x''_i = u'_i(x'_i)$. Then $\bigotimes^m_{i\in I}(u'_i \circ u_i)$ and $(\bigotimes^m_{i\in I} u'_i) \circ (\bigotimes^m_{i\in I} u_i)$ both map $\mathfrak{x}$ upon $\bigotimes_{i\in I} x''_i$. They are therefore both linearizations of the same multilinear mapping of $\prod_{i\in I} M_i$ into $\bigotimes_{i\in I} M''_i$, which proves that they are identical.

If each u_i is an epimorphism, so is $u = \bigotimes^m_{i\in I} u_i$. For $u(\bigotimes_{i\in I} M_i)$ clearly contains every element of the form $\bigotimes_{i\in I} x'_i$ $(x'_i \in M'_i)$, and is therefore the whole of $\bigotimes_{i\in I} M'_i$. If each u_i is an isomorphism, then so is u. For, taking $M''_i = M_i$ and letting $u'_i = \overset{-1}{u_i}$, $(\bigotimes^m_{i\in I} u'_i) \circ u = \bigotimes^m_{i\in I}(u'_i \circ u_i)$ is the identity mapping of $\bigotimes_{i\in I} M_i$, which proves that u is a monomorphism. However, if we assume only that each u_i is a monomorphism, it does not follow in general that $\bigotimes_{i\in I} u_i$ is a monomorphism.

Lemma 4. *Let $(M_i)_{i\in I}$ be a family of modules over R. Let J and K be disjoint subsets of I such that $I = J \cup K$. Set $T = \bigotimes_{i\in I} M_i$, $T_J = \bigotimes_{i\in J} M_i$, $T_K = \bigotimes_{i\in K} M_i$. Then there exists a unique isomorphism Φ of T with $T_J \otimes T_K$ such that*

(1) $$\Phi(\bigotimes_{i\in I} x_i) = (\bigotimes_{i\in J} x_i) \otimes (\bigotimes_{i\in K} x_i)$$

for any $(x_i)_{i\in I} \in \prod_{i\in I} M_i$.

The mapping $(x_i)_{i\in I} \to (\bigotimes_{i\in J} x_i) \otimes (\bigotimes_{i\in K} x_i)$ of $\prod_{i\in I} M_i$ into $T_J \otimes T_K$ is multilinear by lemma 2; thus there exists a unique linear mapping Φ of T into $T_J \otimes T_K$ for which (1) is true. We have to prove that Φ is an isomorphism. Let there be given any element $(a_i)_{i\in K}$ of $\prod_{i\in K} M_i$; for any element $(x_i)_{i\in J}$ of $\prod_{i\in J} M_i$, set $\bar{x}_i = x_i$ if $i \in J$, $\bar{x}_i = a_i$ if $i \in K$. Set $\mathfrak{a} = (a_i)_{i\in K}$; then the mapping $\varphi_{\mathfrak{a}}$: $(x_i)_{i\in J} \to \bigotimes_{i\in I} \bar{x}_i$ is obviously multilinear; let $\lambda_{\mathfrak{a}}$ be the linearization of this mapping. Then the mapping $\mathfrak{a} \to \lambda_{\mathfrak{a}}$ of $\prod_{i\in K} M_i$ into Hom (T_J, T) is multilinear. For, let k be any index in K and let $(a'_i)_{i\in K} = \mathfrak{a}'$ be an element of $\prod_{i\in K} M_i$ such that $a'_i = a_i$ for all $i \neq k$. Set $b_i = a_i = a'_i$ if $i \in K$, $i \neq k$, $b_k = a_k + a'_k$, $\mathfrak{b} = (b_i)_{i\in K}$. If $(x_i)_{i\in J} \in \prod_{i\in J} M_j$, set $\bar{x}_i = \bar{x}'_i = \bar{y}_i = x_i$ if $i \in J$, $\bar{x}_i = a_i$, $\bar{x}'_i = a'_i$, $\bar{y}_i = b_i$ if $i \in K$. Then we have $\bar{y}_i = \bar{x}_i = \bar{x}'_i$ for all $i \in I$, $i \neq k$, and $\bar{y}_k = \bar{x}_k + \bar{x}'_k$, whence

$$\bigotimes_{i\in I} \bar{y}_i = \bigotimes_{i\in I} \bar{x}_i + \bigotimes_{i\in I} \bar{x}'_i.$$

This shows that $\varphi_{\mathfrak{b}} = \varphi_{\mathfrak{a}} + \varphi_{\mathfrak{a}'}$, whence $\lambda_{\mathfrak{b}} = \lambda_{\mathfrak{a}} + \lambda_{\mathfrak{a}'}$; and we see in the same way that $\lambda_{\alpha\mathfrak{a}} = \alpha\lambda_{\mathfrak{a}}$ if $\alpha \in R$. This establishes the multilinearity of the mapping $\mathfrak{a} \to \lambda_{\mathfrak{a}}$. Let Λ be the linearization of this mapping; this is a linear mapping of T_K into Hom (T_J, T). Now, let (t_J, t_K) be any element of $T_J \times T_K$; set

$$B(t_J, t_K) = (\Lambda(t_K))(t_J).$$

Then B is clearly a bilinear mapping of $T_J \times T_K$ into T; let Ψ be its linearization; this is a linear mapping of $T_J \otimes T_K$ into T. We shall now prove that $\Psi \circ \Phi$ is the identity mapping; it will be sufficient to prove that

$$(\Psi \circ \Phi)(\bigotimes_{i\in I} x_i) = \bigotimes_{i\in I} x_i$$

for any $(x_i)_{i\in I} \in \prod_{i\in I} M_i$. This element is

$$\Psi((\bigotimes_{i\in J} x_i) \otimes (\bigotimes_{i\in K} x_i)) = (\Lambda(\bigotimes_{i\in K} x_i))(\bigotimes_{i\in J} x_i).$$

Set $\mathfrak{a} = (x_i)_{i\in K}$; then, Λ being the linearization of the mapping $\mathfrak{a} \to \lambda_{\mathfrak{a}}$, we have

$$\Lambda(\bigotimes_{i\in K} x_i) = \lambda_{\mathfrak{a}}.$$

The value of this element at $\bigotimes_{i\in J} x_i$ is $\varphi_{\mathfrak{a}}((x_i)_{i\in J})$, which is $\bigotimes_{i\in I} x_i$ by definition of $\varphi_{\mathfrak{a}}$; we have thereby proved that $\Psi \circ \Phi$ is the identity mapping. It follows that Φ is a monomorphism. Let A_J (resp.: A_K) be the set of elements of T_J (resp.: T_K) which are of the form $\bigotimes_{i\in J} x_i$ (resp.: $\bigotimes_{i\in K} x_i$); then A_J and A_K are sets of generators of T_J and T_K respectively. Let t_J and t_K be elements of T_J and T_K respectively; then we may write

$t_J = \Sigma_{\sigma=1}^s \alpha_\sigma a_\sigma$, $t_K = \Sigma_{\tau=1}^t \beta_\tau b_\tau$, where $\alpha_\sigma, \beta_\tau \in R$, $a_\sigma \in A_J$, $b_\tau \in A_K$, whence $t_J \otimes t_K = \Sigma_{\sigma=1}^s \Sigma_{\tau=1}^t \alpha_\sigma \beta_\tau a_\sigma \otimes b_\tau$. Now, it is clear that each $a_\sigma \otimes b_\tau$ is contained in the submodule $\Phi(T)$ of $T_J \otimes T_K$; thus, we have also $t_J \otimes t_K \subset \Phi(T)$. This being true for every (t_J, t_K) in $T_J \times T_K$, we have $\Phi(T) = T_J \otimes T_K$, and Φ is an epimorphism. Lemmà 4 is thereby proved.

Theorem 39. *Let $(M_i)_{i \in I}$ be a family of modules over R. Let $I = \bigcup_{k \in K} J_k$ be a partition of I into a finite number of mutually disjoint sets J_k. Then there exists a unique isomorphism Φ of $\bigotimes_{i \in I} M_i$ with $\bigotimes_{k \in K}(\bigotimes_{i \in J_k} M_i)$ such that*

$$\Phi(\bigotimes_{i \in I} x_i) = \bigotimes_{k \in K}(\bigotimes_{i \in J_k} x_i) \tag{2}$$

for every $(x_i)_{i \in I} \in \prod_{i \in I} M_i$.

We proceed by induction on the number ν of elements of K. If $\nu = 0$, then $I = \emptyset$, $K = \emptyset$ and the theorem is obvious in that case. Assume that $\nu > 0$ and that the theorem is true for partitions in $\nu - 1$ sets. Let $k(1), \cdots, k(\nu)$ be the elements of K; set $J(\sigma) = J_{k(\sigma)}$, $T_\sigma = \bigotimes_{i \in J(\sigma)} M_i$ $(1 \leqslant \sigma \leqslant \nu)$, $J' = J(1) \cup \cdots \cup J(\nu - 1)$, $T_{J'} = \bigotimes_{i \in J'} M_i$. Then it follows from lemma 4 that there exists an isomorphism Φ_1 of $T = \bigotimes_{i \in I} M_i$ with $T_{J'} \otimes T_\nu$ such that

$$\Phi_1(\bigotimes_{i \in I} x_i) = (\bigotimes_{i \in J'} x_i) \otimes (\bigotimes_{i \in J(\nu)} x_i)$$

for every $(x_i)_{i \in I} \in \prod_{i \in I} M_i$. Making use of the inductive assumption, there exists an isomorphism Φ_2 of $T_{J'}$ with $\bigotimes_{\sigma=1}^{\nu-1} T_\sigma$ such that

$$\Phi_2(\bigotimes_{i \in J'} x_i) = \bigotimes_{\sigma=1}^{\nu-1}(\bigotimes_{i \in J(\sigma)} x_i).$$

Let I_ν be the identity mapping of T_ν. Then $\Phi_2 \otimes I_\nu$ is an isomorphism of $T_{J'} \otimes T_\nu$ with $(\bigotimes_{\sigma=1}^{\nu-1} T_\sigma) \otimes T_\nu$, and

$$(\Phi_2 \otimes I_\nu)((\bigotimes_{i \in J'} x_i) \otimes (\bigotimes_{i \in J(\nu)} x_i)) = (\bigotimes_{\sigma=1}^{\nu-1}(\bigotimes_{i \in J(\sigma)} x_i)) \otimes (\bigotimes_{i \in J(\nu)} x_i).$$

Finally, using lemma 4 again, we see that there exists an isomorphism Φ_3 of $(\bigotimes_{\sigma=1}^{\nu-1} T_\sigma) \otimes T_\nu$ with $\bigotimes_{\sigma=1}^{\nu} T_\sigma$ such that

$$\Phi_3((\bigotimes_{\sigma=1}^{\nu-1} t_\sigma) \otimes t_\nu) = \bigotimes_{\sigma=1}^{\nu} t_\sigma$$

for every $(t_\sigma) \in \prod_{\sigma=1}^{\nu-1} T_\sigma$. Then $\Phi_3 \circ (\Phi_2 \otimes I_\nu) \circ \Phi_1 = \Phi$ is an isomorphism with the required property. That there exists only one such isomorphism follows immediately from the fact that $\bigotimes_{i \in I} M_i$ is generated by the elements of the form $\bigotimes_{i \in I} x_i$.

Consider in particular the case where $M_i = R$ for every i. Write $\emptyset = \bigcup_{i \in I} J_i$, where $J_i = \emptyset$. Then theorem 39 gives an isomorphism of

$R = \bigotimes_{i \in \emptyset} M_i$ with $\bigotimes_{i \in I}(\bigotimes_{j \in \emptyset} R) = \bigotimes_{i \in I} M_i$. This isomorphism maps 1 upon $\bigotimes_{i \in I} e_i$, where $e_i = 1$ for every i.

The isomorphism Φ of theorem 39 is called the *canonical isomorphism* of $\bigotimes_{i \in I} M_i$ with $\bigotimes_{k \in K}(\bigotimes_{i \in J_k} M_i)$ relative to the partition $I = \bigcup_k J_k$ of the set I; its reciprocal mapping is also called the canonical isomorphism of $\bigotimes_{k \in K}(\bigotimes_{i \in J_k} M_i)$ with $\bigotimes_{i \in I} M_i$.

The notation being as in theorem 39, let furthermore u_i be a linear mapping of M_i into a module M'_i. Let J be the canonical isomorphism of $\bigotimes_{k \in K}(\bigotimes_{i \in J_k} M_i)$ with $\bigotimes_{i \in I} M_i$ and J' the canonical isomorphism of $\bigotimes_{k \in K}(\bigotimes_{i \in J_k} M'_i)$ with $\bigotimes_{i \in I} M'_i$. Set $v_k = \bigotimes^m_{i \in J_k} u_i$, $u = \bigotimes^m_{i \in I} u_i$. Then we have

$$u \circ J = J' \circ (\bigotimes_{k \in K} v_k). \tag{3}$$

For, u and $J' \circ (\bigotimes_{k \in K} v_k) \circ \overset{-1}{J}$ are linear mappings of $\bigotimes_{i \in I} M_i$ into $\bigotimes_{i \in I} M'_i$. These two mappings have the same effect upon an element t of the form $\bigotimes_{i \in I} x_i$ $(x_i \in M_i)$. For, we have $\overset{-1}{J}(t) = \bigotimes_{k \in K}(\bigotimes_{i \in J_k} x_i)$; the image of this element by $\bigotimes_{k \in K} v_k$ is $\bigotimes_{k \in K} v_k(\bigotimes_{i \in J_k} x_i) = \bigotimes_{k \in K}(\bigotimes_{i \in J_k} u_i(x_i))$, whose image by J' is $\bigotimes_{i \in I} u_i(x_i)$: this is equal to $u(t)$. It follows that $u = J' \circ (\bigotimes_{k \in K} v_k) \circ \overset{-1}{J}$.

Consider, for instance, the case where $I = \{1, 2, 3\}$ and $K = \{1, 2\}$. Then we have the following possibilities (excluding those for which one of J_1, J_2 is empty):

$$J_1 = \{1\}, J_2 = \{2, 3\}; J_1 = \{2\}, J_2 = \{1, 3\}; J_1 = \{3\}, J_2 = \{1, 2\};$$
$$J_1 = \{1, 2\}, J_2 = \{3\}; J_1 = \{2, 3\}, J_2 = \{1\}; J_1 = \{1, 3\}, J_2 = \{2\};$$

which give canonical isomorphism of $M_1 \otimes M_2 \otimes M_3$ with the following modules:

$$M_1 \otimes (M_2 \otimes M_3); M_2 \otimes (M_1 \otimes M_3); M_3 \otimes (M_1 \otimes M_2);$$
$$(M_1 \otimes M_2) \otimes M_3; (M_2 \otimes M_3) \otimes M_1; (M_1 \otimes M_3) \otimes M_2.$$

One extends further the notion of canonical isomorphism as follows: the notation being as in theorem 39, let there be given for each k a partition $J_k = \bigcup_{l \in S(k)} H_{k,l}$ of J_k into a finite number of mutually disjoint sets $H_{k,l}$, and let Φ_k be the corresponding canonical isomorphism of $\bigotimes_{i \in J_k} M_i$ with $\bigotimes_{l \in S(k)}(\bigotimes_{i \in H_{k,l}} M_i)$. Then $\bigotimes_{k \in K} \Phi_k$ is an isomorphism of $\bigotimes_{i \in I} M_i$ with $\bigotimes_{k \in K}(\bigotimes_{l \in S(k)}(\bigotimes_{i \in H_{k,l}} M_i))$; such an isomorphism is still called canonical. Finally, all isomorphisms between tensor products which are the reciprocals of those isomorphisms already defined as canonical isomorphisms, or those which are obtained by composition of canonical isomorphisms, are still called canonical.

Let us now consider the case where I is a finite set, and let ϖ be a permutation of I. For any $i \in I$, set $J_i = \{\varpi(i)\}$; then $I = \bigcup_{k \in I} J_k$ is a partition of I into mutually disjoint sets, and we have $\bigotimes_{i \in J_k} M_i = M_{\varpi(i)}$. Thus we have a canonical isomorphism Φ_ϖ of $\bigotimes_{i \in I} M_i$ with $\bigotimes_{i \in I} M_{\varpi(i)}$. Consider more particularly the case where all M_i are identical to some module M. Then Φ_ϖ is an automorphism of $\bigotimes_{i \in I} M_i$, and we have

$$\Phi_{\varpi \circ \varpi'} = \Phi_{\varpi'} \circ \Phi_\varpi$$

for any two permutations ϖ, ϖ' of the set I. For if $\mathfrak{x} = (x_i)_{i \in I}$ is any element of $\prod_{i \in I} M_i$, the image of $\bigotimes_{i \in I} x_i$ under Φ_ϖ is $\bigotimes_{i \in I} x_{\varpi(i)}$, whose image under $\Phi_{\varpi'}$ is $\bigotimes_{i \in I} x_{\varpi(\varpi'(i))} = \Phi_{\varpi \circ \varpi'}(\bigotimes_{i \in I} x_i)$. It follows that $\varpi \to \Phi_\varpi^{-1}$ is a homomorphism of the group of permutations of I into the group of automorphisms of $\bigotimes_{i \in I} M_i$.

Theorem 40. *Let $(M_i)_{i \in I}$ be a finite family of modules. For each $i \in I$, assume that M_i is the sum $\sum_{j \in J(i)} N_{i,j}$ of a family of submodules. For any $f \in \prod_{i \in I} J(i) = P$, let T_f be the submodule of $\bigotimes_{i \in I} M_i$ generated by the elements $\bigotimes_{i \in I} x_i$ such that $x_i \in N_{i,f(i)}$ for every $i \in I$. Then $T = \bigotimes_{i \in I} M_i$ is the sum of the modules T_f for all $f \in \prod_{i \in I} J(i)$. If, for each i, the sum $\sum_{j \in J} N_{i,j}$ is direct, then the sum $\sum_{f \in P} T_f$ is direct; furthermore, if $u_{i,j}$ is the identity mapping of $N_{i,j}$ into M_i, $\bigotimes_{i \in I} u_{i,f(i)} = u_f$ is in this case an isomorphism of $\bigotimes_{i \in I} N_{i,f(i)}$ with T_f.*

Let $(x_i)_{i \in I}$ be any element of $\prod_{i \in I} M_i$, and set $x_i = \sum_{j \in J(i)} x_{i,j}$, $x_{i,j} \in N_{i,j}$. Then it follows from lemma 3 that

$$\bigotimes_{i \in I} x_i = \sum_{f \in P} \bigotimes_{i \in I} x_{i,f(i)},$$

which shows that $\bigotimes_{i \in I} x_i \in \sum_{f \in P} T_f$; this proves the first assertion of theorem 40. Assume now that, for each i, the sum $\sum_{j \in J(i)} N_{i,j}$ is direct; this sum then defines a family of projectors $p_{i,j}$ with $p_{i,j}(M_i) = N_{i,j}$, $\sum_{j \in J(i)} p_{i,j} = v_i$, where v_i is the identity map of M_i. For any $f \in P$, let $q_f = \bigotimes^m_{i \in I} p_{i,f(i)}$; then it follows from lemma 3 that $\sum_{f \in P} q_f = \bigotimes^m_{i \in I} v_i$ is the identity mapping of $\bigotimes_{i \in I} M_i$. Each q_f is a surjection of T on T_f. If f, f' are elements of P, we have $q_f \circ q_{f'} = \bigotimes^m_{i \in I} p_{i,f(i)} \circ p_{i,f'(i)}$; if $f = f'$, this is q_f; if not, then there is an index i such that $f(i) \neq f'(i)$, whence $p_{i,f(i)} \circ p_{i,f'(i)} = 0$ and $q_f \circ q_{f'} = 0$. It follows that the sum $\sum_{f \in P} T_f$ is direct. The mapping $p_{i,j} \circ u_{i,j}$ is the identity mapping of $N_{i,j}$; it follows that $p_f \circ u_f = \bigotimes_{i \in I}^m (p_{i,f(i)} \circ u_{i,f(i)})$ is the identity mapping of $\bigotimes_{i \in I} N_{i,f(i)}$, which shows that u_f is a monomorphism. Since it is also an epimorphism, the last assertion of theorem 40 is proved.

Corollary. *Let the notation be as in theorem 40. A multilinear mapping ψ of $\prod_{i \in I} M_i$ into a module Q is then uniquely determined when its restrictions to the sets $\prod_{i \in I} N_{i,f(i)}$ (for all $f \in P$) are given. Assume now that, for each i, the sum $\sum_{j \in J(i)} N_{i,j}$ is direct. Then, if for any $f \in P$ a multilinear mapping φ_f of $\prod_{i \in I} N_{i,f(i)}$ into a module Q is given, there exists a unique multilinear mapping φ of $\prod_{i \in I} M_i$ into Q which extends all the mappings φ_f.*

The first assertion follows immediately from lemma 3. Assume now that the sums $\sum_{j \in J(i)} N_{i,j}$ are direct. Let λ_f be the linearization of φ_f; then $\lambda_f \circ \overset{-1}{u_f}$ is a linear mapping of T_f into Q. Since $T = \sum_{f \in P} T_f$ (direct), there exists a linear mapping λ of T into Q which extends all mappings λ_f. If we set $\varphi((x_i)_{i \in I}) = \lambda(\bigotimes_{i \in I} x_i)$, then φ is a multilinear mapping which extends all mappings φ_f.

Theorem 41. *Let $(M_i)_{i \in I}$ be a finite family of free modules over a ring R, and let B_i be a base of M_i. Then $\bigotimes_{i \in I} M_i$ is a free module, and has a base composed of the elements $\bigotimes_{i \in I} b_i$, with $b_i \in B_i$ for every i.*

For each i, M_i is the direct sum $M_i = \sum_{b_i \in B_i} Rb_i$; it follows that $\bigotimes_{i \in I} M_i$ is the direct sum of the modules T_b where, for any $b \in \prod_{i \in I} B_i$, T_b is the module generated by all $\bigotimes_{i \in I} x_i$ such that $x_i = \alpha_i b(i)$ for all $i \in I$ (theorem 40); this implies $\bigotimes_{i \in I} x_i = (\prod_{i \in I} \alpha_i) \bigotimes_{i \in I} b(i)$ (lemma 3), whence, if $c_b = \bigotimes_{i \in I} b(i)$, $\bigotimes_{i \in I} M_i = \sum_{b \in \prod_{i \in I} B_i} Rc_b$ (direct). It will therefore be sufficient to prove that $\alpha c_b = 0$ implies $\alpha = 0$, if $\alpha \in R$. Taking into consideration the last assertion of theorem 40, we see that it will be sufficient to consider the case where each B_i consists of a single element $b(i)$; M_i is then isomorphic to R under an isomorphism which maps $b(i)$ upon 1. It follows that $\bigotimes_{i \in I} M_i$ is isomorphic to $\bigotimes_{i \in I} R_i$, where $R_i = R$ for every i, under an isomorphism which maps c_b upon $\bigotimes_{i \in I} e_i$, where $e_i = 1$ for every i. But $\bigotimes_{i \in I} R_i$ is isomorphic to R under an isomorphism which maps $\bigotimes_{i \in I} e_i$ upon 1. Thus, if $\alpha \cdot c_b = 0$, we have $\alpha \cdot \bigotimes_{i \in I} e_i = 0$, $\alpha \cdot 1 = 0$, whence $\alpha = 0$.

Corollary. *The notation being as in theorem 41, let there be given for each $b \in \prod_{i \in I} B_i$ an element ξ_b of a module P. Then there is a unique multilinear mapping φ of $\prod_{i \in I} M_i$ into P such that $\varphi(b) = \xi_b$ for every $b \in \prod_{i \in I} B_i$.*

For, there exists a unique linear mapping λ of $\bigotimes_{i\in I}M_i$ into P such that $\lambda(\bigotimes_{i\in I}b_i) = \xi_b$ for every $b = (b_i)_{i\in I} \in \prod_{i\in I}B_i$. If we set $\varphi((x_i)_{i\in I}) = \lambda(\bigotimes_{i\in I}x_i)$, φ is a multilinear mapping with the required property; and φ is obviously determined uniquely by this property.

Theorem 42. *Let $(M_i)_{i\in I}$ be a finite family of modules over a ring R. For each i, let u_i be an epimorphism of M_i on a module M'_i, and let K_i be the kernel of u_i. Then the kernel of $u = \bigotimes_{i\in I}u_i$ is the submodule K of $\bigotimes_{i\in I}M_i$ which is generated by the elements of the form $\bigotimes_{i\in I}x_i$, where, for at least one index i, x_i belongs to K_i.*

We have $u(\bigotimes_{i\in I}x_i) = \bigotimes_{i\in I}u_i(x_i)$; this is 0 if $x_i \in K_i$ for at least one i, which proves that K is contained in the kernel K' of u. To prove that $K' \subset K$, we proceed by induction on the number ν of elements of I. The theorem is obvious if $\nu = 0$. Assume that $\nu > 0$ and that the theorem is true for $\nu - 1$. Let i be any element of I and J the set of indices $\neq i$ in I. Set $\overline{T} = \bigotimes_{j\in J}M_j$, $\overline{T}' = \bigotimes_{j\in J}M'_j$ and denote by J the canonical isomorphism of $\overline{T} \otimes M_i$ with $\bigotimes_{i\in I}M_i$ and by J' the canonical isomorphism of $\overline{T}' \otimes M'_i$ with $\bigotimes_{i\in I}M'_i$. Then we have, by formula (3),

$$u \circ J = J' \circ (\overline{u} \otimes u_i).$$

Let $\overline{K}$ be the kernel of $\overline{u}$. Since $\overline{u}$ and u_i are epimorphisms, the kernel K^* of $\overline{u} \otimes u_i$ is the module generated by the elements $\overline{x} \otimes x_i$ where either $\overline{x} \in \overline{K}$ or $x_i \in K_i$ (theorem 29, Sect. 8). It follows from our inductive assumption that $\overline{K}$ is the module generated by the elements $\bigotimes_{j\in J}x_j$ where, for at least one $j \in J$, x_j belongs to K_j. For a fixed $x_i \in M_i$, $\overline{x} \to \overline{x} \otimes x_i$ is a linear mapping; it follows that, if $\overline{x} \in \overline{K}$, $\overline{x} \otimes x_i$ may be written as a linear combination of the elements $(\bigotimes_{j\in J}x_j) \otimes x_i$ where $x_j \in K_j$ for at least one $j \in J$. It follows that K^* is generated by the elements $(\bigotimes_{j\in J}x_j) \otimes x_i$, where $(x_k)_{k\in I}$ runs over all elements of $\prod_{i\in I}M_i$ such that $x_k \in K_k$ for at least one $k \in K$. The image of K^* under J is K. Since J is an isomorphism, it follows immediately that K is the kernel of u.

Corollary. *Let $(M_i)_{i\in I}$ be a finite family of modules over R; for each $i \in I$, let K_i be a submodule of M_i and let π_i be the natural mapping of M_i on M_i/K_i. Let φ be a multilinear mapping of $\prod_{i\in I}M_i$ into a module P over R; assume that $\varphi((x_i)_{i\in I}) = 0$ whenever $x_i \in K_i$ for at least one i. Then there exists a unique multilinear mapping φ^* of $\prod_{i\in I}(M_i/K_i)$ into P such that $\varphi^*((\pi_i(x_i))_{i\in I}) = \varphi((x_i)_{i\in I})$ for every $(x_i)_{i\in I} \in \prod_{i\in I}M_i$.*

Let f be the linearization of φ. Then it follows immediately from theorem

42 that the kernel of f contains the kernel of $\bigotimes_{i\in I}\pi_i$. Thus, there exists a unique linear mapping f^* of $\bigotimes_{i\in I}(M_i/K_i)$ into P such that

$$f = f^* \circ (\bigotimes_{i\in I}\pi_i).$$

This linear mapping is the linearization of a multilinear mapping φ^* which obviously has the required property. Conversely, if φ_1^* is any multilinear mapping with this property, and f_1^* its linearization, then $f_1^* \circ (\bigotimes_{i\in I}\pi_i)$ is clearly the linearization f of φ, whence $f_1^* = f^*$ and $\varphi_1^* = \varphi^*$.

11. Transfer of basic rings

In this section, we shall denote by R a ring and by ρ a homomorphism of R into a ring S.

The homomorphism ρ allows us to define on S a left module structure over R, in which the scalar multiplication is the mapping $(\alpha, \beta) \to \rho(\alpha)\beta$ of $R \times S$ into S. For, it is clear that this mapping is bi-additive. Moreover, if $\alpha, \alpha' \in R$, we have $\rho(\alpha\alpha')\beta = \rho(\alpha)(\rho(\alpha')\beta)$, and $\rho(1)\beta = \beta$.

Similarly, we may define on S a right module structure over R by means of the scalar multiplication $(\alpha, \beta) \to \beta\rho(\alpha)$.

The set S now has the following structures: it is a ring, a left module over S, a right module over S, a left module over R and a right module over R. These structures will be denoted by S, ${}_SS$, S_S, ${}_RS$ and S_R respectively. Moreover, the structures ${}_SS$, S_R define S as an $(S; R)$-module, since $\beta(\beta'\rho(\alpha)) = (\beta\beta')\rho(\alpha)$ if $\alpha \in R$, $\beta, \beta' \in S$; we denote this module by ${}_SS_R$. Similarly, ${}_RS$ and S_S define S as an $(R; S)$-module ${}_RS_S$. The structures ${}_RS$ and S_R define S as a double module ${}_RS_R$ over R, since $(\rho(\alpha)\beta)\rho(\alpha') = \rho(\alpha)(\beta\rho(\alpha'))$ if $\alpha, \alpha' \in R$, $\beta \in S$. And, finally, we know that ${}_SS$ and S_S define S as a double module ${}_SS_S$ over S.

Now, let M be any module over S. Then ${}_RS_S \otimes M$ is a module over R. This module is called the *module deduced from* M *by direct transfer of the basic ring to* R, and is denoted by M_R. Since $S_S \otimes M = M$, the elements of M_R are the same as those of M, and the addition in M_R is the same as the addition in M; the scalar multiplication in M_R is the mapping

$$(\alpha, x) \to \rho(\alpha)x \qquad (\alpha \in R, x \in M).$$

Let f be a linear mapping of M into a module M' over S. Then f is also a linear mapping of M_R into M'_R, since $f(\rho(\alpha)x) = \rho(\alpha)f(x)$ if $\alpha \in R$, $x \in M$. The converse is not true in general, except if ρ is an epimorphism.

Now, let M be a module over R. Then ${}_SS_R \otimes M$ is a module over S; this module is called the *module deduced from* M *by inverse transfer of the basic ring to* S; it is denoted by M^S. If $x \in M$, we have $\beta \otimes x = \beta(1 \otimes x)$

for every $\beta \in S$. It follows that, if X is a set of generators of the module M, the elements $1 \otimes x$, $x \in X$, form a set of generators of M^S; if $y = \sum_{x \in X} \alpha_x x$ is any element of M, we have

$$1 \otimes y = \sum_{x \in X}(1 \otimes \alpha_x x) = \sum_{x \in X} \rho(\alpha_x)(1 \otimes x).$$

Let f be a linear mapping of M into a module M' over R. Denote by I the identity mapping of S; then $I \otimes f$ is called the *linear mapping deduced from f by transfer of the basic ring to S* and is denoted by f^S. It is clear that $f \rightarrow f^S$ is a homomorphism of the additive group Hom (M, M') into Hom (M^S, M'^S). If M'' is a third module over R and g a linear mapping of M' into M'', then we have $(g \circ f)^S = g^S \circ f^S$, which follows from the fact that $I \circ I = I$. If R and S are commutative, then Hom (M, M') is a module over R and Hom (M^S, M'^S) a module over S; in that case we have, for $\alpha \in R$,

$$(\alpha f)^S = \rho(\alpha) f^S.$$

For, let x be in R; if $\beta \in S$, we have

$$(\alpha f)^S(\beta \otimes x) = \beta \otimes (\alpha f)(x) = \beta \otimes (\alpha f(x)) = (\beta\rho(\alpha)) \otimes f(x) = (\rho(\alpha)\beta) \otimes f(x)$$
$$= \rho(\alpha)(\beta \otimes f(x)) = \rho(\alpha)(f^S(\beta \otimes x)),$$

which proves our assertion.

If N is a submodule of M, there is a canonical homomorphism τ of N^S into M^S which maps N^S upon the submodule of M^S spanned by the elements $\beta \otimes x$, $\beta \in S$, $x \in N$; we shall say that τ is the transfer of N^S into M^S; τ need not be a monomorphism.

Theorem 43. *Let the module M be the sum of a family $(N_i)_{i \in I}$ of submodules. Let τ_i be the transfer of N_i into M^S; then $M^S = \sum_{i \in I} \tau_i(N_i)$. If the sum $\sum_{i \in I} N_i$ is direct, then so is the sum $\sum_{i \in I} \tau_i(N_i)$, and each τ_i is then a monomorphism.*

This follows immediately from theorem 30, Sect. 8.

Theorem 44. *Assume that the module M has a base $(x_i)_{i \in I}$. Then the elements $1 \otimes x_i$ form a base of M^S.*

The module M is the direct sum of the modules Rx_i; since $\tau(Rx_i) = S(1 \otimes x_i)$, M^S is the direct sum of the modules $S(1 \otimes x_i)$. Since $\alpha \rightarrow \alpha x_i$ is an isomorphism of R (considered as a module overi tself) with Rx_i, $\beta \rightarrow \beta(1 \otimes x_i)$ is an isomorphism of $S^S = {}_S S_R \otimes R$ with $S(1 \otimes x_i)$, which proves theorem 44.

Theorem 45. *Assume that R and S are commutative. Let $(M_i)_{i \in I}$ be a finite family of modules over R. Then there is a unique isomorphism J of $\bigotimes_{i \in I} M_i^S$ with $(\bigotimes_{i \in I} M_i)^S$ such that $J(\bigotimes_{i \in I}(1 \otimes x_i)) = 1 \otimes \bigotimes_{i \in I} x_i$ whenever $x_i \in M_i$ for every i.*

We first consider the case where each M_i has a base $(x_{i,j})_{j\in J(i)}$. Set $P=\prod_{i\in I}J(i)$; then the elements $\bigotimes_{i\in I}x_{i,f(i)}$ (for $f\in P$) form a base of $\bigotimes_{i\in I}M_i$ (theorem 41, Sect. 10); for each i, the elements $1\otimes x_{i,j}\,(j\in J(i))$ form a base of M_i^S, and, consequently, the elements $\bigotimes_{i\in I}(1\otimes x_{i,f(i)})$ form a base of $\bigotimes_{i\in I}M_i^S$. Thus there exists a unique linear mapping J of $\bigotimes_{i\in I}M_i^S$ into $(\bigotimes_{i\in I}M_i)^S$ such that

$$J(\bigotimes_{i\in I}(1\otimes x_{i,f(i)}))=1\otimes\bigotimes_{i\in I}x_{i,f(i)}$$

for every $f\in P$. Moreover, since the elements $1\otimes\bigotimes_{i\in I}x_{i,f(i)}$ form a base of $(\bigotimes_{i\in I}M_i)^S$, J is an isomorphism. Now, for each i, let x_i be an element of M_i; then we may write $x_i=\sum_{j\in J(i)}\alpha_{i,j}x_{i,j}$, $\alpha_{i,j}\in R$, whence

$$1\otimes x_i=\sum_{j\in J(i)}\rho(\alpha_{i,j})\,(1\otimes x_{i,j})$$

and $$\bigotimes_{i\in I}(1\otimes x_i)=\sum_{f\in P}(\prod_{i\in I}\rho(\alpha_{i,f(i)}))\bigotimes_{i\in I}(1\otimes x_{i,f(i)});$$

the image of this element under J is

$$\sum_{f\in P}(\prod_{i\in I}\rho(\alpha_{i,f(i)}))(1\otimes\bigotimes_{i\in I}x_{i,f(i)})$$
$$=\sum_{f\in P}(1\otimes(\prod_{i\in I}\alpha_{i,f(i)})\bigotimes_{i\in I}x_{i,f(i)})=1\otimes(\bigotimes_{i\in I}x_i)$$

which proves that J has the required property.

We consider now the general case. For each i, we can find a free module F_i and an epimorphism u_i of F_i on M_i; let K_i be the kernel of u_i. Denote by J_F the isomorphism constructed above of $\bigotimes_{i\in I}F_i^S$ with $(\bigotimes_{i\in I}F_i)^S$. Let $u=\bigotimes_{i\in I}u_i$, and let u^S be the corresponding linear mapping of $(\bigotimes_{i\in I}F_i)^S$ into $(\bigotimes_{i\in I}M_i)^S$; then $u^S\circ J_F$ is a linear mapping of $\bigotimes_{i\in I}F_i^S$ into $(\bigotimes_{i\in I}M_i)^S$. We shall determine its kernel. Making use of theorem 42, Sect. 10, we see first that the kernel of u^S is generated by the elements $1\otimes z$, where z is in the kernel of u (for, if $\beta\in S$, then $\beta\otimes z=\beta(1\otimes z)$), and then that the kernel of u is generated by the elements $\bigotimes_{i\in I}z_i$, where $z_i\in F_i$ for all i and $z_i\in K_i$ for at least one i. Making use of the characteristic property of J_F, we see that the kernel of $u^S\circ J_F$ is generated by the elements of the form $\bigotimes_{i\in I}(1\otimes z_i)$, where $z_i\in K_i$ for at least one index i. Now, the mapping u_i defines a mapping u_i^S of F_i^S into M_i^S, whose kernel K_i' is generated by the elements $1\otimes z_i$, with $z_i\in K_i$. The kernel of $\bigotimes_{i\in I}u_i^S$ is generated by the elements $\bigotimes_{i\in I}z_i'$, where $z_i'\in K_i'$ for at least one i. This kernel therefore contains the kernel of $u^S\circ J_F$. Conversely, if $z_i'\in F_i^S$, then z_i' may be written in the form $\sum_{j\in J(i)}\beta_{i,j}\,(1\otimes z_{i,j})$, with $z_{i,j}\in F_i$,

$\beta_{i,j} \in S$, and, if $z'_i \in K'_i$, then we may assume that $z_{i,j} \in K_i$ for every j. Thus $\bigotimes_{i \in I} z'_i = \sum_{f \in P} (\prod_{i \in I} \beta_{i,f(i)}) \bigotimes_{i \in I} (1 \otimes z_{i,f(i)})$, where $P = \prod_{i \in I} J(i)$, and it follows that every element of the kernel of $\bigotimes_{i \in I} u_i^S$ is a linear combination of the elements $\bigotimes_{i \in I} (1 \otimes z_i)$ where $z_i \in K_i$ for at least one i. This shows that $u^S \circ F$ and $\bigotimes_{i \in I} u_i^S$ have the same kernel. Since they are both epimorphisms, there is an isomorphism J of $\bigotimes_{i \in I} M_i^S$ with $(\bigotimes_{i \in I} M_i)^S$ such that $J \circ \bigotimes_{i \in I} u_i^S = u^S \circ J_F$. Let $(x_i)_{i \in I}$ be any element of $\prod_{i \in I} M_i$; for each i, let z_i be an element of F_i such that $x_i = u_i(z_i)$, whence $1 \otimes x_i = u_i^S (1 \otimes z_i)$. Then

$$J(\bigotimes_{i \in I}(1 \otimes x_i)) = (J \circ \bigotimes_{i \in I} u_i)(\bigotimes_{i \in I}(1 \otimes z_i))$$
$$= u^S(1 \otimes \bigotimes_{i \in I} z_i) = 1 \otimes (\bigotimes_{i \in I} x_i)$$

which proves that J has the required property. Moreover, a computation similar to the one made above shows that $\bigotimes_{i \in I} M_i^S$ is generated by the elements of the form $\bigotimes_{i \in I}(1 \otimes x_i)$; J is therefore uniquely determined.

If we have not already introduced a tensor product of the modules M_i^S, we see that we may take $(\bigotimes_{i \in I} M_i)^S$ to be such a tensor product. If this is done, then we have

$$\bigotimes_{i \in I}(1 \otimes x_i) = 1 \otimes \bigotimes_{i \in I} x_i.$$

Let now $(N_i)_{i \in I}$ be another family of modules over R, with the same set I of indices as the family $(M_i)_{i \in I}$. For each i, let f_i be a linear mapping of M_i into N_i. Consider $(\bigotimes_{i \in I} M_i)^S$ as a tensor product of the modules M_i^S and $(\bigotimes_{i \in I} N_i)^S$ as a tensor product of the modules N_i^S. Then we have

$$(\bigotimes_{i \in I} f_i)^S = \bigotimes_{i \in I} f_i^S.$$

For, let Z be the set of elements of $(\bigotimes_{i \in I} M_i)^S$ of the form $1 \otimes (\bigotimes_{i \in I} x_i)$, with $x_i \in M_i$ $(i \in I)$. Since the elements of the form $\bigotimes_{i \in I} x_i$ form a set of generators of the module $\bigotimes_{i \in I} M_i$, Z is a set of generators of $(\bigotimes_{i \in I} M_i)^S$. It will therefore be sufficient to prove that $(\bigotimes_{i \in I} f_i)^S$ and $\bigotimes_{i \in I} f_i^S$ map an element $z = 1 \otimes (\bigotimes_{i \in I} x_i)$ of Z upon the same element. We have

$$(\bigotimes_{i \in I} f_i)^S(z) = 1 \otimes ((\bigotimes_{i \in I} f_i)(\bigotimes_{i \in I} x_i)) = 1 \otimes (\bigotimes_{i \in I} f_i(x_i)),$$
$$(\bigotimes_{i \in I} f_i^S)(z) = (\bigotimes_{i \in I} f_i^S)(\bigotimes_{i \in I}(1 \otimes x_i)) = \bigotimes_{i \in I} f_i^S(1 \otimes x_i)$$
$$= \bigotimes_{i \in I}(1 \otimes f_i(x_i)) = 1 \otimes (\bigotimes_{i \in I} f_i(x_i)),$$

and our formula is proved.

Now, let P be a module over R, and let φ be a multilinear mapping of $\prod_{i \in I} M_i$ into P. Its linearization Φ is a linear mapping of $\bigotimes_{i \in I} M_i$ into P; Φ^S is a linear mapping of $\bigotimes_{i \in I} M_i^S$ into P^S. The formula

$$\varphi^S((x_i')_{i \in I}) = \Phi^S(\bigotimes_{i \in I} x_i')$$

(where $x_i' \in M_i^S$ for every $i \in I$) defines a multilinear mapping φ^S of $\prod_{i \in I} M_i^S$; φ^S is called the *multilinear mapping deduced from* φ *by inverse transfer of the basic ring to* S. It is characterized by the property that

$$\varphi^S((1 \otimes x_i)_{i \in I}) = 1 \otimes \varphi((x_i)_{i \in I}). \qquad (x_i \in M_i).$$

In the case where $P = R$, i. e., where φ is a multilinear form, then the preceding formula becomes

$$\varphi^S((1 \otimes x_i)_{i \in I}) = \rho(\varphi((x_i)_{i \in I})).$$

Now, let σ be a homomorphism of S into a third ring T. If M is a module over T, then, by means of σ, we may associate with M a module M_S over S, and, by means of $\sigma \circ \rho$, a module M_R over R. It is clear that

$$(M_S)_R = M_R.$$

Similarly, let M be a module over R; then, using $\sigma \circ \rho$, we associate with M a module M^T over T, and, using σ, with M^S we associate a module $(M^S)^T$ over T.

Theorem 46. *The situation being as described above, there is a unique isomorphism* J *of* $(M^S)^T$ *with* M^T *such that* $J(1_T \otimes (1_S \otimes x)) = 1_T \otimes x$ *for every* $x \in M$. *If* f *is a linear mapping of* M *into a module* M', *and* J' *the similar isomorphism of* $(M'^S)^T$ *with* M'^T, *we have* $J' \circ (f^S)^T = f^T \circ J$.

Consider first the case where M is a free module, with a base $(x_i)_{i \in I}$. Then $(M^S)^T$ is a free module, with the base $(1_T \otimes (1_S \otimes x_i))_{i \in I}$, and M^T is a free module with the base $(1_T \otimes x_i)_{i \in I}$. Thus, there exists a unique isomorphism J of $(M^S)^T$ with M^T which maps $1_T \otimes (1_S \otimes x_i)$ upon $1_T \otimes x_i$ for every $i \in I$. If $x = \sum_{i \in I} \alpha_i x_i$ is any element of M, we have

$$1_S \otimes x = \sum_{i \in I} \rho(\alpha_i)(1_S \otimes x_i)$$

and $$1_T \otimes (1_S \otimes x_i) = \sum_{i \in I} (\sigma \circ \rho)(\alpha_i)(1_T \otimes (1_S \otimes x_i)).$$

The image under J of this element is $\sum_{i \in I} (\sigma \circ \rho)(\alpha_i)(1_T \otimes x_i) = 1_T \otimes x$.

Consider now the general case. We can find a free module F and an epimorphism u of F on M. Let J_F be the isomorphism constructed above of $(F^S)^T$ with F^T; then $u^T \circ J_F$ is an epimorphism of $(F^S)^T$ on M^T. The kernel of u^T being generated by the elements $1_T \otimes z$, where z is in the kernel K

of F, the kernel of $u^T \circ J_F$ is generated by the elements $1_T \otimes (1_S \otimes z)$, $z \in K$. These elements belong to the kernel of $(u^S)^T$. Conversely, an element ζ of the kernel of $(u^S)^T$ is a linear combination of elements $1_T \otimes z'$, where z' is in the kernel of u^S, and z' is a linear combination of elements of the form $1_S \otimes z$, $z \in K$; it follows easily that ζ is a linear combination of elements of the form $1_T \otimes (1_S \otimes z)$, $z \in K$; $(u^S)^T$ and $u^T \circ J_F$ therefore have the same kernel. It follows that there exists an isomorphism J of $(M^S)^T$ with M^T such that $J \circ (u^S)^T = u^T \circ J_F$; it follows immediately that J has the required property. It is easily seen that $(M^S)^T$ is generated by the elements $1_T \otimes (1_S \otimes x)$, $x \in M$, which shows that J is uniquely determined. If $x \in M$, we have

$$\begin{aligned}(J' \circ (f^S)^T)(1_T \otimes (1_S \otimes x)) &= J'(1_T \otimes (1_S \otimes f(x))) = 1_T \otimes f(x) \\ &= f^T(1_T \otimes x) = (f^T \circ J)(1_T \otimes (1_S \otimes x)),\end{aligned}$$

which proves the second assertion of theorem 46.

Theorem 47. *Assume that R and S are commutative. Let M be a module over R and N a module over S. Then there is a unique isomorphism J of $(M^S \otimes N)^T$ with $M^T \otimes N^T$ such that*

$$J(1_T \otimes ((1_S \otimes x) \otimes y)) = (1_T \otimes x) \otimes (1_T \otimes y)$$

for any $x \in M$, $y \in N$.

Let J_1 be the isomorphism of $(M^S)^T \otimes N^T$ with $(M^S \otimes N)^T$ given by theorem 45, and let J_2 be the isomorphism of $(M^S)^T$ with M^T given by theorem 46. Let I be the identity mapping of N^T. Then $(J_2 \otimes I) \otimes \overset{-1}{J_1} = J$ is an isomorphism with the required property. The module M^S is generated by the elements $1_S \otimes x$, $x \in M$; $M^S \otimes N$ is therefore generated by the elements $(1_S \otimes x) \otimes y$, $x \in M$, $y \in N$, and $(M^S \otimes N)^T$ by the elements $1_T \otimes ((1_S \otimes x) \otimes y)$, which proves that J is uniquely determined.

An important special case of the situation considered above is the one in which R is a subring of S and ρ the identity mapping of R into S. In that case, if M is a module over S, M_R is called the *module deduced from M by restriction of the basic ring to R*; and, if M is a module over R, M^S is called the *module deduced from M by extension of the basic ring to S.*

12. Vector spaces

By a *left-* (resp.: *right-*) *vector space* is meant a left (resp.: right) module over a sfield. Unless we indicate otherwise, we shall consider left-vector spaces, which we shall call simply *vector spaces*. The submodules of a vector space V are also called *subspaces* of V.

Theorem 48. *Let V be a vector space generated by a single element $x \neq 0$; then V is a simple module and, if K is the basic sfield of V, the mapping $\alpha \rightarrow \alpha x$ is an isomorphism of K (considered as a vector space over itself) with V.*

Let N be a subspace of K, considered as a vector space over itself. If N contains an element $\alpha \neq 0$, then, for any $\beta \in K$, $\beta = (\beta\alpha^{-1})\alpha$ belongs to N, whence $N = K$; K is therefore a simple module. The epimorphism $\alpha \rightarrow \alpha x$ of K on V does not map K upon $\{0\}$; it is therefore an isomorphism (Schur's lemma), which proves that V is simple.

Theorem 49. *Any vector space V is semi-simple and has a base. All bases of V have the same cardinal number. If $(x_i)_{i \in I}$ is a base of V, W a subspace of V and C a base of W, there is a base of V which contains C and whose other elements (not in C) are among the elements x_i.*

If X is the set of elements $\neq 0$ in V, we have $V = \Sigma_{x \in X} Kx$; making use of theorem 11, Sect. 4, we see that V is semi-simple and is the direct sum of a family $(Kx)_{x \in B}$ (where $B \subset V$) of subspaces each of which is generated by a single element $x \neq 0$. Since $\alpha \rightarrow \alpha x$ is an isomorphism of K with Kx, B is a base of V. It follows from theorem 24, Sect. 7 that all bases of V have the same cardinal number. Making use again of theorem 11, Sect. 4, we see that V is the direct sum of W and of a space of the form $\Sigma_{i \in J} Kx_i$, J being a subset of I; it is clear that the union of C and of the set of elements x_i, for $i \in J$, is a base of V.

Corollary. *Let W be a subspace of a vector space V. Then every linear mapping of W into a vector space U may be extended to a linear mapping of V into U.*

Let f be a linear mapping of W into U. There exists a subspace W' of V such that V is the direct sum of W and W'; there exists a linear mapping f' of V into U which coincides with f on W and which maps W' upon $\{0\}$, which proves the corollary.

Theorem 50. *Let $(x_i)_{i \in I}$ be a family of elements of a vector space V. If the elements x_i are linearly independent, they may be included in a base of V. If they generate V, there is a subset J of I such that $(x_i)_{i \in J}$ is a base of V. If both conditions are satisfied at the same time, then $(x_i)_{i \in I}$ is a base of V.*

If the elements x_i are linearly independent, they are $\neq 0$ and the sum $\Sigma_{i \in I} Kx_i$ is direct. It follows immediately that $(x_i)_{i \in I}$ is a base of the subspace $W = \Sigma_{i \in I} Kx_i$ of V, which proves the third assertion, and also the first, in view of theorem 49. If the elements x_i generate V, then, each subspace Kx_i being either $\{0\}$ or a simple module, it follows from theorem 11, Sect. 4 that there is a subset J of I such that $(x_i)_{i \in J}$ is a base of V.

Theorem 51. *Let V and W be vector spaces over a sfield K, $(x_i)_{i \in I}$ a base of V and $(y_j)_{j \in J}$ a base of W. If $(i, j) \in I \times J$, let E_{ij} be the linear mapping of V into W such that $E_{ij}(x_{i'}) = 0$ if $i' \neq i$, $E_{ij}(x_i) = y_j$. The mappings E_{ij} are then linearly independent; if I is finite, they form a base of* Hom (V, W).

Let α_{ij} be elements of K, almost all zero, such that

$$\Sigma_{(i, j) \in I \times J} \alpha_{ij} E_{ij} = 0.$$

Then we have, for any $i' \in I$, $0 = \Sigma_{i, j} \alpha_{ij} E_{ij}(x_{i'}) = \Sigma_{j \in J} \alpha_{i'j} y_j$, whence $\alpha_{i'j} = 0$ for every j. This shows that the elements E_{ij} are linearly independent. Assume that I is finite, and let f be any linear mapping of V into W. For any $i \in I$, set $f(x_i) = \Sigma_{j \in J} \alpha_{ij} y_j$ (with $\alpha_{ij} = 0$ for almost all $j \in J$). Then we have $\alpha_{ij} = 0$ for almost all $(i, j) \in I \times J$, and, if $f' = \Sigma_{ij} \alpha_{ij} E_{ij}$, $f'(x_i) = f(x_i)$ for every $i \in I$. Since $(x_i)_{i \in I}$ is a base of V, this implies $f = f'$; $(E_{ij})_{(i, j) \in I \times J}$ is therefore a base of Hom (V, W).

Theorem 52. *Let V be a vector space over a sfield K, and $(x_i)_{i \in I}$ a base of V. For any $i \in I$, let f_i be the linear form on V such that $f_i(x_{i'}) = 0$ if $i' \neq i$, $f_i(x_i) = 1$. Then the elements f_i are linearly independent in the dual space V^* of V. The canonical mapping of V into its bidual V^{**} is a monomorphism. If I is finite, then the elements f_i form a base of V^* and the canonical mapping of V into V^{**} is an isomorphism.*

Let α_i $(i \in I)$ be elements of K such that $\Sigma_{i \in I} f_i \alpha_i = 0$. Then we have, for $i' \in I$, $0 = \Sigma_{i \in I}(f_i \alpha_i)(x_{i'}) = \alpha_{i'}$, which proves that the elements f_i are linearly independent in V^*. Let φ be the canonical mapping of V into V^{**}, and let $x = \Sigma_{i \in I} \alpha_i x_i$ $(\alpha_i \in K,\ \alpha_i = 0$ for almost all $i)$ be an element of V such that $\varphi(x) = 0$. Then we have, for every i,

$$0 = (\varphi(x))(f_i) = f_i(x) = \Sigma_{i' \in I} \alpha_i f_i(x_{i'}) = \alpha_i, \quad \text{and} \quad x = 0,$$

which shows that φ is a monomorphism.

Assume now that I is finite, and let f be a linear form on V. Set

$$f(x_i) = \alpha_i,\ f' = \Sigma_{i \in I} f_i \alpha_i;$$

then we have $f'(x_i) = f(x_i)$ for every i, whence $f = f'$, which shows that $(f_i)_{i \in I}$ is a base of V^*. Let x^{**} be any element of V^{**}, and set $x^{**}(f_i) = \alpha_i$, $x = \Sigma_{i \in I} \alpha_i x_i$. Then we have $(\varphi(x))(f_i) = f_i(x) = \alpha_i$ for every i; since the elements f_i form a base of V^*, we have $x^{**} = \varphi(x)$, and φ is an isomorphism.

Corollary. *Let W be a subspace of a vector space V; denote by $\overline{W}$ the set of linear forms on V which map W upon $\{0\}$. Then, if an element x of V is such that $f(x) = 0$ for all $f \in \overline{W}$, x belongs to W.*

Let $(x_i)_{i \in I}$ be a base of V such that there exists a subset J of I with the property that $(x_i)_{i \in J}$ is a base of W. The notation being as in theorem 52,

Let V be a vector space, $\bar{V}$ its dual space. Let A and $\bar{B}$ be subspaces of V and $\bar{V}$, respectively. Define $\bar{A} = \{y \in \bar{V} \mid (\forall x \in A)\ y(x) = 0\}$, $\bar{\bar{B}} = \{x \in V \mid (\forall y \in \bar{B})\ y(x) = 0\}$. $\bar{A}$, $\bar{\bar{B}}$ are subspaces of $\bar{V}$, V. The above corollary shows that, in general, when W is a subspace of V, $W = \bar{\bar{W}}$.

we observe that, if i does not belong to J, then f_i maps W upon $\{0\}$, since $f_i(x_{i'}) = 0$ for every $i' \in J$. Let $x = \sum_{i \in I} \alpha_i x_i$ be the expression of x as a linear combination of the basic elements x_i; we have by assumption $f_i(x) = 0$ if i does not belong to J. Since $f_i(x) = \alpha_i$ for any i, we have $\alpha_i = 0$ whenever i is not in J, which proves that x belongs to W.

One may express the corollary by saying that any subspace of a vector space may be defined by a system of linear equations.

Theorem 53. *Let $(V_i)_{i \in I}$ be a family of vector spaces over a field K; for each i, let W_i be a subspace of V_i. Then the canonical homomorphism of $\bigotimes_{i \in I} W_i$ into $\bigotimes_{i \in I} V_i$ is a monomorphism.*

Let F be this homomorphism. For each i, let p_i be a projector of V_i such that $p_i(V_i) = W_i$. Set $p = \bigotimes_{i \in I} p_i$; then p is a linear mapping of $\bigotimes_{i \in I} V_i$ into $\bigotimes_{i \in I} W_i$, and $p \circ F$ is the identity mapping of $\bigotimes_{i \in I} W_i$, which proves that F is a monomorphism.

It follows that we may consider the subspace W of $\bigotimes_{i \in I} V_i$ generated by the elements $\bigotimes_{i \in I} x_i$ $(x_i \in W_i)$ as a tensor product of the spaces W_i; if we have not already introduced a tensor product of the spaces W_i, we shall denote W by $\bigotimes_{i \in I} W_i$.

Theorem 54. *Let $(V_i)_{i \in I}$ be a finite family of vector spaces over a field K. For each $i \in I$, let u_i be a linear mapping of V_i into some vector space V_i', and let W_i be the kernel of u_i. Then the kernel of $\bigotimes_{i \in I} u_i$ is the subspace W of $\bigotimes_{i \in I} V_i$ generated by the elements $\bigotimes_{i \in I} x_i$ where $x_i \in V_i$ and $x_i \in W_i$ for at least one i.*

Let $W_i' = u_i(V_i)$; denote by u_i' the mapping u_i considered as a mapping of V_i into W_i' and by F the canonical mapping of $\bigotimes_{i \in I} W_i'$ into $\bigotimes_{i \in I} V_i'$, then we have $\bigotimes_{i \in I} u_i = F \circ (\bigotimes_{i \in I} u_i')$. We know that W is the kernel of $\bigotimes_{i \in I} u_i'$ (theorem 42, Sect. 10) and that F is a monomorphism; theorem 54 is thereby proved.

A vector space V whose bases are finite sets is called a *finite dimensional vector space*; the number of elements of a base of V is called the *dimension of* V; it is denoted by $\dim V$.

Theorem 55. *Let V be a vector space and $(W_i)_{i \in I}$ a finite family of finite dimensional subspaces of V. Then $\sum_{i \in I} W_i$ is finite dimensional, and $\dim \sum_{i \in I} W_i \leqslant \sum_{i \in I} \dim W_i$. A necessary and sufficient condition for $\dim \sum_{i \in I} W_i$ to be equal to $\sum_{i \in I} \dim W_i$ is for the sum $\sum_{i \in I} W_i$ to be direct.*

Let B_i be a base of W_i. Then $\bigcup_{i \in I} B_i$ is a set of generators of $W = \Sigma_{i \in I} W_i$ and therefore contains a base B of W. Since $\bigcup_{i \in I} B_i$ is a finite set, W is finite dimensional and $\dim W \leqslant \Sigma_{i \in I} \dim W_i$. In order for the equality to take place, it is necessary and sufficient that $B = \bigcup_{i \in I} B_i$ and that the sets B_i be mutually disjoint; the second assertion therefore follows from theorem 35, Sect. 9.

Theorem 56. *Let V be a vector space and W a subspace of V. In order for V to be finite dimensional, it is necessary and sufficient that W and V/W both be finite dimensional, and we then have* $\dim V = \dim W + \dim V/W$.

Let Z be a subspace of V such that V is the direct sum of W and Z; then Z is isomorphic to V/W. If W and V/W are finite dimensional, then so is Z and it follows from theorem 36 (Sect. 9) that V is finite dimensional and that $\dim V = \dim W + \dim V/W$. The union of a base of W and of a base of Z being a base of V, if V is finite dimensional, so are W and Z, which shows that W and V/W are finite dimensional.

Theorem 57. *Let V be a finite dimensional vector space and W a subspace of V. Then W is finite dimensional, and* $\dim W \leqslant \dim V$; *if* $\dim W = \dim V$, *we have* $W = V$.

This follows from theorem 56 and from the fact that the spaces of dimension 0 are the spaces which consist of their zero elements only.

13. Vector spaces in duality

Let K be a sfield, V a right-vector space over K and W a left-vector space over K. By a *bilinear form* on $V \times W$ we mean a mapping β of $V \times W$ into K which satisfies the following conditions:

a) It is bi-additive;

b) If $\alpha \in K$, $x \in V$, $y \in W$, we have $\beta(x\alpha, y) = \beta(x, y)\alpha$, $\beta(x, \alpha y) = \alpha\beta(x, y)$.

If K is commutative, this is a special case of the notion of multilinear mapping which we have studied in Sect. 10. If, however, K is not commutative, it should be observed that a bilinear form is *not* in general a balanced mapping of $V \times W$.

The bilinear form β is called *nondegenerate* if the following conditions are satisfied: *a*) If x is an element $\neq 0$ of V, there is at least one element $y \in W$ such that $\beta(x, y) \neq 0$; *b*) If y is an element $\neq 0$ of W, there is at least one element $x \in V$ such that $\beta(x, y) \neq 0$.

Examples Let V be a right-vector space over K; then its dual V^* is a left-vector space. If $x \in V$, $x^* \in V^*$, set $\beta(x, x^*) = x^*(x)$; then β is clearly a bilinear form on $V \times V^*$. This bilinear form is nondegenerate. For, if x is an element $\neq 0$ in V, then x may be included in a base $(x_i)_{i \in I}$ of V (theorem 50, Sect. 12); if $x = x_{i_0}$, there is a linear form x^* on V such that $x^*(x_{i_0}) = 1$, $x^*(x_i) = 0$ for all $i \neq i_0$ (theorem 52, Sect. 12), whence $x^*(x) \neq 0$. On the other hand, if x^* is an element $\neq 0$ of V^*, then, by definition, there exists an element $x \in V$ such that $x^*(x) \neq 0$.

If β is a nondegenerate bilinear form on $V \times W$, then we say that V and W are put in *duality with each other* by β.

Let β be a bilinear form on $V \times W$. If x is any element of V, the mapping $y \to \beta(x, y)$ is obviously a linear form on W, i. e., an element of the dual space W^* of W. We shall denote this element by $\beta_{x\cdot}$. The spaces V and W^* are both right-vector spaces over K; the mapping $x \to \beta_{x\cdot}$ of V into W^* is linear. For, let x, x' be elements of V; then

$$\beta_{(x+x')\cdot}(y) = \beta(x + x', y) = \beta(x, y) + \beta(x', y),$$

whence $\beta_{(x+x')\cdot} = \beta_{x\cdot} + \beta_{x'\cdot}$; and if $\alpha \in K$,

$$\beta_{(x\alpha)\cdot}(y) = \beta(x\alpha, y) = \beta(x, y)\alpha = (\beta_{x\cdot}\alpha)(y),$$

whence $\beta_{(x\alpha)\cdot} = (\beta_{x\cdot})\alpha$

Conversely, let φ be any linear mapping of V into W^*; then the mapping β defined by $\beta(x, y) = (\varphi(x))(y)$ of $V \times W$ into K is obviously a bilinear form, and we have $\beta_{x\cdot} = \varphi(x)$ for any $x \in V$.

Similarly, for any $y \in V$, the mapping $\beta_{\cdot y}$: $x \to \beta(x, y)$ is an element of the dual V^* of V (which is a left-vector space), and $y \to \beta_{\cdot y}$ is a linear mapping of W into V^*. Conversely, any linear mapping of W into V^* defines a bilinear form on $V \times W$.

The linear mappings $x \to \beta_{x\cdot}$ and $y \to \beta_{\cdot y}$ are called the linear mappings *associated with* β.

Theorem 58. *Let V be a right-vector space and W a left-vector space over a sfield K. Let β be a bilinear form on $V \times W$. Then, a necessary and sufficient condition for β to be nondegenerate is that the linear mappings $x \to \beta_{x\cdot}$ and $y \to \beta_{\cdot y}$ both be monomorphisms.*

This follows immediately from the definition.

In what follows, we shall consider a right-vector space V and a left-vector space W which are put in duality with each other by means of a fixed bilinear form β. The notions we shall introduce are relative to this fixed form β.

We shall say that a set $A \subset V$ and a set $B \subset W$ are *orthogonal to each other* if $\beta(x, y) = 0$ whenever $x \in A$, $y \in B$. If A (resp.: B) consists of a single element x (resp.: y), then we say also that x and B (resp.: A and y) are orthogonal to each other; if $A = \{x\}$ and $B = \{y\}$, then we say also that x and y are orthogonal to each other.

Let A be any subset of V. Then we shall denote by A^0 the set of elements $y \in W$ which are orthogonal to A. This is clearly the intersection of the sets $\{x\}^0$, x running over the elements of A. Now, $\{x\}^0$ is the kernel of the linear form $\beta_{x\cdot}$, and is therefore a subspace of W. Any intersection of subspaces being a subspace, we see that A^0 is a subspace of W, which is called the *orthogonal space* of A. We define in a similar manner the orthogonal space B^0 of a subset B of W: this is a subspace of V. The following properties follow immediately from the definitions:

If A_1, A_2 are subsets of V such that $A_1 \subset A_2$, we have $A_2^0 \subset A_1^0$. If B_1, B_2 are subsets of W such that $B_1 \subset B_2$, we have $B_2^0 \subset B_1^0$. If A is any subset of V, we have $A \subset (A^0)^0$; if B is any subset of W, we have $B \subset (B^0)^0$.

Let M be a subspace of V. Let x be an element of M; then $\beta_{x\cdot}$ is a linear form whose kernel contains M^0. If π is the natural mapping of W on W/M^0, $\beta_{x\cdot}$ may be written in the form $\varphi(x) \circ \pi$, where $\varphi(x)$ is a uniquely determined linear form on W/M^0. The mapping $\varphi : x \to \varphi(x)$ of M into the dual $(W/M^0)^*$ of W/M^0 is linear. For, let $\bar{y}$ be any element of $(W/M^0)^*$ and y an element of W such that $\pi(y) = \bar{y}$. If x, x' are elements of V, we have

$$(\varphi(x + x'))(\bar{y}) = \beta_{(x+x')\cdot}(y) = \beta_{x\cdot}(y) + \beta_{x'\cdot}(y) = (\varphi(x) + \varphi(x'))(\bar{y}),$$

whence $\varphi(x + x') = \varphi(x) + \varphi(x')$; if $\alpha \in K$, we have

$$(\varphi(x\alpha))(\bar{y}) = \beta_{(x\alpha)\cdot}(y) = (\beta_{x\cdot}(y))\alpha = (\varphi(x)\alpha)(\bar{y}),$$

whence $\varphi(x\alpha) = \varphi(x)\alpha$. The mapping φ defines a bilinear form $\bar{\beta}$ on $M \times (W/M^0)$ such that

$$\bar{\beta}(x, \pi(y)) = \beta(x, y) \qquad (x \in M,\ y \in W).$$

This bilinear form is nondegenerate. For, if x is an element $\neq 0$ of M, there is a $y \in W$ such that $\beta(x, y) \neq 0$, whence $\bar{\beta}(x, \pi(y)) \neq 0$. If $\bar{y}$ is an element $\neq 0$ in W/M^0, let y be an element of W such that $\pi(y) = \bar{y}$. Since $\bar{y} \neq 0$, y is not in M^0, which shows that there exists an $x \in M$ such that $\beta(x, y) = \bar{\beta}(x, \bar{y}) \neq 0$.

Theorem 59. *Let V be a right-vector space over a sfield K and W a left-vector space on K which is put in duality with V by a bilinear form β. If either one of V or W is finite dimensional, so is the other, and they both have the same dimension; moreover, the linear mappings $x \to \beta_{x\cdot}$ of V into the dual W^* of W and $y \to \beta_{\cdot y}$ of W into the dual V^* of V are both isomorphisms.*

Let M be a finite dimensional vector space, and $(z_1, \cdots, z_m)$ a base of M. The dual M^* of M has a base $(z_1^*, \cdots, z_m^*)$ composed of linear forms z_i^* such that $z_i^*(z_j) = 0$ if $j \neq i$, $z_i^*(z_i) = 1$ (theorem 52, Sect. 12); this shows that M^* is finite dimensional and has the same dimension as M. This being said, assume that V is finite dimensional. Since $y \to \beta_{\cdot y}$ is a monomorphism of W into V^*, W is isomorphic to a subspace of V^*; thus W is finite dimensional, and we have $\dim W \leqslant \dim V^* = \dim V$. We see in the same way that the dual of a right-vector space N is finite dimensional and has the same dimension as N; making use of the linear mapping $x \to \beta_{x\cdot}$, we see as above that, if W is finite dimensional, then so is V, and $\dim V \leqslant \dim W$. It follows immediately that, if either V or W is finite dimensional, then so is the other and they have the same dimension. Assuming that this is the case, the image of W under the mapping $y \to \beta_{\cdot y}$ is a space of dimension equal to

$$\dim W = \dim V = \dim V^*$$

and is contained in V^*; this image is therefore the whole of V^*, and $y \to \beta_{\cdot y}$ is an isomorphism of W with V^*. We see in the same way that $x \to \beta_{x\cdot}$ is an isomorphism of V with W^*.

A subspace M of a vector space V is said to be of *finite codimension* if V/M is finite dimensional; the number $\dim V/M$ is then called the codimension of M.

Theorem 60. *Let M be a subspace of a vector space V. In order for M to be of finite codimension, it is necessary and sufficient that there should exist a finite number of linear forms $x_1^*, \cdots, x_n^*$ on V such that M is the set of all $x \in W$ such that $x_i^*(x) = 0$ $(1 \leqslant i \leqslant n)$. This being the case, any linear form on V which takes the value 0 at every element of M is a linear combination of $x_1^*, \cdots, x_n^*$. The linear forms $x_1^*, \cdots, x_n^*$ may be taken to be linearly independent; if this is done, then n is equal to the codimension of M.*

Let V^* be the dual of V; we consider V^* and V as being put in duality with each other by means of the bilinear form $(x^*, x) \to x^*(x)$. Let M^0 be the orthogonal space of M. Denote by $(V/M)^*$ the dual space of V/M and by π the natural homomorphism of V on V/M. If $y^* \in (V/M)^*$, then $y^* \circ \pi$ is a linear form on V which obviously maps M upon $\{0\}$ (since $\pi(M) = \{0\}$) and therefore belongs to M^0. Conversely, if $x^* \in M^0$, then there is a unique $y^* \in (V/M)^*$ such that $x^* = y^* \circ \pi$, since the kernel of x^* then contains M (theorem 14, Sect. 4). Thus, $y^* \to y^* \circ \pi$ is a bijection of $(V/M)^*$ on M^0. This mapping is linear. For, if y_1^*, y_2^* are elements of $(V/M)^*$, then we know that $(y_1^* + y_2^*) \circ \pi = y_1^* \circ \pi + y_2^* \circ \pi$. On the other hand, if α is an element of the basic field K of V, and $x \in V$, then

$$(y^*\alpha \circ \pi)(x) = (y^*\alpha)(\pi(x)) = (y^*(\pi(x)))\alpha = ((y^* \circ \pi)\alpha)(x),$$

whence $y^*\alpha \circ \pi = (y^* \circ \pi)\alpha$. It follows that M^0 is isomorphic to $(V/M)^*$. If M is of finite codimension d, then M^0 is finite dimensional, of dimension d. Let M^{00} be the orthogonal space of M^0. Then we know that there exists a nondegenerate bilinear form on $M^0 \times (V/M^{00})$. Since M^0 is of dimension

d, V/M^{00} is of dimension d (theorem 59). On the other hand, we have $M \subset M^{00}$ and V/M^{00} is isomorphic to $(V/M)/(M^{00}/M)$. Since V/M^{00} and V/M are both of dimension d, M^{00}/M is of dimension 0 (theorem 56, Sect. 12), whence $M^{00} = M$. If $(u_1^*, \cdots, u_d^*)$ is a base of M^0, then, since every element u^* of M^0 is a linear combination of $u_1^*, \cdots, u_d^*$, we have $u^*(x) = 0$ for every point x such that $u_i^*(x) = 0$ $(1 \leqslant i \leqslant d)$. Since $M^{00} = M$, this means that M is the set of elements $x \in V$ such that $u_i^*(x) = 0$ $(1 \leqslant i \leqslant d)$. Conversely, assume that there exist elements $x_1^*, \cdots, x_n^*$ of V^* such that M is the set of all $x \in V$ such that $x_i^*(x) = 0$ $(1 \leqslant i \leqslant n)$. Let P be the subspace of V^* generated by $x_1^*, \cdots, x_n^*$; then it is clear that M is the orthogonal space P^0 of P, and therefore that there exists a non-degenerate bilinear form on $P \times (V/M)$. Since P is finite dimensional, so is V/M, and $\dim V/M = \dim P$. It is clear that $P \subset M^0$, and we have seen above that $\dim M^0 = \dim V/M = \dim P$; it follows that $P = M^0$, and therefore that every linear form on V which takes the value 0 at every point of M is a linear combination of $x_1^*, \cdots, x_n^*$.

Corollary 1. *Let V be a vector space, and V^* its dual space, which is put in duality with V by means of the bilinear form $(x, x^*) \to x^*(x)$. If P is a finite dimensional subspace of V^* and $M = P^0$ its orthogonal space in V, then M is of finite codimension equal to the dimension of P, and P is the orthogonal space of M.*

If $(x_1^*, \cdots, x_n^*)$ is a base of P, then M is clearly the set of elements $x \in W$ such that $x_i^*(x) = 0$ $(1 \leqslant i \leqslant n)$; the corollary therefore follows immediately from theorem 60.

Corollary 2. *The notation being as in corollary 1, assume furthermore that V is of finite dimension n. For every subspace M of V, denote by M^0 the orthogonal space of M; then the mapping $M \to M^0$ is a bijection of the set of subspaces of V on the set of subspaces of V^*. If M is of dimension p, then M^0 is of dimension $n - p$.*

For any subspace M of V, we have $M = (M^0)^0$ by the corollary to theorem 52, Sect. 12; this shows that $M \to M^0$ is an injective mapping. Since V^* is of finite dimension, so is every subspace of V^*, and it follows from corollary 1 above that our mapping is surjective. The dimension of M^0 is equal to the codimension of M, i. e., to $\dim V/M$, which is $n - \dim M$.

Theorem 61. *Let V be a vector space and V^* the dual space of V, which is put in duality with V by means of the bilinear form $(x, x^*) \to x^*(x)$ on $V \times V^*$; for any subspace M of V, denote by M^0 the orthogonal space to M in V^*. If M, M' are subspaces of V, then we have*

$$(M + M')^0 = M^0 \cap M'^0 \qquad (M \cap M')^0 = M^0 + M'^0.$$

The first equality is obvious, and so is the fact that $M^0 + M'^0$ is contained in $(M \cap M')^0$. Let x^* be an element of $(M \cap M')^0$. We may represent M as the direct sum of $M \cap M'$ and of a subspace N; we then have $N \cap M' = \{0\}$, and the sum $N + M'$ is direct. It follows that there exists a linear form x_0^* on $N + M'$ which coincides with x^* on N and which maps M' upon $\{0\}$; x_0^* may be extended to a linear form x_1^* on V, and x_1^* belongs to M'^0. We have $x^*(M \cap M') = \{0\}$, and, since $M \cap M' \subset M'$, $x_1^*(M \cap M') = \{0\}$; on the other hand, $x^* - x_1^*$ maps N upon $\{0\}$. The kernel of $x^* - x_1^*$ therefore contains $(M \cap M') + N = M$, whence $x^* - x_1^* \in M^0$ and $x^* \in M^0 + M'^0$.

14. The rank of a linear mapping

Let V and W be vector spaces over a sfield K and f a linear mapping of V into W. If $f(V)$ is finite dimensional, then we say that f is *of finite rank*, and we call the dimension of $f(V)$ the *rank* of f. Let L be the kernel of f; since $f(V)$ is isomorphic to V/L, a necessary and sufficient condition for f to be of finite rank is that L be of finite codimension, and the rank of f is then the codimension of L.

Let $(x_1^*, \cdots, x_n^*)$ be a finite system of linear forms on V. Set $K_i = K \, (1 \leqslant i \leqslant n)$, $K^n = \prod_{i=1}^n K_i$. Then we may associate with $x_1^*, \cdots, x_n^*$ a linear mapping f of V into K^n; viz., the mapping f defined by

$$f(x) = (x_1^*(x), \cdots, x_n^*(x)).$$

The rank of this mapping is called the *rank of the system* $(x_1^*, \ldots, x_n^*)$ *of linear forms.*

Theorem 62. *Let $x_1^*, \cdots, x_n^*$ be linear forms on a vector space V. The rank of the system $(x_1^*, \cdots, x_n^*)$ is then equal to the dimension of the subspace P of the dual V^* of V which is generated by $x_1^*, \ldots, x_n^*$.*

Let the mapping $f: V \to K^n$ be defined as above, and let L be its kernel. Then L is the set of elements $x \in V$ such that $x_i^*(x) = 0 \, (1 \leqslant i \leqslant n)$. It follows from theorem 60, Sect. 13, that its codimension is equal to the dimension of P.

We have also an analogous notion of rank for a linear mapping of a right-vector space into a right-vector space.

Now, let u be a linear mapping of a vector space V into a vector space W. Then we have associated with u a linear mapping ${}^t u$, the transpose of u, of the dual W^* of W (whch is a right-vector space) into the dual V^* of V. If $y^* \in W^*$, then we have

$$({}^t u)(y^*) = y^* \circ u.$$

Theorem 63. *Let u be a linear mapping of a vector space V into a vector space W, and ${}^tu$ its transpose mapping (of the dual W^* of W into the dual V^* of V). Then a necessary and sufficient condition for ${}^tu$ to be of finite rank is that u be of finite rank; and u and ${}^tu$ are then of the same rank.*

Let $X^* = ({}^tu)(W^*)$, $Y = u(V)$; we shall define a bilinear form β on $X^* \times Y$. Let x^* be an element of X^* and y an element of Y; then we may write $y = u(x)$ for some $x \in V$. The value of $x^*(x)$ depends only on x^* and y. For, let $y^* \in W^*$ be such that $x^* = ({}^tu)(y^*) = y^* \circ u$; then $x^*(x) = y^*(u(x)) = y^*(y)$, which proves our assertion. Set $\beta(x^*, y) = x^*(x)$; for a fixed $x^* \in X^*$, $x^* = ({}^tu)(y^*)$ for some $y^* \in W^*$, we have $\beta(x^*, y) = y^*(y)$, which shows that $y \to \beta(x^*, y)$ is a linear form on Y. For a fixed $y \in Y$, $y = u(x)$ for some $x \in V$, the mapping

$$x^* \to \beta(x^*, y) = x^*(x)$$

is a linear form on X^*. It follows that β is a bilinear form. This form is non-degenerate. For, let x^* be $\neq 0$ in X^*; since x^* is an element $\neq 0$ of V^*, there exists an $x \in V$ such that $x^*(x) \neq 0$, whence $\beta(x^*, u(x)) = x^*(x) \neq 0$. Now, let y be an element $\neq 0$ in Y; then there is a $y^* \neq 0$ in W^* such that $y^*(y) \neq 0$, whence $\beta(({}^tu)(y^*), y) = y^*(y) \neq 0$. Making use of theorem 59, Sect. 13, we see that, if either one of the spaces $u(V)$, $({}^tu)(W^*)$ is finite dimensional, then both are and they have the same dimension, which proves theorem 63.

15. Matrices

Let I and J be sets. By a *matrix* (of type (I, J)) is meant a mapping which assigns to every pair $(i, j) \in I \times J$ an element a_{ij}; the matrix itself is often denoted by the notation $(a_{ij})_{(i,j) \in I \times J}$, or, simply, (a_{ij}).

A matrix of type $(\{1\}, J)$ is called a *row*; a matrix of type $(I, \{1\})$ is called a *column*. If $A = (a_{ij})$ is a matrix of type (I, J) and $i \in I$, the mapping $(1, j) \to a_{ij}$ is called the *row of index* i of A; if $j \in J$, the mapping $(i, 1) \to a_{ij}$ is called the *column of index* j of A. We say that a_{ij} is the element of A at the intersection of the i-th row and the j-th column.

If $I = \{1, \cdots, m\}$, $J = \{1, \cdots, n\}$, where, m, n are integers > 0, then a matrix of type (I, J) is also called a matrix of type (m, n).

A matrix of type (I, I) is called a *square matrix*. A matrix of type (n, n), where n is an integer > 0, is called a *square matrix of degree n*.

Let I and J be sets; for every pair $(i, j) \in I \times J$, let A_{ij} be an additive group. Let $\mathfrak{a}$ be the set of matrices (a_{ij}) of type (I, J) such that $a_{ij} \in A_{ij}$ for every $(i, j) \in I \times J$. The set $\mathfrak{a}$ is by definition the same as $\prod_{(i,j) \in I \times J} A_{ij}$; as such, it is an additive group, in which the addition is defined by the rule

$$(a_{ij}) + (a'_{ij}) = (a_{ij} + a'_{ij}).$$

Moreover, if each A_{ij} is a left module over a fixed ring R, then $\mathfrak{a}$ has a module structure over R, in which the scalar multiplication is defined by

$$\alpha(a_{ij}) = (\alpha a_{ij}).$$

Let M and N be modules over a ring R. Assume that we are given direct sum decompositions $M = \sum_{i \in I} M_i$, $N = \sum_{j \in J} N_j$, where $(M_i)_{i \in I}$ is a family of submodules of M and $(N_j)_{j \in J}$ a family of submodules of N. Let E_{ij} be the group of linear mappings of M_i into N_j. Let f be any linear mapping of M into N. There corresponds to the direct sum decomposition $N = \sum_{j \in J} N_j$ a family of projectors q_j, q_j being a linear mapping of N onto N_j. Let θ_i be the identity mapping of M_i into M. Then $f_{ij} = q_j \circ f \circ \theta_i$ is a linear mapping of M_i into N_j; i. e., an element of E_{ij}. The matrix $F = (f_{ij})_{(j, i) \in J \times I}$ of type (J, I) is called the *representative matrix* of the mapping f. If f and f' are linear mappings of M into N, then, obviously, the representative matrix of $f + f'$ is the sum of the representative matrices of f and f'. If the basic ring R is commutative, then Hom (M, N) and $E_{ij} =$ Hom (M_i, N_j) are modules over R; if $\alpha \in R$, $f \in$ Hom (M, N) the representative matrix of αf is the scalar product by α of the representative matrix of f.

Let f be a linear mapping of M into N. Then f is uniquely determined when its representative matrix $F = (f_{ij})$ is given. For, let x be any element in M_i; then $(q_j \circ f)(x) = f_{ij}(x)$ for every j, whence $f(x) = \sum_{j \in J} f_{ij}(x)$ (there are only a finite number of elements $f_{ij}(x)$ which are $\neq 0$); this shows that the restriction of f to M_i is uniquely determined when F is given; this being true for every i, f is uniquely determined.

Let us now determine under which condition a given matrix $F = (f_{ij})_{(j, i) \in J \times I}$ of type (J, I) represents a linear mapping of M into N (each f_{ij} being assumed to be an element of E_{ij}). Let i be any index in I; then, for any given $x \in M_i$, only a finite number of the elements $f_{ij}(x)$ must be $\neq 0$. This necessary condition is also sufficient. For, assume that it is satisfied. Take any index $i \in I$. Then $x \to (f_{ij}(x))_{j \in J}$ is a linear mapping of M_i into the module $\prod_{j \in J} N_j$, and it follows from our condition that it maps M_i into the weak product $\prod^w_{j \in J} N_j$. Taking into account the isomorphism between $\prod^w_{j \in J} N_j$ and $\sum_{j \in J} N_j$, we see that there exists a linear mapping f_i of M_i into N such that $f_i(x) = \sum_{j \in J} f_{ij}(x)$ for every $x \in M$. Since M is the direct sum of the modules M_i, there exists a unique linear mapping f of M into N which extends all the mappings f_i; it is clear that F is the representative matrix of f.

Now, let P be a third module over the ring R, and let $P = \sum_{k \in K} P_k$ be a direct sum decomposition of P. Let f be a linear mapping of M into N and g a linear mapping of N into P; let $F = (f_{ij})_{(j, i) \in J \times I}$ be the representative matrix of f and $G = (g_{jk})_{(k,j) \in K \times J}$ that of g. We propose to determine the representative matrix $H = (h_{ik})_{(k,i) \in K \times I}$ of $g \circ f = h$. Let x be any element of M_i; then

$$h(x) = g(f(x)) = g(\Sigma_{j \in J} f_{ij}(x)) = \Sigma_{j \in J} g(f_{ij}(x)).$$

Since $(f_{ij}(x)) \in N_j$, we have $g(f_{ij}(x)) = \Sigma_{k \in K} g_{jk}(f_{ij}(x))$ whence

$$h_{ik}(x) = \Sigma_{j \in J}(g_{jk} \circ f_{ij})(x).$$

When J is a finite set, we may write

$$h_{ik} = \Sigma_{j \in J} g_{jk} \circ f_{ij}, \tag{1}$$

and this formula determines the matrix H. If the set J is infinite, it should be observed that there may be infinitely many indices j for which $g_{jk} \circ f_{ij} \neq 0$, although, for any given $x \in M_i$, there are only a finite number of indices j for which $(g_{jk} \circ f_{ij})(x) \neq 0$. It is possible to extend the definition of addition of linear mappings so as to include certain infinite sums and to allow us to write the formula (1) in every case. We shall not go into this here; but we observe that (1) is valid whenever the sum on the right-hand side is defined.

The most important application of the preceding considerations is to the case of modules which have bases. Let M and N be modules over the ring R, which have bases $(x_i)_{i \in I}$ and $(y_j)_{j \in J}$. Then we have direct sum decompositions $M = \Sigma_{i \in I} Rx_i$ and $N = \Sigma_{j \in J} Ry_j$. Let E_{ij} be the group of linear mappings of Rx_i into Ry_j; given any element a of R, there exists a unique $\varphi \in E_{ij}$ such that $\varphi(x_i) = ay_j$: we shall say that a is the representative element of φ. Consider now a linear mapping f of M into N, and let $F = (f_{ij})_{(j,i) \in J \times I}$ be its representative matrix relative to the direct sum decompositions $M = \Sigma_{i \in I} Rx_i$, $N = \Sigma_{j \in J} Ry_j$. Then each f_{ij} has a representative element $a_{ij} \in R$; we shall say that the matrix $(a_{ij})_{(j,i) \in J \times I}$ with elements in R is the *representative matrix of f with respect to the bases* $(x_i)_{i \in I}$, $(y_j)_{j \in J}$.

It is clear that, for any given $i \in I$, there are only a finite number of indices $j \in J$ such that $a_{ij} \neq 0$. In other words, in every column of the matrix (a_{ij}), there are only a finite number of elements $\neq 0$. We shall express this by saying that the matrix (a_{ij}) is *column-finite*. It follows from what we have said above that, conversely, every column-finite matrix represents a linear mapping of M into N.

Let P be a third module, with a base $(z_k)_{k \in K}$, and let g be a linear mapping of N into P. Denote by $A = (a_{ij})_{(j,i) \in J \times I}$ the representative matrix of f with respect to the bases $(x_i)_{i \in I}$ and $(y_j)_{j \in J}$ and by $B = (b_{jk})_{(k,j) \in K \times J}$ the representative matrix of g with respect to the bases $(y_j)_{j \in J}$ and

$(z_k)_{k \in K}$. Then the representative matrix $C = (c_{ik})_{(k,i) \in K \times I}$ of $g \circ f$ with respect to the bases $(x_i)_{i \in I}$ and $(z_k)_{k \in K}$ is given by

$$c_{ik} = \Sigma_{j \in J} a_{ij} b_{jk}.$$

Now, let $\rho : (1, j) \to b_j$ be a row of type $(\{1\}, J)$, and let $\gamma : (j, 1) \to a_j$ be a column of type $(J, \{1\})$. We assume that the elements b_j, a_j are in a ring and that our column is column-finite; i. e., that $a_j = 0$ for almost all j. Then the element $\Sigma_{j \in J} a_j b_j$ is called the product of the row ρ and the column γ, and is denoted by $\rho\gamma$. Let B be any matrix of type (K, J) with elements in R and A any column-finite matrix of type (J, I) with elements in R. If $k \in K$, denote by ρ_k the row of index k of B; if $i \in I$, denote by γ_i the column of index i of A. Then the matrix $(\rho_k \gamma_i)_{(k,i) \in K \times I}$ is called the *product of the matrices B and A*, and is denoted by BA. [It should be observed that there is some inconsistency in our definitions; for, if B is itself a row and A a column, the product BA, according to our first definition, is an element λ of R, while, according to our second definition, it is a matrix with one row and one column, whose unique element is λ; this inconsistency has generally no serious practical consequences.]

With this definition, we obtain the following result:

Theorem 64. *Let M, N, P be modules over a ring R with bases* $(x_i)_{i \in I}$, $(y_j)_{j \in J}$, $(z_k)_{k \in K}$. *Let f be a linear mapping of M into N and g a linear mapping of N into P. Let A (resp.:B) be the representative matrix of f (resp.: g) with respect to the bases* $(x_i)_{i \in I}$ *and* $(y_i)_{j \in J}$ *(resp.: with respect to the bases* $(y_j)_{j \in J}$ *and* $(z_k)_{k \in K}$*). Then the representative matrix of* $g \circ f$ *with respect to the bases* $(x_i)_{i \in I}$ *and* $(z_k)_{k \in K}$ *is BA.*

If I is any set, let R_I be the weak product $\Pi^w_{i \in I} R_i$, where $R_i = R$ for every $i \in I$. This module has a base $(x_i)_{i \in I}$, where x_i is the element of R_I whose i-th coordinate is 1 and whose other coordinates are 0; we shall call this base the *canonical base* of R_I. Let I and J be any two sets; then every column-finite matrix A of type (I, J) with elements in R represents a linear mapping of R_J into R_I with respect to the canonical bases. This fact allows us to translate the properties of linear mappings into properties of matrices. Thus we obtain the following properties, in which $\mathfrak{M}(I, J)$ represents the set of all column-finite matrices of type (I, J) with elements in R:

Each $\mathfrak{M}(I, J)$ *is an additive group, in which addition is defined by*

$$(a_{ij}) + (a'_{ij}) = (a_{ij} + a'_{ij});$$

If R is commutative, then $\mathfrak{M}(I, J)$ *is a module over R, in which scalar multiplication is defined by*

$$\alpha(a_{ij}) = (\alpha a_{ij});$$

If I, J, K are any sets, and $A \in \mathfrak{M}(I, J)$, $B \in \mathfrak{M}(J, K)$, then the matrix product AB is in $\mathfrak{M}(I, K)$, and the mapping $(A, B) \to AB$ of $\mathfrak{M}(I, J) \times \mathfrak{M}(J, K)$ into $\mathfrak{M}(I, K)$ is bi-additive; this mapping is bilinear if R is commutative;

If I, J, K, L are any sets, $A \in \mathfrak{M}(I, J)$, $B \in \mathfrak{M}(J, K)$, $C \in \mathfrak{M}(K, L)$, then we have $(AB)C = A(BC)$.

On the other hand, for any set I, the square matrices of type (I, I) represent the endomorphisms of the module R_I. These endomorphisms form a ring under addition and composition; the unit element of this ring is the identity automorphism, whose representative matrix is (δ_{ij}), where $\delta_{ij} = 1$ if $i = j$, $\delta_{ij} = 0$ if $i \neq j$. This matrix is called the *unit matrix* (of type (I, I)). Thus, *the column-finite matrices of type (I, I) with elements in R form a ring, in which the unit element is the unit matrix.*

A column-finite matrix A of type (I, J) is said to be of *finite rank* if the mapping φ of R_J into R_I which it represents is of finite rank; the rank of this mapping is then called the *rank of the matrix*. Let A be the representative matrix of a linear mapping f of a module M with a base $(x_j)_{j \in J}$ into a module N with a base $(y_i)_{i \in I}$; then a necessary and sufficient condition for f to be of finite rank is that A be of finite rank, and, if this is so, then f and A have the same rank. In fact, there exist isomorphisms u of M with R_J and v of R_I with N with the following properties: if $(\bar{x}_j)_{j \in J}$ is the canonical base of R_J and $(\bar{y}_i)_{i \in I}$ that of R_I, we have $u(x_j) = \bar{x}_j$, $v(\bar{y}_i) = y_i$. We then have $f = v \circ \varphi \circ u$, and, since u and v are isomorphisms, f will be of finite rank if and only if φ is, and f and φ then have the same rank.

Let I, J, K, L be sets, A a column-finite matrix of type (J, K), B a column-finite matrix of type (I, J) and C a column-finite matrix of type (K, L). Then, if A is of finite rank, so are BA and AC, and the ranks of these matrices are at most equal to that of A.

Let M be a module with a base $(x_j)_{j \in J}$. Then every element $x \in M$ may be represented uniquely in the form $\sum_{j \in J} \alpha_j x_j$, the elements α_j being almost all zero. We shall say that the column $(j, 1) \to \alpha_j$ is the *representative column* of x. Every column-finite column of type $(J, \{1\})$ is the representative column of some vector in M. The mapping which assigns to every $x \in M$ its representative column is an isomorphism of the additive group M with the additive group $\mathfrak{M}(J; \{1\})$; it becomes a module isomorphism if we define a scalar multiplication on $\mathfrak{M}(J, \{1\})$ by the formula

$$\alpha(a_{j,1}) = (\alpha a_{j,1})$$

where $(a_{j,1}) \in \mathfrak{M}(J, \{1\})$.

Theorem 65. *Let M and N be modules with bases $(x_i)_{i\in I}$ and $(y_j)_{j\in J}$; denote by f a linear mapping of M into N, and by F its representative matrix with respect to the bases $(x_i)_{i\in I}$ and $(y_j)_{j\in J}$. Then the columns of F are the representative columns of the elements $f(x_i)$ of N with respect to the base $(y_j)_{j\in J}$. If $x \in M$ and if X is the representative column of x with respect to the base $(x_i)_{i\in I}$, the representative column of $f(x)$ with respect to the base $(y_j)_{j\in J}$ is the matrix product FX.*

Let $F = (\alpha_{ij})_{(j,i)\in J\times I}$; we then have $f(x_i) = \sum_{j\in J}\alpha_{ij}y_j$, which proves the first assertion. Let $x = \sum_{i\in I}\xi_i x_i$; then we have

$$f(x) = \sum_{i\in I}\xi_i f(x_i) = \sum_{i\in I, j\in J}\xi_i\alpha_{ij}y_j = \sum_{j\in J}(\sum_{i\in I}\xi_i\alpha_{ij})y_j$$

which proves the second assertion.

Corollary. *Let F be a column-finite matrix of type (I, J) with elements in a sfield. In order for F to be of finite rank, it is necessary and sufficient that the space $\mathfrak{x}$ generated by the columns of F in $\mathfrak{M}(I, \{1\})$ be of finite dimension; and the rank of F is then equal to the dimension of $\mathfrak{x}$.*

Again, let M be a module over R with a base $(x_i)_{i\in I}$. The linear forms on M are the linear mappings of M into R, considered as a module over itself. The module R has a base consisting of the single element 1. If u is a linear form on M, then u is represented by a row relative to the bases $(x_i)_{i\in I}$ of M and (1) of R. This row is called the *representative row of u* with respect to the base $(x_i)_{i\in I}$. Every row of type $(\{1\}, I)$ is the representative row of a linear form on M. If we define a right module structure on $\mathfrak{M}(\{1\}, I)$ by the formula

$$(a_{1,i})\alpha = (a_{1,i}\alpha) \qquad (\alpha \in R),$$

then the right module $\mathfrak{M}(\{1\}, I)$ is isomorphic to the dual space of M.

Theorem 66. *Let f be a linear mapping of a module M with a base $(x_i)_{i\in I}$ into a module N with a base $(y_j)_{j\in J}$; let F be the representative matrix of f with respect to the bases $(x_i)_{i\in I}$ and $(y_j)_{j\in J}$. For any $j \in J$, let u_j be the linear form on N such that $u_j(x_j) = 1$, $u_j(x_{j'}) = 0$ if $j' \neq j$. Then the j-th row of F is the representative row of the linear form $u_j \circ f$ on M with respect to the base $(x_i)_{i\in I}$. Let u be any linear form on N, and U its representative row with respect to the base $(y_j)_{j\in J}$ of N. Then the representative row of $u \circ f$ with respect to the base $(x_i)_{i\in I}$ is the matrix product UF.*

Let $F = (a_{ij})_{(j,i)\in J\times I}$; then $f(x_i) = \sum_{j\in J}a_{ij}y_j$, whence $(u_j \circ f)(x_i) = a_{ij}$, which proves the first assertion. The matrix U is the mapping $(1, j) \to u(y_j)$. On the other hand, we have $(u \circ f)(x_i) = \sum_{j\in J}a_{ij}u(y_j)$, which proves the second assertion.

Corollary. *Let F be a column-finite matrix of type (I, J) with elements in a sfield. A necessary and sufficient condition for F to be of finite rank is that the space R generated by the rows of F in $\mathfrak{M}(\{1\}, J)$ be of finite dimension, and the rank of F is then equal to the dimension of R.*

For, let F represent a linear mapping f of a vector space M with a base $(x_j)_{j\in J}$ into a vector space N with a base $(y_i)_{i\in I}$. Then ${}^tf$ is a linear mapping of N^* into M^*. If f is of finite rank r, then so is ${}^tf$; the elements ${}^tf(u_i)$ $(i \in I)$ (where u_i is the element of N such that $u_i(x_i) = 1$, $u_i(x_{i'}) = 0$ if $i' \neq i$) thus belong to a vector space of finite dimension $\leqslant r$, which shows that R is of dimension $\leqslant r$. Conversely, assume that R is of finite dimension r'; let P^* be the subspace of M^* spanned by the elements $u_i \circ f$, for all $i \in I$; P^* is then of finite dimension r'. Let P be the space of elements $x \in M$ such that $x^*(x) = 0$ for all $x^* \in P^*$; then we know that P is of finite codimension equal to r'. Let x be in P; then we have $u_i(f(x)) = 0$ for every i, since $u_i \circ f \in P^*$; writing $f(x) = \sum_{i\in I}\beta_i y_i$, we have

$$\beta_i = u_i(f(x)) = 0,$$

whence $f(x) = 0$. Thus P is in the kernel of f, and $f(M)$ is contained in the image of M/P under a certain linear mapping of this space into N. Since M/P is of dimension r', $f(M)$ is of finite dimension $\leqslant r'$, and f is of rank $\leqslant r'$. This proves the corollary.

Let M be a module with a base $(x_i)_{i\in I}$. Denote by x an element of M and by X its representative column. Denote by u a linear form on M and by U its representative row. Then the value $u(x)$ of u at x is the product UX of the row U by the column X, as follows immediately from the definitions.

Again, let M be a free module over R. Then we know that any two bases of M are equipotent; we may therefore assume that they are indexed by the same set I. Let $B : (x_i)_{i\in I}$ and $B' : (x'_i)_{i\in I}$ be two bases of M. We may write x'_i in the form

$$x'_i = \sum_{i'\in I} \theta_{ii'} x_{i'}.$$

The matrix $T = (\theta_{ii'})_{(i',i)\in I\times I}$ is called the *transition matrix from the base B to the base B'*. This matrix is column-finite. It is the representative matrix with respect to B of the automorphism θ of M which maps x_i upon x'_i for every index i. *This matrix is invertible in the ring $\mathfrak{M}(I, I)$ of column-finite square matrices of type (I, I), and its inverse is the transition matrix from the base B' to the base B.* For, the fact that T is invertible follows from the fact that it represents an automorphism of M. Let $(\bar\theta_{i'i})$ be its inverse matrix. We have

$$\sum_{i\in I} \bar\theta_{i'i} x'_i = \sum_{i\in I}\sum_{i''\in I} \bar\theta_{i'i}\theta_{ii''} x_{i''}.$$

But $\sum_{i \in I} \overline{\theta}_{i'i} \theta_{ii''}$ is equal to 1 if $i = i''$, to 0 if $i'' \neq i$; thus $x_{i''} = \sum_{i \in I} \theta_{i'i} x'_i$, which proves that T^{-1} is the transition matrix from B' to B.

Let x be any element of M. Denote by X and X' its representative columns with respect to the bases B and B'. Then we have $X = TX'$. For, set $X = \sum_{i \in I} \xi_i x_i = \sum_{i \in I} \xi'_i x'_i$; then

$$\sum_{i \in I} \xi_i x_i = \sum_{i \in I} \sum_{i' \in I} \xi'_i \theta_{ii'} x_{i'}$$

whence $\xi_{i'} = \sum_{i \in I} \xi'_i \theta_{ii'}$, which proves our assertion.

Let M and N be free modules over R, and f a linear mapping of M into N. Let $B = (x_i)_{i \in I}$ and $B' = (x'_i)_{i \in I}$ be bases of M, $C = (y_j)_{j \in J}$ and $C' = (y'_j)_{j \in J}$ bases of N. Let F (resp.: F') be the matrix which represents f with respect to the bases B and C (resp.: B' and C'). Let $T_{B, B'}$ be the transition matrix from B to B' and $T_{C, C'}$ the transition matrix from C to C'. Then we have

$$F' = T^{-1}_{C, C'} F T_{B, B'}$$

Let Θ_i be the column of index i of $T_{B, B'}$; the column of index i of $T^{-1}_{C, C'} F T_{B, B'}$ is then $T^{-1}_{C, C'} F \Theta_i$. But Θ_i is the column which represents x'_i with respect to the base B; thus $F\Theta_i$ is the column which represents $f(x'_i)$ with respect to the base C, and $T_{C, C'} F \Theta_i$ is therefore the column which represents $f(x'_i)$ with respect to the base C'; but this is also the column of index i of F', which proves our formula.

Two column-finite matrices A and B of the same type (I, J), with elements in a ring R, are said to be *equivalent* if there exist invertible column-finite square matrices P of type (I, I) and Q of type (J, J) such that

$$B = PAQ.$$

If A and B are equivalent matrices, there exists a linear mapping f of a module M into a module N such that A and B both represent f, but relative to different choices of bases in M and N. It follows immediately that *if A and B are equivalent matrices, and if one of them is of finite rank, then so is the other and they have the same rank.*

We shall now discuss an important case in which the converse of this statement holds true. But we must first introduce some notation which is frequently useful.

Let A be any matrix of type (I, J); let I' be a subset of I and J' a subset of J. Set $A = (a_{ij})$; then the restriction to $I' \times J'$ of the mapping $(i, j) \to a_{ij}$ is a matrix of type (I', J'), which is called the *matrix of type (I', J') extracted from A.*

Assume that $I = \{1, \cdots, m\}$, $J = \{1, \cdots, n\}$. Let $m_1, \cdots, m_p$ be integers such that

$$1 \leqslant m_1 < m_2 < \cdots < m_p < m$$

and $n_1, \cdots, n_q$ integers such that

$$1 \leqslant n_1 < n_2 < \cdots < n_q < n.$$

Set
$$m_{p+1} = m + 1, \quad n_{q+1} = n + 1.$$

If $1 \leqslant s \leqslant p$, set $I_s = \{m_s, m_s + 1, \cdots, m_{s+1} - 1\}$; if $1 \leqslant t \leqslant q$, set $J_t = \{n_t, n_t + 1, \cdots, n_{t+1} - 1\}$. For every pair (s, t) with $1 \leqslant s \leqslant p$, $1 \leqslant t \leqslant q$, let there be given a matrix A_{st} of type $(m_{s+1} - m_s, n_{t+1} - n_t)$; set $A_{st} = (a_{st;\alpha,\beta})$ $(1 \leqslant \alpha \leqslant m_{s+1} - m_s, 1 \leqslant \beta \leqslant n_{t+1} - n_t)$. Set

$$a_{ij} = a_{st;\, i-m_s+1,\, j-n_t+1} \qquad \text{if } i \in I_s,\ j \in J_t.$$

Then the matrix $A = (a_{ij})$, of type (m, n), is often represented by the symbol

$$A = \begin{pmatrix} A_{11} & \cdots & A_{1q} \\ A_{21} & \cdots & A_{2q} \\ \vdots & & \vdots \\ A_{p1} & \cdots & A_{pq} \end{pmatrix}$$

The matrix of type (I_s, J_t) extracted from A differs from A_{st} only by the way in which its elements are indexed.

This being said, we have the following result:

Theorem 67. *Let A be a matrix of type (m, n) and of rank r with elements in a sfield K. Then A is equivalent to the matrix*

$$\begin{pmatrix} E_r & O_{r,n-r} \\ O_{m-r,r} & O_{m-r,n-r} \end{pmatrix}$$

where E_r is the unit matrix of degree r and $0_{s,t}$ represents the zero matrix of type (s, t).

[If $r = n$, the symbols $0_{r,n-r}$, $0_{m-r,n-r}$ should be omitted; if $r = m$, the symbols $0_{m-r,r}$, $0_{m-r,n-r}$ should be omitted.] The matrix A represents a linear mapping f of an n-dimensional vector space V over K into an m-dimensional vector space W. Let U be the kernel of this mapping, and let V_1 be a subspace of V supplementary to U; then f induces an isomorphism of V_1 with a subspace $f(V_1) = f(V)$ of dimension r of W. Let $(x_1, \cdots, x_n)$ be a base of V which is made up of a base $(x_1, \cdots, x_r)$ of V_1 and a base $(x_{r+1}, \cdots, x_n)$ of U. The elements $y_1 = f(x_1), \cdots, y_r = f(x_r)$ form a base of $f(V)$; let $(y_1, \cdots, y_m)$ be a base of W which contains $y_1, \cdots, y_r$. Since $f(x_i) = y_i$ for $i \leqslant r$, $f(x_i) = 0$ for $i > r$, the matrix which represents f with respect to the bases $(x_1, \cdots, x_n)$ and $(y_1, \cdots, y_m)$ is

$$\begin{pmatrix} E_r & O_{r,n-r} \\ O_{m-r,r} & O_{m-r,n-r} \end{pmatrix}.$$

If, instead of considering linear mappings of a module into another one, we consider endomorphisms of a module, we arrive at a new relationship between matrices. Let M be a module and B a base of M. Let f be an endomorphism of M and F be the matrix which represents f relative to the base B. Let B' be another base of B and T the transition matrix from B' to B. Then it follows from what we have proved that the matrix which represents f with respect to B' is TFT^{-1}. This leads to the following definition: two square column-finite matrices F and F' of type (I, I) with elements in a ring R are called *similar* to each other if there exists a square column-finite invertible matrix T of type (I, I) such that $F' = TFT^{-1}$.

Two similar matrices are equivalent; but the converse is not true in general. The classification of matrices with respect to the relation of similarity is a problem much more difficult than their classification with respect to equivalence. We shall now give an important partial result with regard to this question.

Let f be an endomorphism of a module M over a ring R. An element $x \in M$ is called an "*eigenvector*" of f if $x \neq 0$ and if there is an element $\alpha \in R$ such that $f(x) = \alpha x$; we then say also that α is an "*eigenvalue*" of f, and that x belongs to α. A square matrix $A = (a_{ij})$ of type (I, I) is called *diagonal* if we have $a_{ij} = 0$ whenever $i \neq j$. If $(a_i)_{i \in I}$ is a family of elements of R, the diagonal matrix (a_{ij}) with $a_{ij} = 0$ for $i \neq j$, $a_{ii} = a_i$ is denoted by $\operatorname{diag}(a_i)_{i \in I}$.

Theorem 68. *Let f be an endomorphism of a vector space M over a field K. Assume that M is generated by a set of eigenvectors. Then there is a base $B = (x_i)_{i \in I}$ of M composed of eigenvectors. The matrix which represents f with respect to B is a diagonal matrix* $\operatorname{diag}(\alpha_i)_{i \in I}$; *each α_i is an eigenvalue, and conversely, if α is any eigenvalue of f, α occurs among the elements α_i. If* $\operatorname{diag}(\alpha'_i)_{i \in I}$ *is a diagonal matrix which is similar to* $\operatorname{diag}(\alpha_i)_{i \in I}$, *there is a permutation ϖ of I such that $\alpha'_i = \alpha_{\varpi(i)}$ for every i. Conversely, if ϖ is any permutation of I, the matrix* $\operatorname{diag}(\alpha_{\varpi(i)})_{i \in I}$ *is similar to* $\operatorname{diag}(\alpha_i)_{i \in I}$.

If x is an eigenvector, then Kx is a subspace of dimension 1 of M, and therefore simple. It follows from our assumption that M is the sum of the spaces Kx generated by all eigenvectors; it is therefore the *direct* sum of a family $(Kx_i)_{i \in I}$ of subspaces generated by eigenvectors. This means that there is a base $B = (x_i)_{i \in I}$ of M composed of eigenvectors. If $f(x_i) = \alpha_i x_i$, then the matrix which represents f with respect to B is $\operatorname{diag}(\alpha_i)_{i \in I}$. Let $B' = (x'_i)_{i \in I}$ be another base of M such that f is represented with respect to B' by a diagonal matrix $\operatorname{diag}(\alpha'_i)_{i \in I}$. Then we have $f'(x'_i) = \alpha'_i x'_i$, and each x'_i is an eigenvector belonging to α'_i. Now, let x be any eigenvector of f, belonging to an eigenvalue α. Write $x = \sum_{i \in I} \xi_i x_i$; then we have

$$f(x) = \sum_{i \in I} \xi_i f(x_i) = \sum_{i \in I} \xi_i \alpha_i f(x_i) = \alpha f(x) = \sum_{i \in I} \alpha \xi_i x_i$$

whence $\xi_i\alpha_i = \alpha\xi_i = \xi_i\alpha$ for every i. Since $x \neq 0$, there is at least one $i \in I$ such that $\xi_i \neq 0$, whence $\alpha = \alpha_i$, which shows that α occurs among the elements α_i. Moreover, we have $\xi_i = 0$ for any $i \in I$ such that $\alpha_i \neq \alpha$, which shows that every eigenvector belonging to α is in the space M_α generated by those basic elements x_i for which $\alpha_i = \alpha$. Conversely, it is clear that every element $\neq 0$ of M_α is an eigenvector belonging to α. Similar considerations apply to the base B'. If, for any $\alpha \in K$, we denote by I_α (resp.: I'_α) the set of indices $i \in I$ such that $\alpha_i = \alpha$ (resp.: $\alpha'_i = \alpha$), we see that $(x_i)_{i \in I_\alpha}$ and $(x'_i)_{i \in I'_\alpha}$ are both bases of M_α. This implies that I_α and I'_α are equipotent for every $\alpha \in K$. It follows immediately that there is a permutation ϖ of I such that $\alpha'_i = \alpha_{\varpi(i)}$. Conversely, let ϖ be any permutation of I. Set $x'_i = x_{\varpi(i)}$; then we have $f(x'_i) = \alpha_{\varpi(i)} x'_i$; it follows that the matrix which represents f with respect to the base $(x'_i)_{i \in I}$ is diag $(\alpha'_i)_{i \in I}$.

Let M be a module over a ring R which has a *finite* base $(x_i)_{i \in I}$, and let M^* be the dual module of M. Let x^*_i be the linear form on M such that $x^*_i(x_i) = 1$, $x^*_i(x_j) = 0$ for $i \neq j$. Then the elements x^*_i form a base of the right module M^* (theorem 52, Sect. 12); we say that this base is the *dual base* of the base $(x_i)_{i \in I}$. Let N be another module over R, with a finite base $(y_j)_{j \in J}$, and let $(y^*_j)_{j \in J}$ be the dual base of the dual N^* of N. Now, let f be a linear mapping of M into N, represented by a matrix $F = (a_{ij})_{(j,i) \in J \times I}$ with respect to the bases $(x_i)_{i \in I}$ and $(y_j)_{j \in J}$. Then the transpose ${}^tf$ of f is a linear mapping of N^* into M^*. We shall determine the matrix which represents ${}^tf$ with respect to the dual bases $(y^*_j)_{j \in J}$ and $(x^*_i)_{i \in I}$. The linear form $({}^tf)(y^*_j)$ is by definition $y^*_j \circ f$; its value at x_k is $y^*_j(f(x_k)) = \Sigma_{s=1}^n y^*_j(a_{ks}y_s) = a_{ik}$. Since we have $(\Sigma_{i=1}^m x^*_i a_{ij})(x_k) = a_{ik}$, we see that

$$({}^tf)(y^*_j) = \Sigma_{i=1}^m x^*_i a_{ij}$$

and the matrix which represents ${}^tf$ is $F' = (a_{ij})_{(i,j) \in I \times J}$. The element at the intersection of the i-th row and j-th column of F' is the element at the intersection of the j-th row and i-th column of F.

In general, if $F = (a_{ij})_{(j,i) \in J \times I}$ is any matrix of type (J, I), the matrix of type (I, J) defined by the mapping $(i, j) \to a_{ij}$ of $I \times J$ is called the *transpose* of the matrix F, and is denoted by ${}^tF$. Thus we have proved:

Theorem 69. *Let M and N be modules over a ring R with finite bases $(x_i)_{i \in I}$ and $(y_j)_{j \in J}$. Let $(x^*_i)_{i \in I}$ and $(y^*_j)_{j \in J}$ be the dual bases of the dual modules M^* and N^*. Let f be a linear mapping of M into N, represented by a matrix F relative to the bases $(x_i)_{i \in I}$ and $(y_j)_{j \in J}$. Then the matrix which represents ${}^tf$ with respect to the bases $(y^*_j)_{j \in J}$ and $(x^*_i)_{i \in I}$ is the transpose of F.*

A remark on notations.

When a matrix is represented in the notation (a_{ij}), which does not indicate explicitly the sets of indices corresponding respectively to the rows and columns of the matrix, it is understood that a_{ij} is the element in the i-th row and the j-th column of the matrix. If F is the representative matrix of a linear mapping f of a module M with a base $(x_i)_{i\in I}$ into a module N with a base $(y_j)_{j\in J}$, and if $f(x_i)=\sum_{j\in J}a_{ij}y_j$, then F is the matrix $(a_{ij})_{j\in J,\, i\in I}$, which means that a_{ij} is in the row of index j and the column of index i; thus, in the abbreviated notation, we have $F=(a_{ji})$. In the future, we shall prefer to write $f(x_i)=\sum_{j\in J}a'_{ji}y_j$, with $a'_{ji}=a_{ij}$, and the representative matrix of f is then (a'_{ij}).

16. Systems of linear equations

Let K be a sfield. By a system of linear equations with coefficients in K is meant a system of equations of the form

$$\sum_{j=1}^{n}\xi_j a_{ij}=b_i \qquad (1\leqslant i\leqslant n) \tag{1}$$

where $\xi_1, \cdots, \xi_n$ are the unknowns, and the a_{ij}'s, b_i's are given elements of K.

Let A be the matrix (a_{ij}); A is called the matrix of the system. Let $\mathfrak{K}$ be the vector space of column matrices of type $(n, 1)$ with elements in K; denote by B the column matrix whose i-th row element is b_i. Let $x_1, \cdots, x_n$ be elements of K; denote by X the column matrix whose i-th row element is x_i. Then $(x_1, \cdots, x_n)$ will be a solution of (1) if and only if the matrix equality

$$AX=B$$

holds. If this is so, then we say that X is the representative column of the solution $(x_1, \cdots, x_n)$.

Let f be the mapping $X\to AX$ of $\mathfrak{K}$ into itself. This is obviously a linear mapping. Let $(E_1, \cdots, E_n)$ be the canonical base of $\mathfrak{K}$; E_i is therefore the column whose j-th row element is 0 if $j\neq i$, 1 if $j=i$. Then $f(E_i)$ is the i-th column of A, and the rank of f is equal to the rank of A.

Assume first that A is of rank n. Then $f(\mathfrak{K})$ is of dimension n, and therefore identical with $\mathfrak{K}$; f is then an automorphism of $\mathfrak{K}$, which proves that for any system of elements $b_1, \cdots, b_n$ of K, the system (1) has a unique solution.

Assume now that A is of rank $r<n$. Then $f(\mathfrak{K})$ is a subspace $\neq\mathfrak{K}$ of $\mathfrak{K}$, of dimension r; a necessary and sufficient condition for the system (1) to have a solution is for B to belong to the space $f(\mathfrak{K})$. Assume that this condition is satisfied; then, if X_1 is any column such that $AX_1=B$, a

necessary and sufficient condition for X to be the representative column of a solution of (1) is that $A(X - X_1) = 0$; i. e., that $X - X_1$ should belong to the kernel $\mathfrak{N}$ of f. The latter is a vector space of dimension $n - r$. Thus we proved:

Theorem 70. *Let* $(\Sigma) : \sum_{j=1}^{n} \xi_j a_{ij} = b_i$ $(1 \leqslant i \leqslant n)$ *be a system of linear equations with coefficients in a sfield* K. *If the matrix* A *of the system is of rank* n, *then the system has a unique solution. If the rank* r *of* A *is* $< n$, *then, depending on the values of* $b_1, \cdots b_n$, *the system* (Σ) *has either no solution or several solutions. Assuming that it has one, represented by a column* X_1, *then the solutions of the system are represented by the columns* $X_1 + Y$, *where* Y *runs over all column matrices such that* $AY = 0$; *these column matrices form a vector space of dimension* $n - r$.

Corollary. *In order for the system of equations* $\sum_{j=1}^{n} \xi_j a_{ij} = 0$ *to have a solution composed of elements not all* 0 *of* K, *it is necessary and sufficient that the rank of the matrix of the system be* $< n$,

Returning to the case where A is of rank n, we observe that A is in that case invertible. The relation $AX = B$ therefore gives $X = A^{-1}B$. Thus, the solution of the system (1) may be computed explicitly as soon as the inverse matrix A^{-1} is known. Later we shall give explicit formulas for the computation of A^{-1} in the case where K is a field.

Assume now that A is of rank $r < n$. Then, using the same notation as above, a necessary and sufficient condition for (1) to have a solution is that B should belong to the space $f(\mathfrak{K})$. Let $\mathfrak{K}^*$ be the dual space of $\mathfrak{K}$; then we know that a necessary and sufficient condition for B to belong to $f(\mathfrak{K})$ is that $u(B) = 0$ for every linear form $u \in \mathfrak{K}^*$ which is zero on $f(\mathfrak{K})$. But every element u of $\mathfrak{K}^*$ may be represented by a row U with respect to the canonical base $(E_1, \cdots, E_n)$ of $\mathfrak{K}$, and we have $u(X) = UX$ for every $X \in \mathfrak{K}$. The space $f(\mathfrak{K})$ is generated by the columns $f(E_i)$ $(1 \leqslant i \leqslant n)$ of the matrix A; thus, in order for u to map $f(\mathfrak{K})$ upon $\{0\}$, it is necessary and sufficient that $UX = 0$ for every column X of A; i. e., that $UA = 0$. If we denote by λ_i the i-th column element of U, the j-th column element of the row UA is $\sum_{i=1}^{n} a_{ij}\lambda_i$. Thus we obtain the following result:

Theorem 71. *Let* $(\Sigma) : \sum_{j=1}^{n} \xi_j a_{ij} = b_i$ $(1 \leqslant i \leqslant n)$ *be a system of linear equations with coefficients in a sfield* K. *In order for this system to have a solution, it is necessary and sufficient that* $\sum_{i=1}^{n} b_i \lambda_i = 0$ *whenever* $\lambda_1, \cdots, \lambda_n$ *are elements of* K *such that* $\sum_{i=1}^{n} a_{ij}\lambda_i = 0$ *for* $1 \leqslant j \leqslant n$.

17. Graded modules

Let R be a ring and Γ a set. By a *graded module over* R, with Γ as its set of degrees, we mean an object consisting of a module M over R and a direct sum decomposition $M = \sum_{\gamma \in \Gamma} M_\gamma$ of M into a family of submodules M_γ, indexed by the set Γ.

Let M be a graded module over R, with Γ as its set of degrees. An element x of M is called *homogeneous* if it belongs to M_γ for at least one $\gamma \in \Gamma$; if $x \in M_\gamma$, then we say that x is *homogeneous of degree* γ. The element 0 is therefore homogeneous of any degree; on the other hand, if $x \neq 0$, then there cannot exist more than one element $\gamma \in \Gamma$ such that x is homogeneous of degree γ; if there exists one, then we say that γ is the *degree of* x. If x is any element of M, then it is possible to represent x in one and only one way in the form

$$x = \sum_{\gamma \in \Gamma} x_\gamma$$

where, for each γ, x_γ is homogeneous of degree γ. We say that x_γ is the *homogeneous component of degree* γ of x, and that the elements x_γ, for all $\gamma \in \Gamma$, are the *homogeneous components of* x; only a finite number of these components are $\neq 0$.

A submodule N of M is called *homogeneous* if it satisfies the following condition: if x is any element of N, then the homogeneous components of x are in N. This condition may also be formulated as follows: we have $N = \sum_{\gamma \in \Gamma}(M_\gamma \cap N)$. For, if N is homogeneous, and $x \in N$, we have $x = \sum_{\gamma \in \Gamma} x_\gamma$, where the x_γ's are the homogeneous components of x; since $x_\gamma \in N$ by assumption, we have $x \in \sum_{\gamma \in \Gamma}(M_\gamma \cap N)$. Conversely, assume that the condition is satisfied; then, if $x \in N$, we may write $x = \sum_{\gamma \in \Gamma} x_\gamma$, where, for each $\gamma \in \Gamma$, x_γ belongs to $N \cap M_\gamma$. Since $x_\gamma \in M_\gamma$, x_γ is the homogeneous component of degree γ of x; since $x_\gamma \in N$, the homogeneous components of x belong to N. If N is homogeneous, then the decomposition $N = \sum_{\gamma \in \Gamma}(N \cap M_\gamma)$ defines on N the structure of a graded module, with Γ as its set of degrees.

Theorem 72. *Let M be a graded module, with Γ as its set of degrees. Let N be a submodule of M. In order for N to be homogeneous, it is necessary and sufficient that N should have a set of module generators composed of homogeneous elements.*

If N is homogeneous, it is obviously generated by the set of homogeneous components of its elements. Conversely, assume that N has a set of generators S composed of homogeneous elements. Then every $x \in N$ may be written in the form $\sum_{u \in S} \alpha_u u$, with $\alpha_u \in R$, $\alpha_u = 0$ for almost all $u \in S$. If u is of degree γ, $\alpha_u u$ belongs to $N \cap M_\gamma$, whence $N = \sum_{\gamma \in \Gamma}(N \cap M_\gamma)$.

Let N be a homogeneous submodule of the graded module M. Denote by π the natural mapping of M on M/N. The notation being as above, we have

$M/N = \sum_{\gamma \in \Gamma} \pi(M_\gamma)$. We shall see that this sum is direct. Assume that $\sum_{\gamma \in \Gamma} \pi(x_\gamma) = 0$, where, for each γ, $x_\gamma \in M_\gamma$, and $\pi(x_\gamma) = 0$ for almost all γ's. Then we may assume that $x_\gamma = 0$ for almost all γ's, and, if we set $x = \sum_{\gamma \in \Gamma} x_\gamma$, then $\pi(x) = 0$, whence $x \in N$. Since x_γ is the homogeneous component of degree γ of x, it follows that $x_\gamma \in N$, whence $\pi(x_\gamma) = 0$. This shows that the sum $\sum_{\gamma \in \Gamma} \pi(M_\gamma)$ is direct. Thus, M/N has the structure of a graded module, with Γ as its set of degrees, in which the homogeneous elements of degree γ are those of $\pi(M_\gamma)$.

Let M and N be graded modules over a ring R, with the same set of degrees Γ. We assume further that Γ is a commutative additive group. Let f be a linear mapping of M into N, and let σ be an element of Γ. Denote by M_γ, N_γ the sets of homogeneous elements of degree γ of M, N. Then we say that f is *homogeneous of degree* σ if we have

$$f(M_\gamma) \subset N_{\gamma+\sigma}$$

for every $\gamma \in \Gamma$.

Assume that this is the case. Let g be a linear mapping of N into a third graded module P, with the same group of degrees as M and N. Then, if g is homogeneous of degree τ for some $\tau \in \Gamma$, $g \circ f$ is homogeneous of degree $\sigma + \tau$: this follows immediately from the definition.

Theorem 73. *Let M and N be graded modules over a ring R, with the same set of degrees Γ, which is a commutative additive group. For any $\sigma \in \Gamma$, let H_σ be the set of homogeneous linear mappings of degree σ of M into N. Then each H_σ is a subgroup of* Hom (M, N), *and the sum $\sum_{\sigma \in \Gamma} H_\sigma$ is direct. If R is commutative, then each H_σ is a submodule of* Hom (M, N).

Let f and g be in H_σ for some σ. If $x \in M_\gamma$, then $f(x)$ and $g(x)$ are in $N_{\gamma+\sigma}$, whence $(f - g)(x) \in N_{\gamma+\sigma}$, which proves that $f - g \in H_\sigma$: this shows that H_σ is a subgroup of Hom (M, N). Let $(f_\sigma)_{\sigma \in \Gamma}$ be a family of elements of Hom (M, N) such that $f_\sigma \in H_\sigma$ for every $\sigma \in \Gamma$, $f_\sigma = 0$ for almost every σ and $\sum_{\sigma \in \Gamma} f_\sigma = 0$. Let x be in M_γ for some $\gamma \in \Gamma$; then we have $0 = \sum_{\sigma \in \Gamma} f_\sigma(x)$, and $f_\sigma(x) \in N_{\gamma+\sigma}$ for every σ. Since $\gamma + \sigma \neq \gamma + \sigma'$ if $\sigma \neq \sigma'$, it follows from the fact that the sum $\sum_{\gamma \in \Gamma} N_\gamma$ is direct that $f_\sigma(x) = 0$ for every σ. Thus f_σ maps each M_γ upon $\{0\}$, whence $f_\sigma = 0$. This shows that the sum $\sum_{\sigma \in \Gamma} H_\sigma$ is direct. If R is commutative, then Hom (M, N) is a module over R; if $f \in H_\sigma$, $\alpha \in R$, $x \in M_\gamma$, then $(\alpha f)(x) = \alpha f(x) \in N_{\gamma+\sigma}$, whence $\alpha f \in H_\sigma$; this shows that H_σ is a submodule of Hom (M, N).

It should be observed that the sum $\sum_{\sigma \in \Gamma} H_\sigma$ is not in general the whole of Hom (M, N). If an element f belonging to $\sum_{\sigma \in \Gamma} H_\sigma$ is represented in the form $\Sigma_{\sigma \in \Gamma} f_\sigma$, with $f_\sigma \in H_\sigma$ for every $\sigma \in \Gamma$, then f_σ, which is uniquely determined (in view of theorem 73), is called the *homogeneous component of degree* σ *of* f.

We have defined the notion of gradation for modules (i. e., left modules over a ring R). We have, of course, entirely similar definitions and results for right modules over R. Now, let M be a graded right module over R and N a graded left module over R; let Γ and Δ be the sets of degrees of M and N. If $\gamma \in \Gamma$ (resp.: $\delta \in \Delta$), denote by M_γ (resp.: N_δ) the set of homogeneous elements of degree γ (resp.: δ) of M (resp.: N). Form the tensor product $M \otimes N$; since M is the direct sum of the right modules M_γ and N the direct sum of the modules N_δ, we may consider $\Theta(M_\gamma, N_\delta)$ (in the notation of theorem 30, Sect. 8) as a tensor product $M_\gamma \otimes N_\delta$ and $M \otimes N$ is the direct sum of the groups $M_\gamma \otimes N_\delta$ (*loc. cit.*). This direct sum decomposition defines on $M \otimes N$ the structure of a graded group (i. e., module over $\underline{Z}$) with $\Gamma \times \Delta$ as its set of degrees. If R is commutative, then $M \otimes N$ is a module over R, each $M_\gamma \otimes N_\delta$ is a submodule of $M \otimes N$, and we have defined on $M \otimes N$ the structure of a graded module over R. Moreover, the preceding considerations may easily be extended to the case of the tensor product of any finite family of modules over R.

Let M be a graded module over a ring R, with a set of degrees Γ. Let φ be a mapping of Γ into a set Δ. If $\gamma \in \Gamma$, let M_γ be the set of homogeneous elements of degree γ of M. For any $\delta \in \Delta$, let P_δ be the sum of the modules M_γ for all γ such that $\varphi(\gamma) = \delta$. Then we have the direct sum decomposition $M = \Sigma_{\delta \in \Delta} P_\delta$ (theorem 8, Sect. 4), which defines on M a new graded structure, with Δ as its set of degrees. The most important applications of this construction are the following. First, let M be a graded module with the set $\underline{Z}$ of integers as its set of degrees. Then we may associate with M a new graded module M', with $\underline{Z}_2$ as its set of degrees, by means of the natural homomorphism φ of $\underline{Z}$ on $\underline{Z}_2$. Let M_ν be the set of homogeneous elements of degree ν of M (if $\nu \in \underline{Z}$); then M' is defined by the direct sum decomposition

$$M' = (\Sigma_{\nu \text{ even}} M_\nu) + (\Sigma_{\nu \text{ odd}} M_\nu).$$

The second application is as follows. Let M be a graded right module and N a graded left module over a ring R, the sets of degrees of M and N being both identical to a certain commutative additive group Γ. Then we have defined above the structure of a graded group on $M \otimes N$, with $\Gamma \times \Gamma$ as its set of degrees. Now, $\Gamma \times \Gamma$ is also a commutative additive group, and the mapping φ of $\Gamma \times \Gamma$ into Γ defined by $\varphi(\gamma, \gamma') = \gamma + \gamma'$ is a homomorphism. Thus we obtain on $M \otimes N$ a new structure of graded group, with Γ as its set of degrees, where, for each $\sigma \in \Gamma$, the set of homogeneous elements of degree σ is $\Sigma_{\gamma+\gamma'=\sigma} M_\gamma \otimes N_{\gamma'}$ (M_γ and $N_{\gamma'}$ being the sets of homogeneous elements of degrees γ, γ' of M and N respectively). The projections of $\Gamma \times \Gamma$ on its two factors are also homomorphisms of $\Gamma \times \Gamma$ into Γ; they define on $M \otimes N$ graded structures in which the sets of homogeneous elements of degree γ are $M_\gamma \otimes N$ and $M \otimes N_\gamma$ respectively. The various gradations on $M \otimes N$ are distinguished from each other by the following names. The one defined originally, in which the set of degrees is $\Gamma \times \Gamma$, is called the *bigradation*; the one in which the set of homogeneous elements of degree σ is $\sum_{\gamma+\gamma'=\sigma} M_\gamma \otimes N_{\gamma'}$ is called the *total gradation*; the one in which the set of homogeneous elements of degree γ is $M_\gamma \otimes N$ is called the *first partial gradation*, and the one in which the set of homogeneous elements of degree γ is $M \otimes N_\gamma$ is called the *second partial gradation*. Correspondingly, we have for homogeneous elements the notions of bi-degree, of total degree, of first and second partial degree.

Exercises on Chapter III

1. Let R be a set with two laws of composition (addition and multiplication) which satisfy the following conditions: *a*) R is a group under addition; *b*) R is a monoid under multiplication; *c*) if a, b, c are in R, then we have $a(b + c) = ab + ac$, $(a + b)c = ac + bc$. Show that the addition of R is commutative, and that R is therefore a ring [compute in two different manners the element $(a + b)(1 + 1)$].

2. Let R be a set with two laws of composition (addition and multiplication) which satisfy the following conditions: *a*) R is a commutative group under addition; *b*) the multiplication in R is associative; *c*) if $a, b, c \in R$, then we have $(a + b)c = ac + bc$, $a(b + c) = ab + ac$. Define a multiplication on the additive group $R \times \underline{Z}$ such that $(a, 0)(b, 0) = (ab, 0)$ if a, b are in R in such a way that $R \times \underline{Z}$ becomes a ring with this multiplication.

3. Let E be a set, R a ring and M the set of mappings of E into R. If f, g are in M, let $f + g$ and fg be the mappings $x \to f(x) + g(x)$ and $x \to f(x)g(x)$ respectively. Show that, with these laws of composition, M is a ring; under which condition is M commutative? Show that, if each one of the sets E and R has at least 2 elements, then M has a zero divisor $\neq 0$.

4. Let G be a finite group and M the set of mappings of G into a ring R. If f, g are in M, the mapping $f * g$ defined by the formula

$$(f * g)(t) = \textstyle\sum_{s \in G} f(s)g(s^{-1}t) \qquad (t \in G)$$

is called the convolution of f and g. Addition in M being defined as in ex. 3, show that M is a ring under the operations of addition and convo-

Map. $G \xrightarrow{q} M$: $s_q(x) = 0$ when $x \neq s$, $= 1$ when $x = s$.

(1_M is the identity for M.)

lution. Show that the multiplicative monoid of elements of M contains a submonoid isomorphic to G. Show that, if G and R are commutative, then M is commutative. Show that, if each of G and R contains at least two elements, M has a zero divisor $\neq 0$.

5. Show that the ring of endomorphisms of the additive group $\underline{Z}$ is isomorphic to the ring $\underline{Z}$ and that the ring of endomorphisms of the additive group $\underline{Q}$ is isomorphic to the field $\underline{Q}$. Show that the ring of endomorphisms of the additive group $\underline{Z} \times \underline{Z}$ is not commutative and has zero divisors $\neq 0$.

6. Show that there does not exist any ring whose additive group is the group $\underline{Q}/\underline{Z}$ [show that the only bi-additive mapping of $(\underline{Q}/\underline{Z}) \times (\underline{Q}/\underline{Z})$ into $\underline{Q}/\underline{Z}$ is the zero mapping].

7. Let n be an integer > 0; denote by e the image of 1 under the natural mapping of $\underline{Z}$ on $\underline{Z}_n = \underline{Z}/n\underline{Z}$. Show that there exists a unique ring having $\underline{Z}_n$ as its additive group and e as its unit element. What is the characteristic of this ring? Under which condition is this ring a field?

8. Let p be a prime number. Show that all fields with p elements are isomorphic to each other.

9. Show that the condition that the additive group M be commutative could be dropped in the definition of a module at the beginning of Sect. 3 [cf. ex. 1].

10. Let G be the additive group $\underline{Q}/\underline{Z}$. Let E be any set of prime numbers and f a mapping of E into the set of integers $\geqslant 0$. Denote by $\underline{Q}_{f,E}$, the set of rational numbers r which satisfy the following condition: r may be written in the form a/b, where a and b are integers and, if $p \in E$, b is not divisible by $p^{f(p)+1}$. Let $H_{f,E}$ be the image of $\underline{Q}_{f,E}$ under the natural mapping of $\underline{Q}$ on G. Show that $H_{f,E}$ is a subgroup of G and that, conversely, every subgroup of G may be defined in this manner. Show that, for any integer $n > 0$, G has a unique subgroup isomorphic to $\underline{Z}_n$. Which subgroups of G are direct summands?

11. Show that the set S of submodules of a given module is a monoid under the law of composition $(A, B) \to A + B$. Show that the neutral element is the only invertible element of S.

12. Show by an example that there may exist three submodules A, B, C of a module M such that $A \cap B = B \cap C = C \cap A = \{0\}$ but such that the sum $A + B + C$ is not direct [let P and Q be isomorphic modules; take $M = P \times Q$, $A = P \times \{0\}$, $B = \{0\} \times Q$ and define C suitably].

13. Show by an example that a direct summand P of a module M may have several supplementary modules [use ex. 12].

14. Let M be a module. Show that the set of submodules N of M such that M/N is semi-simple has a smallest element R, and that, if M has at least one submodule N such that M/N is simple, then R is the intersection

of all submodules with this property. What is R when $M = \underline{Z}$? when $M = \underline{Q}/\underline{Z}$?

15. Let M be a module; show that the set of semi-simple submodules of M has a largest element S. What is S when M is $\underline{Z}$? when M is $\underline{Q}/\underline{Z}$?

16. If f is a mapping of a set A into a set B, the set of elements of $A \times B$ of the form $(a, f(a))$ $(a \in A)$ is called the graph of f. Show that a necessary and sufficient condition for a mapping f of a module A into a module B (over the same ring) to be linear is that the graph of f be a submodule of $A \times B$.

17. A module M over a ring R is called projective if the following condition is satisfied: if N is a module over R and f an epimorphism of N on M, there exists a linear mapping g of M into N such that $f \circ g$ is the identity mapping. Show that a module is projective if and only if it is isomorphic to a direct summand of a free module. Conclude that any module is isomorphic to a quotient module of some projective module.

18. A submodule M of a module N is called antiprimitive if every submodule $\neq \{0\}$ of N has an element $\neq 0$ in common with M. Show that, if M is an antiprimitive submodule of a module P and P an antiprimitive submodule of a module N, then M is an antiprimitive submodule of N. Show that, if M is a submodule of a module N, the set of submodules of N which contain M as an antiprimitive submodule has at least one maximal element [use Zorn's lemma]. Show that, if f is a monomorphism of a module M into a module N, there exists a submodule H of N with the following properties: $H \cap f(M)$ is $\{0\}$, and, if π is the natural mapping of N on N/H, then $\pi(f(M))$ is an antiprimitive submodule of N/H. [Show by Zorn's lemma that the set of submodules of N which have only 0 in common with $f(M)$ has a maximal element H.]

19. A module M is called injective if the following condition is satisfied: if f is any monomorphism of M into a module N, $f(M)$ is a direct summand of N. Show that a necessary and sufficient condition for M to be injective is that the following condition be satisfied: if f is any monomorphism of M into a module N such that $f(M)$ is antiprimitive in N, we have $f(M) = N$ [use ex. 18].

    Let R be a ring $\neq \{0\}$ which has no zero divisor $\neq 0$; show that a necessary and sufficient condition for R (considered as a module over itself) to be injective is that R be a sfield.

    Show that the module $\underline{Q}/\underline{Z}$ over $\underline{Z}$ is injective.

20. Let M be a submodule of a module N over a ring R, and let z be an element of N. Let a be the set of elements $\alpha \in R$ such that $\alpha z \in M$, and let φ be the mapping $\alpha \to \alpha z$ of a into M. Show that a is a submodule of R (considered as a module over itself) and that φ is a homomorphism of a into M. Let conversely φ be any linear mapping of a submodule a of R into M. Show that there exists a monomorphism of M into a module N

and an element z of N with the following properties: a is the set of elements $\alpha \in R$ such that $\alpha z \in f(M)$ and we have $\alpha z = f(\varphi(\alpha))$ if $\alpha \in a$. [Show that the elements $(\alpha, \varphi(\alpha))$, $\alpha \in a$, form a submodule H of $R \times M$, and take $N = (R \times M)/H$.]

21. Let R be a ring, and let P be a property that a module over R may or may not have. Assume that the following is true: a) if $\mathfrak{M}$ is a set of submodules of a module N such that, of any two modules M, M' belonging to $\mathfrak{M}$, one at least is a submodule of the other, and if every module in $\mathfrak{M}$ has the property P, then the union of all modules in $\mathfrak{M}$ has the property P; b) there exists a set E with the following property: every module with the property P is equipotent to a subset of E. Show that there exists a module M with the following properties: M has the property P; if f is any monomorphism of M into a module M' which has the property P, then $f(M) = M'$. [Let E_1 be the set of subsets of E; consider the set M of triplets (X, a, μ), where X is a subset of E_1, a a mapping of $X \times X$ into X and μ a mapping of $R \times X$ into X such that X, together with the addition a and the scalar multiplication μ, is a module over R, which is denoted by $M_{(X, a, \mu)}$; show that the set of all those modules of the form $M_{(X, a, \mu)}$ which have the property P has a maximal element.]

22. Let M be a module over a ring R. Let Φ be the set of linear mappings into M of submodules of R (considered as a module over itself). If ψ, ψ' are in Φ, we write "$\psi \leqslant \psi'$" if the mapping ψ is a restriction of the mapping ψ' to a submodule of its domain of definition. A subset E of Φ is called well ordered if every non-empty subset F of E contains an element ψ such that $\psi' \leqslant \psi$ for every $\psi' \in F$. Assuming that E is well ordered and that $\psi \in E$, the set of all $\psi' \in E$ such that $\psi' \leqslant \psi$ and $\psi' \neq \psi$ is called the segment determined by ψ in E and is denoted by $S(\psi; E)$.
Assume that M is an antiprimitive submodule of a module N (cf. ex. 18). If $x \in N$, let a_x be the set of $\alpha \in R$ such that $\alpha x \in M$, and let φ_x be the mapping $\alpha \to \alpha x$ of a_x into M (cf. ex. 20). Show that, if x, y are elements of N such that $\varphi_x = \varphi_y$, $x \neq y$, then we have $\varphi_x \leqslant \varphi_{x-y}$, $\varphi_y \leqslant \varphi_{x-y}$ and that φ_x, φ_y are both distinct from φ_{x-y}.
Let E be a well ordered subset of Φ. A mapping λ of E into N is called semi-convergent if there exists an $x \in N$ such that $\varphi_{x-\lambda(\psi)} = \psi$ for every $\psi \in E$; x is then called a cluster point of the mapping λ. Let $\mathfrak{L}$ be the set of all semi-convergent mappings of well ordered subsets of Φ into N, and let L be a mapping of $\mathfrak{L}$ into N which assigns to every $\lambda \in \mathfrak{L}$ a cluster point of λ.
Let F be the set of sets $\mathfrak{E}$ of well ordered subsets of Φ with the following properties: if E belongs to a set $\mathfrak{E} \in F$, then every segment of E belongs to $\mathfrak{E}$; if $\mathfrak{E} \in F$, there is a uniquely determined mapping ξ of $\mathfrak{E}$ into N such that, for every $E \in \mathfrak{E}$, the mapping λ_E: $\psi \to \xi(S(\psi; E))$ is semi-convergent and $\xi(E) = L(\lambda_E)$. Show that F contains a maximal

element. [Show that, if $\mathfrak{E}$, $\mathfrak{E}'$ are in F and $\mathfrak{E} \subset \mathfrak{E}'$, then the mapping ξ of the set $\mathfrak{E}$ is a restriction of the mapping ξ' of the set $\mathfrak{E}'$; then, apply Zorn's lemma.] From now on, let $\mathfrak{E}_0$ be a maximal element of F and let ξ be the mapping of $\mathfrak{E}_0$ into N with the properties stated above. If E is a well ordered subset of Φ whose segments belong to $\mathfrak{E}_0$, the mapping $\psi \to \xi(S(\psi; E))$ of E into N will be denoted by μ_E. Show that, if μ_E is semi-convergent, then E belongs to $\mathfrak{E}_0$.

Let x be an element of N; let $\mathfrak{E}_0(x)$ be the set of elements $E \in \mathfrak{E}_0$ such that x is a cluster point of μ_E. Show that, if G is a subset of $\mathfrak{E}_0(x)$ such that, if E, E' are any sets in G, one of E, E' is a segment of the other, the union of the sets of G is in $\mathfrak{E}_0(x)$. Show that $\mathfrak{E}_0(x)$ contains a set E which is not a segment of any other set in $\mathfrak{E}_0(x)$; show that $\xi(E) = x$. [Were this not the case, derive a contradiction from the consideration of the set $E \cup \{\varphi_{x-\xi(E)}\}$.] Conclude that N is equipotent to a subset of the set of well ordered subsets of Φ.

Show that, if M is any module, there exists a monomorphism of M into an injective module [use ex. 19 and 21].

23. Let M be a module over a ring R and $(N_i)_{i \in I}$ a non empty family of modules over R; for each $i \in I$, let there be given a monomorphism f_i of M into N_i. For each $i \in I$, let ψ_i be the natural injection of N_i into $\prod^w_{i \in I} N_i$, and let H be the submodule of $\prod^w_{i \in I} N_i$ generated by all elements $\psi_i(f_i(x)) - \psi_j(f_j(x))$, for all $x \in M$ and $i, j \in I$. Set $S = (\prod^w_{i \in I} N_i)/H$. Show that there exists a monomorphism g of M into S and, for each $i \in I$, a monomorphism g_i of N_i into S such that $g = g_i \circ f_i$.

24. Let (M_n) be a sequence of modules over a ring R. Assume that, for every integer $n > 0$, there is given an epimorphism f_n of M_{n+1} on M_n. Let P be the set of elements (a_n) in $\prod_{n>0} M_n$ such that $f_n(a_{n+1}) = a_n$ for every $n > 0$. Show that P is a submodule of $\prod_{n>0} M_n$. Denote by π_n the restriction to P of the projection of $\prod_{n>0} M_n$ on M_n. Show that π_n is an epimorphism of P on M_n and that $f_n \circ \pi_{n+1} = \pi_n$. Assume that we have, for every $n > 0$, a homomorphism g_n of a fixed module Q into M_n and that $f_n \circ g_{n+1} = g_n$ for every $n > 0$; show that there exists a unique homomorphism g of Q into P such that $\pi_n \circ g = g_n$ for every $n > 0$. The module P is called the projective limit of the modules M_n relative to the homomorphisms f_n; π_n is called the natural homomorphism of P on M_n.

25. Let p be a prime number; for each $n > 0$, let M_n be the module $\underline{Z}/p^n\underline{Z}$, and let ω_n be the natural mapping of $\underline{Z}$ on M_n. Show that there exists a unique homomorphism f_n of M_{n+1} into M_n such that $\omega_n \circ f_n = \omega_{n+1}$, and that f_n is an epimorphism. Let P be the projective limit of the modules M_n relative to the homomorphisms f_n (cf. ex. 24), and let π_n be the natural homomorphism of P on M_n. Each M_n being made into a ring in the manner explained in ex. 7, show that f_n is a ring homomorphism. Show

that it is possible in one and only one way to define a multiplication in P in such a way that P becomes a ring and each π_n a ring homomorphism. The ring P obtained in this manner is called the ring of p-adic integers; show that it is a domain of integrity.

26. Show that the ring of endomorphisms of a simple module is a sfield.

27. Let M be a module over a domain of integrity R. If $x \in M$, call annihilator of x the set of elements $\alpha \in R$ such that $\alpha x = 0$. Show that the set of elements of M whose annihilators are $\neq \{0\}$ is a submodule N, and that the annihilator of every element of M/N is $\{0\}$.

28. Let M be a module. Show that the additive group Hom (M, M), together with the law of composition $(f, g) \rightarrow f \circ g$ in Hom (M, M), constitutes a ring E. Show that the mapping $(f, x) \rightarrow f(x)$ of $E \times M$ into M is the scalar multiplication of a module structure over E on the additive group M; let M' be this module. Show that, if M is semi-simple and isotypic, then M' is simple; conclude that, whenever M is semi-simple, so is M'.

29. Let R be a ring. Denote by R_r (resp.: R_l) the ring R considered as a right (resp.: left) module over itself; let R_a be the additive group of R. Let $\mathfrak{a}$ be a submodule of R_r and $\mathfrak{b}$ a submodule of R_l; show that $(R_r/\mathfrak{a}) \otimes (R_l/\mathfrak{b})$ is isomorphic to $R_a/(\mathfrak{a} + \mathfrak{b})$.

30. Let R be a commutative ring, and let M, N be modules over R; denote by M^* and N^* the dual modules of M and N. Show that there exists a linear mapping λ of $M^* \otimes N^*$ into $(M \otimes N)^*$ such that

$$(\lambda(u \otimes v))(x \otimes y) = u(x)v(y)$$

whenever $u \in M^*$, $v \in N^*$, $x \in M$, $y \in N$. Show by an example that λ is not always a monomorphism. [Take R $= \underline{Z}_4$ (cf. ex. 7), $M = N = \underline{Z}_4/2\underline{Z}_4$]. Show by an example that λ is not always an epimorphism. [Take R to be a field and M, N to be infinite dimensional vector spaces.] Show that, if M and N both have finite bases, then λ is an isomorphism.

31. Let M be the module $\underline{Z}$ (considered as a module over the ring $\underline{Z}$) and $N = \underline{Z}_2$; set $P = 2\underline{Z}$. Denote by u the identity mapping of P into M and by v the identity mapping of N into itself. Show that $u \otimes v$ is the zero mapping of $P \otimes N$ into $M \otimes N$, but that $P \otimes N \neq \{0\}$.

32. Let R be a ring, M a right module over R and N a module over R. Show that, if N has a base, then $M \otimes N$ is the direct sum of a family of groups isomorphic to the additive group of M.

33. Let R be a ring and M a module over R which has a base B. Show that there is a right module over R which has the same additive group as M and which is such that $x\alpha = \alpha x$ for every $x \in B$.

34. Let r be an integer > 0; if $e_1, \cdots, e_r$ are integers $\geqslant 0$, denote by $\nu(e_1, \cdots, e_r)$ the number of partitions of a fixed set E with $e_1 + \cdots + e_r$ elements into r sets with respectively $e_1, \cdots, e_r$ elements. Show that

$\nu(e_1, \cdots, e_r) = \sum_{e_i > 0} \nu(e_{i1}, \cdots, e_{ir})$ where $e_{ij} = e_j$ *if* $i \neq j$, $e_{ii} = e_i - 1$,

Show that, for any integer $n > 0$, $\sum_{e_1 + \cdots + e_r = n} \nu(e_1, \cdots, e_r) = r^n$. Show that $\sum_{e_1 + e_2 = n} (-1)^{e_1} \nu(e_1, e_2) = 0$.

35. Let K be a field; set $K_n = K$ for every integer $n > 0$, and let $S = \prod_{n>0} K_n$ be the vector space whose elements are all sequences of elements of K. Make the convention of saying that a sequence (a_n) of elements of K converges to an element a when there is an integer n_0 such that $a_n = a$ for all $n \geqslant n_0$. By a generalized limit function is meant a linear form λ on S such that $\lambda(\sigma) = \alpha$ whenever the sequence σ converges to α. Show that, if λ is a generalized limit function, we have $\lambda((a_n)) = \lambda((a'_n))$ if there exists an integer n_0 such that $a_n = a'_n$ for all $n \geqslant n_0$. If σ is any sequence which does not converge and α any element of K, show that there exists a generalized limit function λ such that $\lambda(\sigma) = \alpha$.

36. Let U and V be vector spaces over a field. Let $u, u_1, \cdots, u_h$ be elements of U and $v, v_1, \cdots, v_h$ elements of V such that $u \otimes v = \sum_{k=1}^{k} u_k \otimes v_k$. Show that u is a linear combination of $u_1, \cdots, u_h$.

Assume that U and V are both of the same finite dimension n. Show that every element of $U \otimes V$ may be represented as the sum of n elements each of which is of the form $u \otimes v$ ($u \in U$, $v \in V$), but that there are elements of $U \otimes V$ which cannot be represented as sums of $n - 1$ elements of this form.

37. Let K be a field; set $K_n = K$ for every $n > 0$, and let P be the vector space $\bigotimes_{n>0} K_n$. Let λ be a generalized limit function on the set of sequences of elements of K (cf. ex. 35). Show that there is a linear form u on P such that $u\left(\bigotimes_{n>0} a_n\right) = \lambda((p_n))$, where (p_n) is the sequence defined by $p_n = a_1 \cdots a_n$.

38. Let $(M_n)_{n>0}$ be a sequence of modules over a commutative ring R. Set $T_n = M_{2n-1} \otimes M_{2n}$, $P = \bigotimes_{n>0} M_n$, $Q = \bigotimes_{n>0} T_n$. Show that there exists a linear mapping θ of P into Q such that $\theta\left(\bigotimes_{n>0} x_n\right) = \bigotimes_{n>0} t_n$, where (x_n) is any element of $\prod_{n>0} M_n$ and $t_n = x_{2n-1} \otimes x_{2n} \in T_n$. Show by an example that θ is not always a monomorphism [take R to be a field with more than 2 elements and $M_n = R$; take a sequence (x_n) such that $x_{2n-1} x_{2n} = 1$ for every n, but $x_{2n-1} \neq 1$; set $x'_n = 1$; show that

$$\theta\left(\bigotimes_{n>0} x_n\right) = \theta\left(\bigotimes_{n>0} x'_n\right);$$

show by making use of ex. 37 that $\bigotimes_{n>0} x_n \neq \bigotimes_{n>0} x'_n$]. Show by an example that θ is not always an epimorphism [take R to be field; take $M_{2n-1} = M_{2n} = V_n$, where V_n is a vector space of dimension n; let t_n be an element of T_n which is not the sum of fewer than n elements of the form $x \otimes y$ with $x, y \in V_n$ (cf. ex. 36); show that $\bigotimes_{n>0} t_n$ does not belong to $\theta(P)$; assuming that this element were the sum of h elements of the form $\bigotimes_{n>0} x_n$, $x_n \in M_n$, derive a contradiction from the consideration of the isomorphism of Q with $T_{h+1} \otimes \bigotimes_{n \neq h+1} T_n$ and from the results of ex. 36].

39. Let V and W be respectively a right vector space and a left vector space over a sfield K which are put in duality with each other by a bilinear form on $V \times W$; if E is a subset of V or W, let E^0 be the orthogonal space to E. Show that $((E^0)^0)^0 = E^0$.

40. Let V and W be respectively a right vector space and a left vector space over a sfield K; assume that V and W are finite dimensional and have the same dimension. Let β be a bilinear form on $V \times W$. Show that, if for every $x \in V$, there exists a $y \in W$ such that $\beta(x, y) \neq 0$, then β is non degenerate.

41. Let u and v be linear mappings of a vector space V into a vector space W; assume that u and v are of finite ranks, and denote their ranks by r and s. Show that $u + v$ is of finite rank and that its rank lies between $|r - s|$ and $r + s$.

42. Let M be a module over a ring R and M^* its dual. Define a multiplication on the group $T = M^* \otimes M$ such that $(\lambda' \otimes x')(\lambda \otimes x) = \lambda \otimes \lambda'(x)x'$ whenever λ, λ' are in M^* and x, x' in M. Show that this multiplication is associative and that the mapping $(\theta, \theta') \to \theta\theta'$ of $T \times T$ into itself is biadditive. Show that there exists a homomorphism ρ of the additive group T into Hom (M, M) such that $(\rho(\lambda \otimes x))(y) = \lambda(y)x$ whenever $\lambda \in M^*, x, y \in M$; show that $\rho(\theta\theta') = \rho(\theta) \circ \rho(\theta')$ whenever θ, θ' are in T. Show by an example that ρ is not always a monomorphism [construct a ring R of the form $\underline{Z} \cdot 1 \times \underline{Z} \cdot x_0$, with $x_0^2 = 0$, and take $M = \underline{Z}x_0$]. Assuming that R is a sfield, show that ρ is a monomorphism, that $\rho(T)$ is the set of endomorphisms of finite ranks of M and that a necessary and sufficient condition for the multiplication in T to have a unit element is that M be finite dimensional.

CHAPTER IV

Algebras

1. Definition

Let R be a *commutative ring*. By an *algebra over* R is meant an object composed of a module A over R and of a bilinear mapping of $A \times A$ into A, called the multiplication in A; the image of an element $(x, y) \in A \times A$ under the multiplication is denoted by xy and is called the product of x and y in A.

It should be noted that we do not require that the multiplication in A should be associative, nor that it should have a unit element.

EXAMPLES: *a*) Let S be any ring. Being an additive group, S may be considered as a module over the ring $\underline{Z}$ of integers. This module, together with the multiplication in S, defines on S the structure of an algebra over $\underline{Z}$, as can be verified immediately. Thus, any ring may be considered as an algebra over $\underline{Z}$.

b) Let A be an algebra over a commutative ring R, and let ρ be a homomorphism of R into a commutative ring R'. Let $A^{R'}$ be the module over R' deduced from A by transfer of the basic ring to R' by means of ρ. Let μ be the multiplication in A; then μ defines a bilinear mapping $\mu^{R'}$ of $A^{R'} \times A^{R'}$ into $A^{R'}$ (cf. Chapter III, Sect. 11). The module $A^{R'}$, together with the multiplication $\mu^{R'}$, is an algebra over R'; we call this algebra the algebra deduced from A by transfer of the basic ring to R' by means of ρ.

c) Let M be any module over a commutative ring R. Then the set E of endomorphisms of M has the structure of a module over R (Chapter III, Sect. 5). The mapping $(f, g) \rightarrow f \circ g$ of $E \times E$ into E is bilinear (Chapter III, Sect. 10). It defines on E the structure of an algebra over R, the algebra of endomorphisms of M.

d) Let A be an algebra over R. The mapping

$$(x, y) \rightarrow xy - yx$$

of $A \times A$ into A is obviously bilinear. Taking it as a new multiplication, we obtain a new algebra structure on A with the same underlying module as the algebra A but with a different multiplication.

e) Let M be any set in which there is defined a law of composition, denoted multiplicatively. Let (A, ψ) be a free module on M over a commutative ring R. Since the elements $\psi(x)$, $x \in M$, form a base of A over R, there exists a unique bilinear mapping of $A \times A$ into A which maps $(\psi(x), \psi(y))$ upon $\psi(xy)$ for any $x, y \in M$. This mapping defines on A the structure of an algebra. An algebra obtained in this manner is called an *algebra of M over R.*

f) Let A be a free module over a commutative ring R, and $(x_i)_{i \in I}$ a base of A. Let there be given a family $(\gamma_{ijk})_{(i, j, k) \in I \times I \times I}$ of elements of A such that for every pair $(i, j) \in I \times I$, there are only a finite number of elements $k \in I$ such that $\gamma_{ijk} \neq 0$. Then there is a uniquely determined algebra structure on A such that

$$x_i x_j = \Sigma_{k \in I} \gamma_{ijk} x_k$$

for every $(i, j) \in I \times I$. For, it follows from the corollary to theorem 41, Chapter III, Sect. 10, that there exists a uniquely determined bilinear mapping μ of $A \times A$ into A such that $\mu(x_i, x_j) = \Sigma_{k \in I} \gamma_{ijk} x_k$ for every $(i, j) \in I \times I$; we then define the multiplication in A by the formula $xy = \mu(x, y)$. When an algebra A is defined in this manner, we say that the γ_{ijk}'s are its *constants of structure* with respect to the base $(x_i)_{i \in I}$.

2. Subalgebras

Let A be an algebra. Assume that a subset B of A is a submodule of A and is stable under the multiplication of A. Then the restriction to $B \times B$ of the multiplication in A, together with the module structure of B, defines on B the structure of an algebra. An algebra defined in this manner is called a *subalgebra* of A. It is clear that any intersection of subalgebras of an algebra A is a subalgebra of A. Therefore, given any subset S of A, there is a smallest subalgebra of A containing S; it is called the *subalgebra generated by S.*

Theorem 1. *Let A be an algebra and S a subset of A such that the product of any two elements of S is in S. Then the submodule B of A generated by S is a subalgebra.*

For, let t and u be elements of B. We may write $t = \Sigma_{s \in S} \alpha_s s$, $u = \Sigma_{s \in S} \beta_s s$, the α_s and β_s being elements of the ring over which A is an algebra, of which only a finite number are $\neq 0$. We then have $xy = \Sigma_{s, s' \in S} \alpha_s \beta_{s'} ss'$, which shows that xy is a linear combination of elements of S, whence $xy \in B$.

3. Homomorphisms

Let A and B be algebras over the same commutative ring R. By a *homomorphism* of A into B is meant a mapping f of A into B which is linear and which has the property that

$$f(xy) = f(x)f(y)$$

whenever x, y are in A.

If S is any ring, considered as an algebra over the ring $\underline{Z}$ of integers, the notion of homomorphism of the algebra S, as we have just defined it, coincides with the notion of homomorphism of a ring, as introduced in Chapter III, Sect. 1.

If f is a homomorphism of an algebra A into an algebra B, and g a homomorphism of B into an algebra C, then $g \circ f$ is a homomorphism of A into C. On the other hand, if f is also a bijection of A on B, then $\overset{-1}{f}$ is a homomorphism of B into A; f is then called an *isomorphism* of A with B. The notions of monomorphism, epimorphism, endomorphism, automorphism are defined for algebras in the same manner as they have been defined for monoids (Chapter I, Sect. 3).

Let f be a homomorphism of an algebra A into an algebra B. Then f, as a linear mapping of A into B, has a kernel K, which is a submodule of A. By an *ideal* in A is meant a submodule of A which is the kernel of some homomorphism of A.

Theorem 2. *Let A be an algebra and K a submodule of A. In order for K to be an ideal in A, it is necessary and sufficient that the following condition be satisfied: if u is any element of K and x any element of A, then xu and ux are in K.*

Assume first that K is the kernel of a homomorphism of A. Then we have $f(xu) = f(x)f(u) = f(x)0 = 0$, $f(ux) = 0f(x) = 0$, which shows that xu and ux are in K. Next, assume that the condition is satisfied. Observe that the multiplication in A defines a linear mapping μ of the module $A \otimes A$ into A, such that $\mu(x \otimes y) = xy$ for any $x, y \in A$. Let π be the natural mapping of A into A/K; then $\pi \otimes \pi$ is a linear mapping of $A \otimes A$ into $(A/K) \otimes (A/K)$, whose kernel is the group generated by the elements $x \otimes u$ and $v \otimes y$, with u, v in K and x, y in A (theorem 29, Chapter III, Sect. 8). This kernel is contained in the kernel of $\pi \circ \mu$; for, if $x \in A$, $v \in K$, $(\pi \circ \mu)(x \otimes v) = \pi(xv) = 0$ since $xv \in K$, and, similarly, $(\pi \circ \mu)(v \otimes x) = 0$. It follows that $\pi \circ \mu$ may be factored in the form $\mu^* \circ (\pi \otimes \pi)$, where μ^* is a linear mapping of $(A/K) \otimes (A/K)$ into A/K. Define a multiplication in A/K by setting

$x^*y^* = \mu^*(x^* \otimes y^*)$ if $x^*, y^* \in A/K$. Then A/K becomes an algebra relative to this multiplication. If x, y are in A, then

$$\pi(xy) = \pi(\mu(x \otimes y)) = \mu^*((\pi \otimes \pi)(x \otimes y)) = \pi(x)\pi(y),$$

which proves that π is a homomorphism with kernel K of the algebra A.

Corollary. *Let $(K_i)_{i\in I}$ be a family of ideals in an algebra A. Then $\bigcap_{i\in I}K_i$ and $\sum_{i\in I}K_i$ are ideals.*

This follows immediately from theorem 2.

The algebra A/K which was defined in the proof of theorem 2 is called the *quotient algebra* of A by the ideal K.

Theorem 3. *Let f be a homomorphism of an algebra A into an algebra B and K an ideal of A contained in the kernel of f. Denote by π the natural homomorphism of A on A/K. Then there exists a unique homomorphism g of the algebra A/K into B such that $f = g \circ \pi$.*

There is a unique linear mapping g of A/K into B such that $f = g \circ \pi$. Let $x^* = \pi(x)$ and $y^* = \pi(y)$ be elements of A/K, with $x, y \in A$. Then we have $g(x^*y^*) = f(xy) = f(x)fy) = g(x^*)g(y^*)$, and g is a homomorphism.

Theorem 4. *Let f and g be homomorphisms of an algebra A into an algebra B, and let S be a subset of A. Assume that we have $f(x) = g(x)$ whenever x is in S; then $f(x) = g(x)$ whenever x belongs to the subalgebra A' of A generated by S.*

Let A'' be the set of all elements $x \in A$ such that $f(x) = g(x)$. This is the kernel of the linear mapping $f - g$, which shows that A'' is a submodule of A. If x, y are in A'', then we have $f(xy) = f(x)f(y) = g(x)g(y) = g(xy)$, whence $xy \in A''$; A'' is therefore a subalgebra of A. Since $S \subset A''$, we have $A' \subset A''$, which proves theorem 4.

Theorem 5. *Let A and B be algebras over the same ring, and let f be a linear mapping of the module A into the module B. Let S be a set of module generators of A. If we have $f(xy) = f(x)f(y)$ whenever x, y are in S, then f is a homomorphism of the algebra A.*

The mapping $(x, y) \to f(xy) - f(x)f(y)$ of $A \times A$ into B is obviously bilinear; since it maps $S \times S$ upon $\{0\}$, it is the zero mapping (cf. lemma 3, Chapter III, Sect. 10), which proves that f is a homomorphism.

4. Products

Let $(A_i)_{i\in I}$ be a family of algebras on the ring R. We may define the structure of an algebra on the module $\prod_{i\in I}A_i$ by the formula

$$(a_i)_{i\in I} \cdot (b_i)_{i\in I} = (a_ib_i)_{i\in I} \tag{1}$$

for we have

$$((a_i)_{i\in I} + (a'_i)_{i\in I})(b_i)_{i\in I} = (a_i + a'_i)_{i\in I}(b_i)_{i\in I} = (a_ib_i + a'_ib_i)_{i\in I}$$
$$= (a_i)_{i\in I}(b_i)_{i\in I} + (a'_i)_{i\in I}(b_i)_{i\in I}$$

and we see in the same way that

$$(a_i)_{i\in I}((b_i)_{i\in I} + (b'_i)_{i\in I})$$
$$= (a_i)_{i\in I}(b_i)_{i\in I} + (a_i)_{i\in I}(b'_i)_{i\in I};$$

moreover, if α is any element of R,

$$(\alpha(a_i)_{i\in I})(b_i)_{i\in I} = (\alpha a_i)_{i\in I}(b_i)_{i\in I} = (\alpha a_ib_i)_{i\in I}$$
$$= \alpha((a_i)_{i\in I}(b_i)_{i\in I})$$

and we see in the same way that

$$(a_i)_{i\in I}(\alpha(b_i)_{i\in I}) = \alpha((a_i)_{i\in I}(b_i)_{i\in I});$$

this proves that the multiplication defined by (1) is bilinear. The algebra defined in this way is called the *product of the algebras* A_i, and is denoted by $\prod_{i\in I}A_i$. For any $i \in I$, the projection π_i of $\prod_{i\in I}A_i$ on A_i is a homomorphism.

It follows immediately from the definition that $\prod^w_{i\in I}A_i$ is a subalgebra of $\prod_{i\in I}A_i$.

5. Free algebra

Let S be a set. An algebra F over a commutative ring R, together with a mapping ψ of S into F, is said to be a *free algebra over* S if the following condition is satisfied: given any mapping φ of S into an algebra A over R, there exists a unique homomorphism f of F into A such that $f\circ\psi = \varphi$.

If (F, ψ) is a free algebra over S, then $\psi(S)$ is a set of generators of F. Moreover, if (F, ψ) and (F', ψ') are free algebras over S, there is a unique isomorphism J of F with F' such that $J\circ\psi = \psi'$. These statements are proved exactly in the same way as the analogous ones for monoids (Chapter I, Sect. 4) or for modules (Chapter III, Sect. 9).

We shall now prove the existence of a free algebra over S. We shall construct inductively a sequence $(S_n)_{1\leqslant n<\infty}$ of sets S_n as follows. We set $S_1 = S$. If $S_1, \cdots, S_n$ are already defined, we set

$$T_n = \bigcup_{i+j=n+1} S_i \times S_j$$

and we take S_{n+1} to be a set equipotent to T_n which has no element in common with $S_1 \cup \cdots \cup S_n$; we shall denote by J_n a bijection of T_n on S_{n+1}. It is clear that the sets S_n, $1 \leqslant n < \infty$, are mutually disjoint; let M be the union of these sets. We shall define a law of composition in M. Let x and y

An illuminating diagram.

S
S_1 S_1
$T_1 = S_1\times S_1$ T_1
$T_2 = S_2\times S_1 \cup S_1\times S_2$ T_2
$T_3 = S_3\times S_1 \cup S_2\times S_2 \cup S_1\times S_3$ T_3

If, for example, $S = \{\alpha, \beta, (\alpha,\beta)\}$; then $S_1 \cap (S_1\times S_1) \neq \emptyset$. It is actually necessary to replace T_n by S_{n+1}.

be elements of M, and let i, j be the indices such that $x \in S_i$, $y \in S_j$. Then we have $i + j > 1$, and $(x, y) \in S_i \times S_j$; we then set

$$xy = J_{i+j-1}(x, y).$$

See p. 138, e).
Let F be an algebra of M over R; we then have a mapping ψ_M of M upon a subset of F, which is a base of the module F. We shall denote by ψ_0 the restriction of ψ_M to the subset S of M.

Now, let φ be any mapping of S into an algebra A. We shall extend φ to a mapping Φ of M into A. Set $\varphi_1 = \varphi$. Assume that, for some n, we have already defined for each $i \leqslant n$ a mapping φ_i of S_i into A. Let u be any element of S_{n+1}; then we have $u = J_n(u')$, where $u' \in T_n$. The sets $S_1, \cdots, S_n$ being mutually disjoint, there exist uniquely determined indices $i \leqslant n$, $j \leqslant n$ and elements $x \in S_i$, $y \in S_j$ such that $i + j = n + 1$ and $u' = (x, y)$. We then set $\varphi_{n+1}(u) = \varphi_i(x)\varphi_j(y)$, which defines φ_{n+1}. Since the sets S_n are mutually disjoint, there exists a unique mapping Φ of M into A which extends all mappings φ_n. It follows immediately from our definition that

$$\Phi(xy) = \Phi(x)\Phi(y) \qquad (x, y \in M).$$

Since (F, ψ_M) is a free module over M, there is a unique linear mapping f of F into A such that $f \circ \psi_M = \Phi$, whence $f \circ \psi_0 = \varphi$. We shall see that f is a homomorphism of the algebra F. If $x, y \in M$, then

$$f(\psi_M(x)\psi_M(y)) = f(\psi_M(xy)) = \Phi(xy) = \Phi(x)\Phi(y) = f(\psi_M(x))f(\psi_M(y)).$$

Consider now the mapping $\beta : (\xi, \eta) \to f(\xi\eta) - f(\xi)f(\eta)$ of $F \times F$ into A; this mapping is obviously bilinear. Moreover, we have $\beta(\xi, \eta) = 0$ whenever ξ, η belong to $\psi_M(M)$. Since the elements of $\psi_M(M)$ form a base of F, it follows that $\beta = 0$, i. e. that f is a homomorphism. Conversely, let f' be any homomorphism of F into A such that $f' \circ \psi_0 = \varphi$. In order to prove that $f' = f$, it is clearly sufficient to prove that $f'(\psi_M(x)) = f(\psi_M(x))$ for any $x \in M$. Set $\Phi' = f' \circ \psi_M$; since f' is a homomorphism, we have $\Phi'(xy) = \Phi'(x)\Phi'(y)$ for any $x, y \in M$. We have to prove that $\Phi' = \Phi$. Since $f \circ \psi_0 = \varphi$, the restriction of Φ' to $S_1 = S$ is $\varphi = \varphi_1$. Assume that, for some $n \geqslant 1$, we have already proved that Φ' coincides with Φ on $S_1 \cup \cdots \cup S_n$. Let u be any element of S_{n+1}; then we may write $u = xy$ with $x \in S_i$, $y \in S_j$, i, j being indices such that $i + j = n + 1$, whence $i \leqslant n$, $j \leqslant n$. We then have $\Phi'(u) = \Phi'(x)\Phi'(y) = \Phi(x)\Phi(y) = \Phi(u)$, which proves our assertion for $n + 1$. It follows that $\Phi' = \Phi$. Thus, we have proved that (F, ψ_0) is a free algebra on S.

Classes of algebras defined by identities

Let S be a finite set with ν elements $x_1, \cdots, x_\nu$. Let (F, ψ) be a free algebra on S over the ring Z of integers, and let $L_1, \cdots, L_h$ be a finite number of elements of F. Let A be an algebra over a commutative ring R.

Then the additive group of A may be considered as a module over the ring $\underline{Z}$ of integers; this module, together with the multiplication in A, defines on A an algebra structure A_0 over $\underline{Z}$. Let $\xi_1, \cdots, \xi_\nu$ be any elements of A. Then there is a unique homomorphism f of F into A_0 such that $f(x_i) = \xi_i$ $(1 \leqslant i \leqslant \nu)$. Assume now that, *for all possible choices of* $\xi_1, \cdots, \xi_\nu$ *in* A, we have $f(L_1) = \cdots = f(L_h) = 0$. Then we say (although improperly) that the identities $L_1 = 0, \cdots, L_h = 0$ are valid in A. Some important classes of algebras are defined by the condition that a certain number of identities are valid in these algebras.

Consider, for instance, the case where $\nu = 3$, $h = 1$, $L_1 = x_1(x_2x_3) - (x_1x_2)x_3$. Then the algebras in which the identity $L_1 = 0$ is valid are called the *associative algebras*: they are the algebras in which the multiplication is associative.

The case where $\nu = 2$, $h = 1$, $L_1 = x_1x_2 - x_2x_1$ leads to the *commutative algebras.*

The case where $\nu = 3$, $h = 2$, $L_1 = x_1x_1$, $L_2 = x_1(x_2x_3) + x_2(x_3x_1) + x_3(x_1x_2)$ leads to the *Lie algebras.*

The case where $\nu = 2$, $h = 2$, $L_1 = x_1x_2 - x_2x_1$, $L_2 = ((x_1x_1)x_2)x_1 - (x_1x_1)(x_2x_1)$ leads to the *Jordan algebras.*

The case where $\nu = 2$, $h = 2$, $L_1 = (x_1x_1)x_2 - x_1(x_1x_2)$, $L_2 = x_2(x_1x_1) - (x_2x_1)x_1$ leads to the *alternative algebras.*

Exercises on Chapter IV

1. Let $\mathfrak{L}$ be a finite set of elements of a free algebra on a finite set S over a ring R. Call algebras of type $\mathfrak{L}$ the algebras in which the identities $L = 0$ (for $L \in \mathfrak{L}$) are valid. Show that any subalgebra or quotient algebra of an algebra of type $\mathfrak{L}$ is of type $\mathfrak{L}$.

2. Let A be an algebra over a ring R, and let ρ be a homomorphism of R into a commutative ring S; denote by A^S the algebra over S deduced from A by transfer of the basic ring to S by means of the homomorphism ρ. Show that, if A is an associative algebra (resp.: a Lie algebra, an alternative algebra), then A^S is an associative algebra (resp.: a Lie algebra, an alternative algebra). Show that the corresponding statement would not be true for Jordan algebras. [Take $R = \underline{Z}_2$, $A = Rx + Ry$, where $x^2 = x$, $y^2 = y$, $xy = yx = x + y$; prove that there exists a monomorphism of R into a field S with 4 elements.]

3. Show that, in a Lie algebra $\neq \{0\}$, the multiplication cannot have a neutral element.

4. Let A be an algebra. If x, y, z are in A, set $(x, y, z) = (xy)z - x(yz)$ Show that

$$(xy, z, t) - (x, yz, t) + (x, y, zt) = x(y, z, t) + (x, y, z)t$$

if x, y, z, t are any elements of A.

5. Let A be an alternative algebra.

a) The symbol (x, y, z) being defined as in ex. 4, show that

$$-(x, y, z) = (y, x, z) = (x, z, y) = (z, y, x), \quad (x, y, z) = (y, z, x) = (z, x, y).$$

b) Call strongly associative a subset E of A such that $(x, y, z) = 0$ whenever x, y are in E and z in A. Show that, if E is strongly associative and $x, y \in E$, then $E \cup \{xy\}$ is strongly associative; show that the subalgebra of A generated by a strongly associative set is strongly associative [use ex. 4].

c) Let S be a set of generators of A and A_1 a submodule of A containing S and such that $xA_1 \subset A_1$, $A_1x \subset A_1$ whenever $x \in S$; show that $A_1 = A$. [Let $\mathfrak{A}$ be the set of submodules M of A such that $xM \subset M$, $Mx \subset M$ whenever $x \in S$, and let A_0 be the intersection of all modules $M \in \mathfrak{A}$ which contain S; let B be the set of $y \in A$ such that $yA_0 \subset A_0$, $A_0y \subset A_0$; show that $B \in \mathfrak{A}$.]

d) Show that the subalgebra of A generated by two strongly associative sets B and C is associative [let D be the set of elements z such that $(x, y, z) = 0$ whenever $x \in B$ and $y \in C$; making use of ex. 4, show that $xD \subset D$, $Dx \subset D$ whenever x is in either B or C].

e) Show that, if x, y are in A, the subalgebra of A generated by x and y is associative.

6. Let A be an associative algebra. Define a new law of composition on A by the mapping $(x, y) \to xy - yx$ (resp.: $(x, y) \to xy + yx$). Show that this new law of composition defines on the module A a Lie (resp.: Jordan) algebra structure.

7. Let A be an algebra over a ring R. A linear mapping D of the module A into itself is called a derivation of A if we have $D(xy) = D(x)y + xD(y)$ for any x, y in A. Show that the derivations of A form a submodule of Hom (A, A) and that, if D, D' are derivations of A, then $D \circ D' - D' \circ D$ is again a derivation of A. Show that, in order for A to be a Lie algebra, it is necessary and sufficient that the following condition be satisfied: if $x \in A$, then the mapping $y \to xy$ is a derivation and maps x upon 0.

8. Let D be a derivation of an algebra A; assume that $D \circ D = 0$. Show that, if α is any element of the ring R over which A is an algebra, then the mapping $x \to x + \alpha D(x)$ is an automorphism s_α of A; show that the automorphisms s_α, for all $\alpha \in R$, form a group.

9. Let D be a derivation of an algebra A. Show that, if $x, y \in A$, then $D^n(xy) = \sum_{k=0}^{n} C_n^k (D^k x)(D^{n-k} y)$, where the C_n^k are the binomial coefficients.

CHAPTER V

Associative algebras

1. Definitions

We have introduced in the last chapter the very general notion of an algebra. We shall henceforth have to consider only algebras A which satisfy the following conditions:

a) The multiplication in A is associative;

b) A has a unit element relative to the operation of mutliplication.

In order to avoid repetition, we adopt the convention that, henceforth, the term algebra will refer to an algebra which has the properties *a*) and *b*).

We shall review briefly the definitions and results of Chapter IV in the light of this new definition.

First, we shall modify the notion of a subalgebra. By a subalgebra of an algebra A, we shall now mean a subset of A which is a submodule, which is stable under the multiplication of A and, moreover, which contains the unit element of A. Then the restriction to $B \times B$ of the multiplication in A defines on B the structure of an algebra in the new sense.

It should be observed that an algebra A in the new sense may have subalgebras B in the sense of Chapter IV which are algebras in the new sense but are not subalgebras of A in the new sense: this will happen if B has a unit element which is not the unit element of A.

With our new definition, it is still true that, given any subset S of an algebra A, there is a smallest subalgebra B of A containing S: B is the algebra generated by $S \cup \{1\}$ in the sense of chapter IV. We shall say from now on that B is the *subalgebra of A generated by S.*

Theorem 1. Chapter IV, Sect. 2 has to be modified as follows:

Theorem 1. *Let A be an algebra and let S be a subset of A such that the product of any two elements of S is in S. Then the submodule of A generated by $\{1\} \cup S$ is a subalgebra of A.*

Let now S be any subset of an algebra A, and let M be the submonoid of the multiplicative monoid of elements of A which is generated by S. Then M is clearly contained in the subalgebra B of A generated by S; since M is stable under multiplication, it follows from the preceding result that M is a set of module generators of B. On the other hand, every element of M is a product of a finite number of elements of S (theorem 15, Chapter I, Sect. 6). The elements of the subalgebra generated by S are therefore the linear combinations of products of finite sequences of elements of S.

Let B be a subalgebra (in the new sense) of an algebra A. Let σ be the restriction to $B \times A$ of the multiplication of A. Then σ is the scalar multiplication of the structure of a module over B on the additive group of elements of A, as can be verified immediately. Assume further that every element of B commutes with every element of A (which implies that B is a commutative ring). Then the structures of a ring and of a module over B on A combine with each other to give a structure of an algebra over B on A. In order to prove this, we have to establish that the multiplication of A is bilinear relative to the module structure of A over B. Since this multiplication is bi-additive, it will be sufficient to prove that $(bx)y = x(by) = b(xy)$ if $b \in B$, $x \in A$, $y \in A$; this is true because A is associative and $xb = bx$.

Let A and B be algebras over the same ring R. By a homomorphism of A into B, we shall henceforth mean a mapping f which is a homomorphism in the sense of Chapter IV, Sect. 3, and, in addition, which maps the unit element of A upon that of B. If f is a homomorphism of A into B and g a homomorphism of B into a third algebra C, then $g \circ f$ is a homomorphism of A into C. If f is a homomorphism of A into B and, at the same time, a bijection of A on B, then $\overset{-1}{f}$ is a homomorphism of B into A; f is then called an isomorphism.

By an ideal in an algebra A is meant a subset of A which is the kernel of some homomorphism of A into an algebra. The statement of theorem 2, Chapter IV, Sect. 3, remains true without modification for our new definitions. For, let K be a subset of A. If K is the kernel of a homomorphism of A in the new sense, it is also the kernel of a homomorphism in the sense of Chapter IV, which shows that the conditions of theorem 1 are still necessary. Assume that they are satisfied. Then A/K is an algebra in the sense of Chapter IV, and the natural mapping f of A onto A/K is a homomorphism in the sense of Chapter IV. If x, y, z are elements of A/K, and u, v, w elements of A such that $f(u) = x$, $f(v) = y$, $f(w) = z$, then we have $(xy)z = f((uv)w)$, $x(yz) = f(u(vw))$; since $(uv)w = u(vw)$, we have $(xy)z = x(yz)$, which shows that the multiplication in A/K is associative. If 1 is the unit element of A, then we have, for any $u \in A$, $f(1)f(u) = f(1 \cdot u) = f(u)$ and similarly $f(u)f(1) = f(u)$; this shows that $f(1)$ is the unit element in A/K. Thus, A/K is an algebra in the new sense, and f a homomorphism in the new sense.

The corollary to theorem 2 remains true without any modification.

Theorem 3, Chapter IV, Sect. 3, remains true without any modification. For, the notation being as in this theorem, we have $f(1) = g(\pi(1))$; but $\pi(1)$ is the unit element of A/K and $f(1)$ is the unit element of B, which shows that g is a homomorphism in the new sense.

Theorem 4, Chapter IV, Sect. 3, remains true without any modification. For, let the notation be as in this theorem. Then the set of elements $x \in A$ such that $f(x) = g(x)$ is a subalgebra of A in the sense of Chapter IV, and contains 1, since $f(1)$ and $g(1)$ are both equal to the unit element of B. This set is therefore a subalgebra in the new sense, which proves the theorem.

Theorem 5, Chapter IV, Sect. 3, remains true provided we add the assumption that $f(1) = 1$.

If $(A_i)_{i \in I}$ is a family of algebras in the new sense, then $\prod_{i \in I} A_i$ is an algebra in the new sense, whose unit element is $(e_i)_{i \in I}$ where e_i is, for each i, the unit element of A_i. However, if I is infinite, then $\prod^w_{i \in I} A_i$ is in general not an algebra in the new sense.

The free algebra on a set S in the sense of Chapter IV, Sect. 5, is in general not associative.

Let A be an algebra over the ring R in the sense of Chapter IV. Assume that S is a subset of A which is a set of generators of the module structure of A over R, and that we have $(xy)z = x(yz)$ whenever x, y and z belong to S. Then the multiplication in A is associative. For, let ν be the mapping of $A \times A \times A$ into A defined by the formula $\nu(u, v, w) = (uv)w - u(vw)$; it is clear that ν is trilinear. It follows from our assumption that every element of A may be written as a linear combination of the elements of S. Making use of lemma 3, Chapter III, Sect. 10, we see that, for any u, v, w, in A, $\nu(u, v, w)$ may be written as a linear combination of the elements $\nu(x, y, z)$ where x, y, z are in S; since $\nu(x, y, z) = 0$ by assumption, it follows that $\nu = 0$, which proves our assertion.

In particular, let A be a free module over a commutative ring R, and let $(x_i)_{i \in I}$ be a base of A. Let an algebra structure in the sense of Chapter IV be defined on A by means of its constants of structure γ_{ijk} with respect to the base $(x_i)_{i \in I}$. In order for this algebra to be associative, it is necessary and sufficient that we should have $(x_i x_j)x_k = x_i(x_j x_k)$ for any i, j, k in I. The corresponding necessary and sufficient conditions on the constants γ_{ijk} are that

$$\sum_{l \in I} \gamma_{ijl}\gamma_{lkm} = \sum_{l \in I} \gamma_{ilm}\gamma_{jkl}$$

for all $(i, j, k, m) \in I \times I \times I \times I$. Assume that these conditions are satisfied, and assume further that there exist elements e_i $(i \in I)$ of R, of which only a finite number are $\neq 0$, such that

$$\sum_{j \in I} \gamma_{ijk} e_j = \delta_{ik} \quad \sum_{i \in I} \gamma_{ijk} e_i = \delta_{jk}$$

where $\delta_{ij} = 1$ if $j = i$, $\delta_{ij} = 0$ if $i \neq j$. Then $e = \sum_{i \in I} e_i x_i$ is the unit element for the algebra A. For, it follows from our conditions that $x_i e = x_i$, $e x_j = x_j$ for any $i, j \in I$. The mappings $x \to xe - x$ and $x \to ex - x$ are then linear mappings of A into itself which map the basic elements x_i upon 0, whence $xe = ex = x$ for every $x \in A$.

In particular, *an algebra A of a monoid M over a commutative ring R is an algebra (in our new sense of the word)*. For, there exists a base $(\psi(x))_{x \in M}$ of the module A such that $\psi(x)\psi(y) = \psi(xy)$ for any $x, y \in M$. The constants of structure $\gamma_{x,y,z}$ with respect to this base are given by

$$\gamma_{x,y,z} = 1 \text{ if } z = xy \text{ in } M, \qquad \gamma_{x,y,z} = 0 \text{ if } z \neq xy;$$

since the multiplication in M is associative, we see immediately that the multiplication in A is associative. If e is the unit element of M, we have

$$\gamma_{x,e,z} = \gamma_{e,x,z} = 1 \text{ if } z = x, \qquad \gamma_{x,e,z} = \gamma_{e,x,z} = 0 \text{ if } z \neq x;$$

it follows immediately that $\psi(e)$ is the unit element in A.

Let A be an algebra over R (in the new sense of the word). Let S be any subset of A. Then the intersection of all ideals of A which contain S is an ideal, which is called the *ideal generated by S*.

Theorem 2. *Let A be an algebra, S a subset of A and K the ideal generated by S in A. Then the elements of K are all elements of A which may be represented in the form $\sum_{i \in I} a_i x_i b_i$, where I is a finite set, a_i and b_i are elements of A and the x_i's elements of S.*

For each $x \in S$, let K_x be the ideal generated by $\{x\}$. Then $\sum_{x \in S} K_x$ is an ideal (corollary to theorem 2, Chapter IV, Sect. 3), which contains S and which is clearly contained in every ideal containing S, whence $K = \sum_{x \in S} K_x$. It follows immediately that it will be sufficient to prove theorem 2 in the case where $S = \{x\}$ consists of a single element. Let then K' be the set of all elements of the form $\sum_{i \in I} a_i x b_i$. If a, b are in A, then $axb \in K$, whence $K' \subset K$. It will therefore be sufficient to prove that K' is an ideal. Let $\sum_{i \in I} a_i x b_i$ be an element of K', α an element of R, and a and b elements of A. Then

$$\alpha\left(\sum_{i \in I} a_i x b_i\right) = \sum_{i \in I} (\alpha a_i) x b_i \in K', \quad a\left(\sum_{i \in I} a_i x b_i\right) = \sum_{i \in I} (a a_i) x b_i \in K'$$

and
$$\left(\sum_{i \in I} a_i x b_i\right) b = \sum_{i \in I} a_i x (b_i b) \in K';$$

it follows first that K' is a submodule of A, and then, by theorem 2, Chapter IV, Sect. 3, that K' is an ideal.

2. Graded algebras

Let A be an algebra over a ring R. Assume that we have defined a gradation on the underlying module of A whose set of degrees is a commutative additive group Γ. Then we say that this algebra and this gradation define a *graded algebra* if the following condition is satisfied: *If x and x' are homogeneous elements of A of respective degrees γ and γ', then xx' is homogeneous of degree $\gamma + \gamma'$.*

This condition may also be expressed as follows: If x is a homogeneous element of degree γ of A, then the left and right multiplication by x (i. e., the mappings $y \rightarrow xy$ and $y \rightarrow yx$) are homogeneous of degree γ.

Lemma 1. *Let A be a graded algebra. Then the unit element of A is homogeneous of degree* 0.

For, let $1 = \Sigma_{\gamma \in \Gamma} e_\gamma$ be the decomposition of 1 into its homogeneous components. Denote by E_γ the left multiplication by e_γ; then E_γ is homogeneous of degree γ, and $\Sigma_{\gamma \in \Gamma} E_\gamma = I$ (the identity mapping of A). Since I is homogeneous of degree 0, we have $E_0 = I$ (theorem 73, Chapter III, Sect. 17). We see in the same way that the right multiplication by e_0 is I. It follows that e_0 is a unit element in A, whence $e_0 = 1$, which proves lemma 1.

If A is graded algebra and B a subalgebra of A, then B is called a homogeneous subalgebra if it is a homogeneous submodule of A. If this is so, then, obviously, B becomes a graded algebra if equipped with the gradation induced by that of A.

Theorem 3. *Let A be a graded algebra and B a subalgebra of A. In order for B to be homogeneous, it is necessary and sufficient that B should have a set of algebra generators composed of homogeneous elements.*

If B is homogeneous, the set of homogeneous elements of B is a set of module generators, and, *a fortiori*, of algebra generators of B. Conversely, assume that B has a set S of homogeneous algebra generators. It is clear that the set of homogeneous elements of A is a submonoid of the multiplicative monoid of all elements of A. Therefore, the multiplicative monoid M generated by S is composed of homogeneous elements. Let B' be the submodule of A generated by M; since $S \subset B$, we have $M \subset B$ whence $B' \subset B$. If $\Sigma_{i \in I} \alpha_i x_i = x$ and $\Sigma_{j \in J} \beta_j y_j = y$ are elements of B' (with x_i, $y_j \in M$, α_i, $\beta_j \in R$), we have $xy = \Sigma_{(i,j) \in I \times J} \alpha_i \beta_j x_i y_j \in B'$ since $x_i y_j \in M$. Since $1 \in M \subset B'$, B' is a subalgebra. Since $S \subset B' \subset B$, we have $B' = B$. But B' is a homogeneous submodule of A (theorem 72, Chapter III, Sect. 17); B is therefore a homogeneous subalgebra.

If L is an ideal in a graded algebra A, L is called a homogeneous ideal if it is a homogeneous submodule of A. Assume that this is the case. Then A/L is an algebra and has a graded module structure; and we verify immediately that A/L is a graded algebra. The natural homomorphism from A to A/L is homogeneous of degree 0.

Theorem 4. *Let L be an ideal in a homogeneous algebra A. A necessary and sufficient condition for L to be homogeneous is for L to have a set of homogeneous ideal generators.*

If L is homogeneous, the homogeneous elements of L form a set of module generators of L, and, *a fortiori*, of ideal generators of L. Assume conversely that L has a set S of homogeneous ideal generators. Let S' be the set of elements of the form axb, where $x \in S$, and where a and b are homogeneous elements of A. The elements of S' are homogeneous. Let u and v be arbitrary elements of A, and $x \in S$; we may then write $u = \sum_{i \in I} a_i$, $v = \sum_{j \in J} b_j$, where the a_i's and b_j's are homogeneous, whence $uxv = \sum_{(i,j) \in I \times J} a_i x b_j$: uxv is a sum of elements of S'. Taking theorem 2 into account, we see that every element of L is a sum of elements of S'; thus S' is a set of module generators of L, which shows that L is homogeneous.

A graded algebra A over a ring R is called a *regularly graded algebra* if it satisfies the following conditions: *a*) the group of degrees of A is the additive group of integers; *b*) A has no homogeneous element $\neq 0$ of degree < 0; *c*) every homogeneous element of degree 0 of A is of the form $\alpha \cdot 1$, with $\alpha \in R$, and the condition $\alpha \cdot 1 = 0$ implies $\alpha = 0$.

Let A be a regularly graded algebra. For any integer n, denote by A_n the set of homogeneous elements of degree n of A; we then have

$$A = \sum_{n=0}^{\infty} A_n \text{ (direct)}$$

and the product of an element of A_m by an element of A_n is in A_{m+n}. It is clear that A_0 is a subalgebra of A; as a ring, A_0 is isomorphic to R under the isomorphism $\alpha \to \alpha \cdot 1$. For any integer $n > 0$, set

$$L_n = \sum_{i \geqslant n} A_i.$$

Then L_n is a homogeneous ideal. For, let $x = \sum_{i \geqslant n} x_i$ be in L_n, with $x_i \in A_i$ for all i. Let $a = \sum_{j \geqslant 0} a_j$ be any element of A. Then $ax = \sum_{i \geqslant n, j \geqslant 0} a_j x_i$ belongs to L_n, since $a_j x_i \in A_{j+i}$; and we see in the same way that $xa \in L_n$. Since L_n is obviously a homogeneous submodule of A, it is a homogeneous ideal. We have

$$A = \sum_{i=0}^{n-1} A_i + L_n \text{ (direct)}.$$

Theorem 5. *Let A be a regularly graded algebra, and let n be an integer > 0. Let L be an ideal of A which is generated by homogeneous elements of degrees $\geqslant n$. Then A/L is a regularly graded algebra. If A_i (resp.: $(A/L)_i$) is the set of homogeneous elements of degree i of A (resp.: A/L), then the natural mapping π of A to A/L induces a module isomorphism of $\sum_{i=0}^{n-1} A_i$ with $\sum_{i=0}^{n-1}(A/L)_i$.*

We use the same notation as above. Since L_n is an ideal and contains a set of generators of L, we have $L \subset L_n$. Since $A = \sum_{i=0}^{n-1} A_i + L_n$ is a direct sum, we have $L \cap \sum_{i=0}^{n-1} A_i = \{0\}$, and π induces a monomorphism of $\sum_{i=0}^{n-1} A_i$. Since $\pi(A_i) = (A/L)_i$ by definition, the last assertion of theorem 5 is proved. Since $n > 0$, π induces an isomorphism of A_0 with $(A/L)_0$, from which it follows immediately that A/L is regularly graded.

Let A be a graded algebra and Γ its group of degrees. Let φ be a homomorphism of Γ into an additive group Δ. Then φ defines on A a structure of graded module A' with Δ as its set of degrees. If A_γ is the set of homogeneous elements of degree γ of A, then, for any $\delta \in \Delta$, the set A'_δ of homogeneous elements of degree δ of A' is

$$A'_\delta = \sum\nolimits_{\varphi(\gamma)=\delta} A_\gamma.$$

Let δ and δ' be elements of Δ, x an element of A'_δ and x' an element of $A'_{\delta'}$; we shall see that $xx' \in A'_{\delta+\delta'}$. Write $x = \sum_{\varphi(\gamma)=\delta} y_\gamma$, $y_\gamma \in A_\gamma$, and $x' = \sum_{\varphi(\gamma')=\delta'} y'_{\gamma'}$, $y'_{\gamma'} \in A_{\gamma'}$. Then $xx' = \sum_{\varphi(\gamma)=\delta,\, \varphi(\gamma')=\delta'} y_\gamma y'_{\gamma'}$. But $y_\gamma y'_{\gamma'}$ belongs to $A_{\gamma+\gamma'}$, and, if $\varphi(\gamma) = \delta$, $\varphi(\gamma') = \delta'$, we have $\varphi(\gamma + \gamma') = \delta + \delta'$, whence $xx' \in A'_{\delta+\delta'}$. It follows that the graded module A', with the multiplication of A, defines a graded algebra having Δ as its group of degrees.

3. Tensor algebras

Let R be a commutative ring and M a module over R. Let there be given an algebra T over R and a linear mapping ψ of M into T. Then we say that the pair (T, ψ) is a *tensor algebra* on M if the following condition is satisfied: If φ is any linear mapping of M into an algebra A over R, there exists a unique homomorphism f of the algebra T into A such that $f \circ \psi = \varphi$.

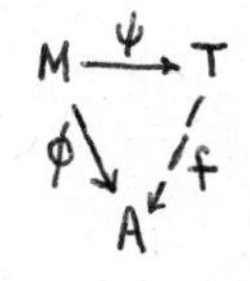

If (T, ψ) and (T', ψ') are tensor algebras over the same module M, then there exists a unique isomorphism J of T with T' such that $J \circ \psi = \psi'$. This is proved in the same way as the corresponding statements for monoids (Chapter I, Sect. 6) and for modules (Chapter III, Sect. 9).

We shall now construct a tensor algebra over a given module M. For any $n \geqslant 0$, we construct a tensor product T'_n of n modules identical with M. Let $T = \prod_n^w T'_n$ be the weak product of the modules T'_n. Then T is the direct sum of modules T_n $(0 \leqslant n < \infty)$ respectively isomorphic to the

$T = R \oplus M \oplus (M \otimes M) \oplus (M \otimes M \otimes M) \oplus \cdots$

modules T'_n. Thus, we have for each n an n-linear mapping τ_n of the product of n modules identical with M into T_n such that (T_n, τ_n) is a tensor product of n modules identical with M.

We shall now define a multiplication in T. Let m and n be integers $\geqslant 0$. Then there is a canonical isomorphism $\theta_{m,n}$ of $T_m \otimes T_n$ with T_{m+n} such that

$$\theta_{m,n}(\tau_m(x_1, \cdots, x_m), \tau_n(y_1, \cdots, y_n)) = \tau_{m+n}(x_1, \cdots, x_m, y_1, \cdots, y_n)$$

(theorem 39, Chapter III, Sect. 10). On the other hand, since $T = \sum_{n=0}^{\infty} T_n$ (direct), we may write

$$T \otimes T = \sum_{m,n=0}^{\infty} T_m \otimes T_n \text{ (direct)}$$

(theorem 40, Chapter III, Sect. 10). Let θ be the linear mapping of $T \otimes T$ into T which extends all mappings $\theta_{m,n}$ $(0 \leqslant m, n < \infty)$ (corollary 2 to theorem 20, Chapter III, Sect. 6). We define the multiplication in T by the formula

$$xy = \theta(x \otimes y) \qquad (x, y \in T).$$

Then the mapping $(x, y) \to xy$ is obviously bilinear. We shall prove that our multiplication is associative. For each n, let P_n be the set of elements of T_n of the form $\tau_n(x_1, \cdots, x_n)$ (with $x_i \in M$); then we know that P_n is a set of module generators of T_n. It will be sufficient to prove that $(xy)z = x(yz)$ when $x, y, z \in P = \bigcup_{n=0}^{\infty} P_n$ (cf. Sect. 1). Assume that $x = \tau_m(x_1, \cdots, x_m)$, $y = \tau_n(y_1, \cdots, y_n)$, $z = \tau_p(z_1, \cdots, z_p)$, where the elements x_i, y_j, z_k are in M. Then

$$xy = \tau_{m+n}(x_1, \cdots, x_m, y_1, \cdots, y_n)$$
$$yz = \tau_{n+p}(y_1, \cdots, y_n, z_1, \cdots, z_p);$$

$(xy)z$ and $x(yz)$ are both equal to $\tau_{m+n+p}(x_1, \cdots, x_m, y_1, \cdots, y_n, z_1, \cdots, z_p)$, which proves the associativity of our multiplication.

We shall now prove that our multiplication admits a unit element. Let e be the image under τ_0 of the empty sequence of elements of M. Then it follows immediately from the definition of the multiplication that $ex = xe = x$ for any $x \in P$. Since the mappings $x \to ex$ and $x \to xe$ are linear and P is a set of module generators of T, it follows that $ex = xe = x$ for every $x \in T$: e is the unit element of T. We shall henceforth denote it by 1.

We have proved that T, with the multiplication defined on it, is an algebra.

Set $\psi = \tau_1$; then ψ is an isomorphism of M with a submodule of T. Let φ be any linear mapping of M into an algebra A over R. For any $n \geqslant 0$, the mapping

$$\varphi_n : (x_1, \cdots, x_n) \to \prod_{i=1}^{n} \varphi(x_i)$$

of the product of n modules identical to M into A is obviously multilinear. Thus there exists a linear mapping f_n of T_n into A such that $f_n \circ \tau_n = \varphi_n$.

Let f be the linear mapping of T into A which extends all mappings f_n. We shall see that f is an algebra homomorphism. The set P is stable under the multiplication of T and is a set of module generators of T; it will therefore be sufficient to prove that $f(xy) = f(x)f(y)$ if $x, y \in P$. Assume that $x = \tau_m(x_1, \cdots, x_m)$, $y = \tau_n(y_1, \cdots, y_n)$, with $x_i, y_j \in M$; then

$$xy = \tau_{m+n}(x_1, \cdots, x_m, y_1, \cdots, y_n),$$

and

$$f(xy) = (\Pi_{i=1}^m \varphi(x_i))(\Pi_{j=1}^n \varphi(y_j)),$$

$$f(x) = \Pi_{i=1}^m \varphi(x_i),\ f(y) = \Pi_{j=1}^n \varphi(y_j),$$

whence $f(xy) = f(x)f(y)$; f is therefore a homomorphism. Since $\psi = \tau_1$, we have $f \circ \psi = \varphi$.

In order to prove the uniqueness of the homomorphism f such that $f \circ \psi = \varphi$, it will be sufficient to prove that $\psi(M) = T_1$ is a set of algebra generators of T. Let $x_1, \cdots, x_n$ be elements of M; then we have $\Pi_{i=1}^n \psi(x_i) = \tau_n(x_1, \cdots, x_n)$. This is true if $n = 0$. Assume that $n > 0$ and that the statement is true for $n - 1$. We have

$$\Pi_{i=1}^n \psi(x_i) = (\Pi_{i=1}^{n-1} \psi(x_i))\psi(x_n) = \tau_{n-1}(x_1, \cdots, x_{n-1})\tau_1(x_n) = \tau_n(x_1, \cdots, x_n)$$

which proves that the statement is true for n. It follows that the subalgebra T' of T generated by $\psi(M)$ contains P_n for every $n \geqslant 0$, whence $P \subset T'$. Since P is a set of module generators of T, we have $T' = T$.

Thus we have proved that (T, ψ) is a tensor algebra over M. Moreover, our construction yields the following results:

Theorem 6. *Let M be a module over a commutative ring R and (T, ψ) a tensor algebra over M. For any $n \geqslant 0$, let τ_n be the multilinear mapping of the product of n modules identical with M into T defined by*

$$\tau_n(x_1, \cdots, x_n) = \psi(x_1) \cdots \psi(x_n).$$

Let T_n be the submodule of T generated by the elements $\tau_n(x_1, \cdots, x_n)$, for all $x_1, \cdots, x_n \in M$. Then we have $T = \Sigma_{n=0}^{\infty} T_n$ (direct) *and (T_n, τ_n) is a tensor product of n modules identical with M.*

The elements of T which are of the form $\psi(x_1) \cdots \psi(x_n)$ are called the *decomposable elements.*

Theorem 7. *Let M be a free module over a commutative ring R, $(x_i)_{i \in I}$ a base of M and (T, ψ) a tensor algebra over M. For any finite sequence $\sigma = (i_1, \cdots, i_n)$ of elements of I, set $t_\sigma = \Pi_{j=1}^n \psi(x_{i_j})$; then the elements t_σ, for all finite sequences σ, form a base of the module T over R.*

For each n, the elements t_σ for the sequences σ of n elements form a base of T_n (in the notation of theorem 6) by virtue of theorem 41, Chapter III, Sect. 10; theorem 6 follows immediately.

We shall now define on T the structure of a graded algebra. The notation being as in theorem 6, we further define T_n to be $\{0\}$ if $n < 0$; whence $T = \sum_{-\infty}^{+\infty} T_n$ (direct). This formula defines on T the structure of a graded module with the group $\underline{Z}$ of integers as its set of degrees. If $x_1, \cdots, x_m, y_1, \cdots, y_n$ are in M, the product $\tau_m(x_1, \cdots, x_m)\tau_n(y_1, \cdots, y_n) = \tau_{m+n}(x_1, \cdots, x_m, y_1, \cdots, y_n)$ is in T_{m+n}. It follows immediately that, if m, n are any integers, the product of an element of T_m and an element of T_n is in T_{m+n} (this product is 0 if either m or n is < 0); T is therefore a graded algebra, with $\underline{Z}$ as its group of degrees.

Theorem 8. *Let T be a tensor algebra over a module; then T is a regularly graded algebra.*

Using the same notation as above, (T_0, τ_0) is a tensor product of the empty family of modules. Thus T_0 is isomorphic to R. The unit element 1 of T is the image under τ_0 of the empty sequence of elements of M; it follows immediately that there exists an isomorphism φ of R with T_0 such that $\varphi(1) = 1$. Since φ is an isomorphism, we have $\alpha \cdot 1 \neq 0$ for every $\alpha \neq 0$ in R. Since $T = T_0 + \sum_{n>0} T_n$ (direct), theorem 8 is proved.

Theorem 9. *Let M be a module over a ring R, (T, ψ) a tensor algebra over M and φ a linear mapping of M into a graded algebra A over R whose group of degrees is the additive group of integers; assume that the elements of $\varphi(M)$ are homogeneous of degree* 1 *in A. Then the homomorphism f of T into A such that $f \circ \psi = \varphi$ is homogeneous of degree* 0.

We use the same notation as above. If $x_1, \cdots, x_n$ are elements of M, then $f(\tau_n(x_1, \cdots, x_n)) = \prod_{i=1}^{n} \varphi(x_i)$ is homogeneous of degree n in A. It follows that the elements of $f(T_n)$ are homogeneous of degree n if $n \geqslant 0$; if $n < 0$, then $f(T_n) = \{0\}$; theorem 9 is thereby proved.

4. Tensor products of graded algebras

See problem 7, p. 229.

Let $A_1, \cdots, A_n$ be graded algebras over a commutative ring R, all admitting the group $\underline{Z}$ of integers as their group of degrees. The multiplication in A_i is a bilinear mapping of $A_i \times A_i$ into A_i; the linearization of this mapping is a linear mapping μ_i of $A_i \otimes A_i$ into A_i. Let $T = A_1 \otimes \cdots \otimes A_n$ be a tensor product of the modules $A_1, \cdots, A_n$. We shall denote by $A_{i;k}$ the module of homogeneous elements of degree k of A_i. If $(k) = (k_1, \cdots, k_n)$ is any element of $\underline{Z}^n$ (the product of n groups identical to $\underline{Z}$), we shall denote by $T_{(k)}$ the submodule of T generated by the elements $a_1 \otimes \cdots \otimes a_n$,

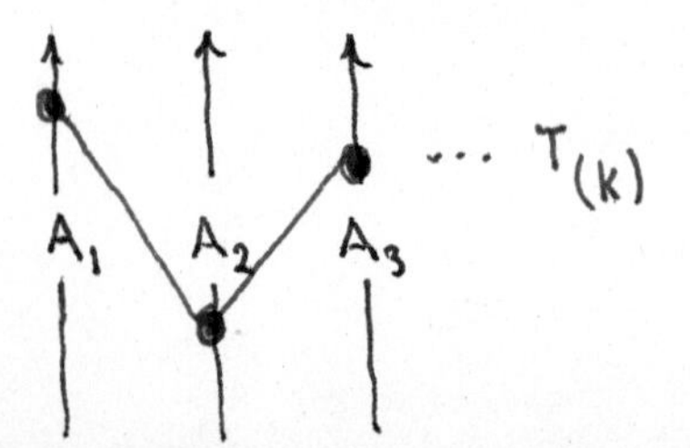

where $a_i \in A_{i;k_i}$ for each i; $T_{(k)}$ may be regarded as a tensor product of the modules $A_{i;k_i}$ $(1 \leqslant i \leqslant n)$, and T is the direct sum of the modules $T_{(k)}$ for all $(k) \in \underline{Z}^n$. If k, k' are any integers, we denote by $\mu_{i;k,k'}$ the restriction of μ_i to $A_{i;k} \otimes A_{i;k'}$, this last module being considered as a submodule of $A_i \otimes A_i$. If $(k) = (k_1, \cdots, k_n)$ and $(k') = (k'_1, \cdots, k'_n)$ are in $\underline{Z}^n$, there is a canonical isomorphism $\omega_{(k),(k')}$ of $T_{(k)} \otimes T_{(k')}$ with

$$(A_{1;k_1} \otimes A_{1;k'_1}) \otimes \cdots \otimes (A_{n;k_n} \otimes A_{n;k'_n})$$

which maps the element $(a_1 \otimes \cdots \otimes a_n) \otimes (a'_1 \otimes \cdots \otimes a'_n)$ upon $(a_1 \otimes a'_1) \otimes \cdots \otimes (a_n \otimes a'_n)$ (cf. theorem 39, Chapter III, Sect. 10). Set

$$N((k), (k')) = \Sigma_{i>j} k_i k'_j, \qquad \varphi_{(k),(k')} = (-1)^{N((k),(k'))} \omega_{(k),(k')}.$$

Finally, set

$$\mu_{(k),(k')} = (\mu_{1;k_1,k'_1} \otimes \cdots \otimes \mu_{n;k_n,k'_n}) \circ \varphi_{(k),(k')}.$$

Then $\mu_{(k),(k')}$ is a linear mapping of $T_{(k)} \otimes T_{(k')}$ into $T_{(k)+(k')}$. We may assume that the modules $T_{(k)} \otimes T_{(k')}$ are taken to be submodules of $T \otimes T$, and that $T \otimes T$ is their direct sum (cf. theorem 40, Chapter III, Sect. 10). We shall then denote by μ the linear mapping of $T \otimes T$ into T which extends all the mappings $\mu_{(k),(k')}$. If a, a' are any elements of T, we set

$$aa' = \mu(a \otimes a');$$

this formula defines a bilinear multiplication in T, and we have

$$(a_1 \otimes \cdots \otimes a_n)(a'_1 \otimes \cdots \otimes a'_n) = (-1)^{N((k),(k'))}(a_1 a'_1) \otimes \cdots \otimes (a_n a'_n)$$

if $(k) = (k_1, \cdots, k_n)$, $(k') = (k'_1, \cdots, k'_n)$, $a_i \in A_{i;k_i}$, $a'_i \in A_{i;k'_i}$ $(1 \leqslant i \leqslant n)$. We shall prove that the multiplication we have just defined turns T into an algebra. Consider the mappings $(a, a', a'') \to (aa')a''$ and $(a, a', a'') \to a(a'a'')$ of $T \times T \times T$ into T; these two mappings are obviously trilinear; denote them by M and M'. If $(k) = (k_1, \cdots, k_n)$ is any element of $\underline{Z}^n$, denote by $S_{(k)}$ the set of elements of T of the form $a_1 \otimes \cdots \otimes a_n$, where $a_i \in A_{i;k_i}$ for each i; then the union S of the sets $S_{(k)}$ for all (k) in $\underline{Z}^n$ is a set of generators of the module T (for, each $S_{(k)}$ is a set of generators of $T_{(k)}$). In order to prove that $M = M'$, it will therefore be sufficient to prove that $M(a, a', a'') = M'(a, a', a'')$ when a, a', a'' are in S. Assume then that $a \in S_{(k)}$, $a' \in S_{(k')}$, $a'' \in S_{(k'')}$, with $(k) = (k_1 \cdots, k_n)$, $(k') = (k'_1, \cdots, k'_n)$, $(k'') = (k''_1, \cdots, k''_n)$; set $a = a_1 \otimes \cdots \otimes a_n$, $a' = a'_1 \otimes \cdots \otimes a'_n$, $a'' = a''_1 \otimes \cdots \otimes a''_n$, with $a_i \in A_{i;k_i}$, $a'_i \in A_{i;k'_i}$, $a''_i \in A_{i;k''_i}$. Then we have

$$M(a, a', a'') = (-1)^{N((k),(k'))+N((k)+(k'),(k''))}(a_1 a'_1 a''_1) \otimes \cdots \otimes (a_n a'_n a''_n)$$

$$M'(a, a', a'') = (-1)^{N((k'),(k''))+N((k),(k')+(k''))}(a_1 a'_1 a''_1) \otimes \cdots \otimes (a_n a'_n a''_n).$$

But $N((k), (k')) + N((k) + (k'), (k''))$ and $N((k'), (k'')) + N((k), (k') + (k''))$ are both equal to $\Sigma_{i>j}(k_i k'_j + k_i k''_j + k'_i k''_j)$, and the equality of the

the "multiplier condition"

mappings M, M' is established. This shows that our multiplication on T is associative. Let 1_i be the unit element of A_i; set $1 = 1_1 \otimes \cdots \otimes 1_n$. Since each 1_i is homogeneous of degree 0, it follows immediately from the definition of our multiplication that $1a = a1 = a$ whenever $a \in S$; since the mappings $a \to 1a$, $a \to a1$, $a \to a$ are linear, 1 is the unit element for our multiplication in T. This completes the proof of the fact that T, with the multiplication we have defined on it, constitutes an algebra. If $(k) = (k_1, \cdots, k_n) \in \underline{Z}^n$, set $s((k)) = k_1 + \cdots + k_n$; for any integer p, set $T_p = \sum_{s((k))=p} T_{(k)}$; then T is the direct sum of the modules T_p, and this direct sum decomposition defines on T the structure of a graded module (this is a generalization of the gradation of the tensor product of two modules by the total degree). It follows immediately from our definition of the multiplication in T that the product of an element of $T_{(k)}$ by an element of $T_{(k')}$ is in $T_{(k)+(k')}$, and therefore that the product of an element of T_p by an element of $T_{p'}$ is in $T_{p+p'}$. Thus, T is a graded algebra; we shall call this graded algebra a *tensor product of the graded algebras* $A_1, \cdots, A_n$.

Theorem 10. *Let $A_1, \cdots, A_n$ be graded algebras over a commutative ring R. Let $r_1, \cdots, r_h$ be integers $\geqslant 0$ such that $r_1 + \cdots + r_h = n$. Set $q_0 = 0$, $q_j = r_1 + \cdots + r_j$, and let U_j be a tensor product of the algebras $A_{q_{j-1}+1}, \cdots, A_{q_j}$; denote by T a tensor product of the algebras $A_1, \cdots, A_n$. Let ω be the isomorphism of the module T with $U_1 \otimes \cdots \otimes U_n$ which maps $a_1 \otimes \cdots \otimes a_n$ upon $(a_1 \otimes \cdots \otimes a_{q_1}) \otimes \cdots \otimes (a_{q_{h-1}+1} \otimes \cdots \otimes a_n)$ if $a_i \in A_i$ $(1 \leqslant i \leqslant n)$. Then ω is an isomorphism of the algebra T with the algebra $U_1 \otimes \cdots \otimes U_h$, and is homogeneous of degree 0.*

Let the subset S of T be defined as above. If $n = 0$, then $S = \{1\}$; if not, then, if $a_1 \otimes \cdots \otimes a_n$ (with each a_i homogeneous in A_i) belongs to S, $-a_1 \otimes \cdots \otimes a_n = (-a_1) \otimes \cdots \otimes a_n$ belongs to S; thus, the product of two elements of S is in S. Since S is a set of module generators of T, in order to prove that ω is an algebra homormophism, it will be sufficient to prove that $\omega(aa') = \omega(a)\omega(a')$ if a, a' are in S (cf. theorem 5, Chapter IV, Sect. 3 and Sect. 1). Set $a = a_1 \otimes \cdots \otimes a_n$, $a' = a'_1 \otimes \cdots \otimes a'_n$, with a_i homogeneous of degree k_i and a'_i homogeneous of degree k'_i. Set

$$b_j = a_{q_{j-1}+1} \otimes \cdots \otimes a_{q_j} \qquad b'_j = a'_{q_{j-1}+1} \otimes \cdots \otimes a'_{q_j}$$
$$c_j = (a_{q_{j-1}+1}a'_{q_{j-1}+1}) \otimes \cdots \otimes (a_{q_j}a'_{q_j})$$
$$d_j = k_{q_{j-1}+1} + \cdots + k_{q_j} \qquad d'_j = k'_{q_{j-1}+1} + \cdots + k'_{q_j}.$$

Denote by M the number $\sum_{i>i'} k_i k'_{i'}$, by M_j the number $\Sigma k_i k'_{i'}$ where the sum is extended to the pairs (i, i') such that $q_{j-1} + 1 \leqslant i' < i \leqslant q_j$, by M' the number $\sum_{j>j'} d_j d'_{j'}$. Then we have $aa' = (-1)^M (a_1a'_1) \otimes \cdots \otimes (a_na'_n)$ whence

$$\omega(aa') = (-1)^M c_1 \otimes \cdots \otimes c_h.$$

On the other hand, we have $\omega(a) = b_1 \otimes \cdots \otimes b_h$, $\omega(a') = b'_1 \otimes \cdots \otimes b'_h$, and b_j, b'_j are homogeneous of respective degrees d_j and d'_j, whence

$$\omega(a)\omega(a') = (-1)^{M'}(b_1b'_1) \otimes \cdots \otimes (b_hb'_h).$$

But $b_jb'_j$ is equal to $(-1)^{M_j}c_j$; it will therefore be sufficient to show that $M = M' + \sum_{j=1}^{h} M_j$. For each index i between 1 and n, denote by $p(i)$ the integer j between 1 and h such that $q_{j-1} + 1 \leqslant i \leqslant q_j$. If $i > i'$, then we have $p(i) \geqslant p(i')$; and, if i, i' are indices such that $p(i) > p(i')$, then $i > i'$. Denote by P the set of pairs (i, i') such that $1 \leqslant i' < i \leqslant n$; if j, j' are indices between 1 and h, let $P_{j,j'}$ be the set of pairs $(i, i') \in P$ such that $p(i) = j$, $p(i') = j'$. These sets are mutually disjoint, and their union is P; moreover, $P_{j,j'}$ is empty if $j < j'$; if $j > j'$, then $P_{j,j'}$ is the set of all pairs (i, i') such that $p(i) = j$, $p(i') = j'$. It follows that $\sum_{(i,i') \in P_{j,j'}} k_ik'_{i'} = d_jd'_{j'}$ if $j > j'$, $\sum_{(i,i') \in P_{j,j}} k_ik'_i = M_j$, which proves the formula $M = M' + \sum_{j=1}^{h} M_j$ Thus we have proved that ω is an algebra homomorphism (and therefore, isomorphism, since ω is a module isomorphism). On the other hand, if $a \in S_{(k)}$, $(k) = (k_1 \cdots, k_n)$, then each b_j is homogeneous of degree d_j (with the notation used above) and $\omega(a)$ is homogeneous of degree $\sum_{j=1}^{h} d_j = \sum_{i=1}^{n} k_i$, which shows that ω is homogeneous of degree 0.

Theorem 11. *Let $A_1, \cdots, A_n, B_1, \cdots B_n$ be graded algebras over a commutative ring R, all admitting $\underline{Z}$ as their group of degrees. For each i, let θ_i be a homogeneous homomorphism of degree 0 of A_i into B_i. Then $\theta_1 \otimes \cdots \otimes \theta_n$ is a homogeneous homomorphism of degree 0 of the graded algebra $A_1 \otimes \cdots \otimes A_n$ into $B_1 \otimes \cdots \otimes B_n$.*

Set $T = A_1 \otimes \cdots \otimes A_n$, and define the sets $A_{i,k}$, $S_{(k)}$, S as above; set $\theta = \theta_1 \otimes \cdots \otimes \theta_n$. The set S is a set of module generators of T and the product of any two elements of S is in S; thus, to prove that θ is an algebra homomorphism, it is sufficient to prove that $\theta(aa') = \theta(a)\theta(a')$ when a, a' belong to S. Set $a = a_1 \otimes \cdots \otimes a_n$, $a' = a'_1 \otimes \cdots \otimes a'_n$, with $a_i \in A_{i;k_i}$, $a'_i \in A_{i;k'_i}$. Then we have

$$aa' = (-1)^M(a_1a'_1) \otimes \cdots \otimes (a_na'_n)$$

with $M = \sum_{i>j} k_ik'_j$. Thus, $\theta(aa') = (-1)^M(\theta_1(a_1)\theta_1(a'_1)) \otimes \cdots \otimes (\theta_n(a_n)\theta_n(a'_n)))$ On the other hand, we have

$$\theta(a) = \theta_1(a_1) \otimes \cdots \otimes \theta_n(a_n) \qquad \theta(a') = \theta_1(a'_1) \otimes \cdots \otimes \theta_n(a'_n),$$

and, for each i, $\theta_i(a_i)$ and $\theta_i(a'_i)$ are homogeneous of respective degrees k_i and k'_i. It follows immediately that $\theta(aa') = \theta(a)\theta(a')$.

If we set $(k) = (k_1, \cdots, k_n)$, then, using the same notation as above, $\theta(a)$ is homogeneous of degree $k_1 + \cdots + k_n$ if $a \in S_{(k)}$. It follows immediately that the image under θ of any homogeneous element of degree p of T is homogeneous of degree p in $B_1 \otimes \cdots \otimes B_n$; this shows that θ is homogeneous of degree 0.

5. Anticommutative algebras

Let A be a graded algebra over a commutative ring R, having $\underline{Z}$ as its group of degrees; denote by A_k the module of homogeneous elements of degree k of A. The algebra A is called *anticommutative* if it satisfies the following conditions: if a, a' are homogeneous elements of A of respective degrees k and k', then $a'a = (-1)^{kk'}aa'$; if a is a homogeneous element of odd degree of A, then $a^2 = 0$. Observe that the first condition implies that $2a^2 = 0$ if a is homogeneous of odd degree; but it does not imply $a^2 = 0$, as follows for instance from the fact that $2a^2 = 0$ is satisfied for every commutative algebra over a field of characteristic 2.

In the subsequent discussion, we shall use the following notations. A finite sequence $\sigma = (i_1, \cdots, i_h)$ of integers will be called *strictly increasing* if $i_k < i_{k+1}$ for $1 \leqslant k < h$; the number h will be called the *length* of the sequence. If σ and τ are strictly increasing finite sequences of integers, we shall denote by $\sigma \vee \tau$ the strictly increasing sequence whose terms are the integers which occur either in σ or in τ, these integers being arranged by order of magnitude. We shall introduce a number $\eta(\sigma, \tau)$ defined as follows: $\eta(\sigma, \tau) = 0$ if some integer occurs both in σ and in τ; if not, then

$$\eta(\sigma, \tau) = (-1)^{N(\sigma, \tau)} \tag{1}$$

where $N(\sigma, \tau)$ is the number of pairs (i, j) of integers with the following properties: i occurs in σ, j occurs in τ and $i > j$.

Theorem 12. *Let A be a graded algebra over a commutative ring R, having $\underline{Z}$ as its group of degrees. Assume that A has a finite set $S = \{x_1, \cdots, x_n\}$ of generators which satisfies the following conditions: each x_i is homogeneous of odd degree d_i; we have $x_i^2 = 0$ and $x_ix_j + x_jx_i = 0$ $(1 \leqslant i, j \leqslant n)$. Then A is anticommutative. If $\sigma = (i_1, \cdots, i_h)$ is any strictly increasing sequence of integers between 1 and n, set $t(\sigma) = x_{i_1} \cdots x_{i_h}$. Then every element of A is a linear combination of the elements $t(\sigma)$, for all strictly increasing sequences σ; we have*

$$t(\sigma)t(\tau) = \eta(\sigma, \tau)t(\sigma \vee \tau) \tag{2}$$

for any two strictly increasing sequences σ and τ. If the condition $\alpha x_1 \cdots x_n = 0$ (where $\alpha \in R$) implies $\alpha = 0$, then the elements $t(\sigma)$ form a base of the module A.

We first show that, if $(i_1, \cdots, i_h)$ is any finite sequence (strictly increasing or not) of integers between 1 and n, and if there exist indices p and q such that $p < q$, $i_p = i_q$, then $x_{i_1} \cdots x_{i_h} = 0$. We proceed by induction on $q - p$. Our assertion is true if $q - p = 1$, since $x_{i_p}^2 = 0$. Assume that $q - p > 1$

and that our assertion is true for smaller values of $q-p$. Set $i'_k = i_k$ if $k < p$, $i'_p = i_{p+1}$, $i'_{p+1} = i_p$, $i'_k = i_k$ if $k > p+1$. Since $x_{i_p}x_{i_{p+1}} = -x_{i_{p+1}}x_{i_p}$, we have $x_{i_1}\cdots x_{i_h} = -x_{i'_1}\cdots x_{i'_h}$; but the right side of this equality is 0 by virtue of our inductive assumption, since $i'_{p+1} = i'_q$. This being said, we shall establish the validity of formula (2). This formula is true if there is an index which occurs in both σ and τ, because then $t(\sigma)t(\tau) = 0$ by what we have just proved, and $\eta(\sigma, \tau) = 0$. Assume now that this is not the case. Then we shall proceed by induction on the length h of σ. If $h = 0$, then $t(\sigma) = 1$, $N(\sigma, \tau) = 0$ and $\sigma \vee \tau = \tau$; the formula is therefore true in that case. Assume that $h > 0$ and that (2) is valid when σ is of length $< h$. If σ is of length h, we may write $\sigma = (i) \vee \sigma'$, where i is the first term of σ and where σ' is a strictly increasing sequence of length $h-1$ whose terms are $> i$. We then have $t(\sigma) = x_i t(\sigma')$, and therefore, by our inductive assumption, $t(\sigma)t(\tau) = \eta(\sigma', \tau)x_i t(\sigma' \vee \tau)$. Denote by p the number of terms of the sequence τ which are $< i$; we shall prove that $x_i t(\sigma' \vee \tau) = (-1)^p t(\sigma \vee \tau)$. Since all terms of σ' are $> i$, p is equal to the number of terms of $\sigma' \vee \tau$ which are $< i$, whence $p = N((i), \sigma' \vee \tau)$. If $h > 1$, then the formula $x_i t(\sigma' \vee \tau) = (-1)^p t(\sigma \vee \tau)$ follows from our inductive assumption, applied to the pair $((i), \sigma' \vee \tau)$. If $h = 1$, we proceed by induction on p. In that case, we have $\sigma' \vee \tau = \tau$. The formula is obvious if $p = 0$, for i is then the first term of $\sigma \vee \tau$. Assume that $p > 0$ and that the formula is true for smaller values of p. Set $\tau = (j_1, \cdots, j_m)$; then $x_i t(\tau) = -x_{j_1}x_i x_{j_2}\cdots x_{j_m}$, and the number of terms of the sequence $(j_2, \cdots, j_m)$ which are $< i$ is $p-1$, whence, by the inductive assumption $x_i x_{j_2}\cdots x_{j_m} = (-1)^{p-1}t((i) \vee \tau')$, if $\tau' = (j_2, \cdots, j_m)$, and $x_i t(\tau) = (-1)^p x_{j_1} t((i) \vee \tau') = (-1)^p t((i) \vee \tau)$, since j_1 is the first term of $(i) \vee \tau$. Thus we have $t(\sigma)t(\tau) = (-1)^p \eta(\sigma', \tau)t(\sigma \vee \tau)$. Since $N(\sigma, \tau)$ is obviously equal to $p + N(\sigma', \tau)$, formula (2) is proved in the case where σ is of length h.

If we denote by T the set composed of 0 and of the elements $t(\sigma)$, $-t(\sigma)$, for all strictly increasing sequences σ of integers between 1 and n, then T contains the set S of generators of A and formula (2) shows that the product of two elements of T is in T. Since $1 \in T$, it follows that every element of A is a linear combination of elements of T (cf. theorem 1, Chapter IV, Sect. 2).

If $\sigma = (i_1, \cdots, i_h)$, set $d(\sigma) = d_{i_1} + \cdots + d_{i_h}$; then $t(\sigma)$ is homogeneous of degree $d(\sigma)$. If $x = \Sigma_\sigma \alpha(\sigma)t(\sigma)$ (with $\alpha(\sigma) \in R$) is an element of A, then we may write $x = \Sigma_{p\in Z}(\Sigma_{d(\sigma)=p}\alpha(\sigma)t(\sigma))$, and, since $\Sigma_{d(\sigma)=p}\alpha(\sigma)t(\sigma)$ belongs to A_p, it is the homogeneous component of degree p of x. In particular, the elements $t(\sigma)$ for all σ such that $d(\sigma) = p$ form a set of module generators of A_p. If we prove that $\eta(\tau, \sigma) = (-1)^{d(\sigma)d(\tau)}\eta(\sigma, \tau)$ for any two strictly increasing sequences σ, τ, it will follow that $yx = (-1)^{pq}xy$ for any x in A_p and y in A_q.

The formula is obviously true if there is an index which occurs in both σ and τ. Assume that this is not the case, and denote by h and k the lengths of σ and τ. It is clear that $N(\sigma, \tau) + N(\tau, \sigma)$ is the number of all pairs (i, j) of integers such that i occurs in σ and j in τ; this number is therefore hk, whence $\eta(\tau, \sigma) = (-1)^{hk}\eta(\sigma, \tau)$. Since each d_i is odd, we have $d(\sigma) \equiv h \pmod 2$, $d(\tau) \equiv k \pmod 2$, and our formula is proved.

Let $x = \Sigma_{d(\sigma)=p}\alpha(\sigma)t(\sigma)$ be a homogeneous element of odd degree p. Let $\sigma_1, \cdots, \sigma_M$ be all the strictly increasing sequences of indices between 1 and n such that $d(\sigma) = p$. Then we have

$$x^2 = \Sigma_{1 \leqslant k < k' \leqslant M}\alpha(\sigma_k)\alpha(\sigma_{k'})(t(\sigma_k)t(\sigma_{k'}) + t(\sigma_{k'})t(\sigma_k)) + \Sigma_{k=1}^{M}(\alpha(\sigma_k))^2(t(\sigma_k))^2.$$

Since p is odd, we have $t(\sigma_k)t(\sigma_{k'}) + t(\sigma_{k'})t(\sigma_k) = 0$. Moreover, no σ_k may be the empty sequence, whence $(t(\sigma_k))^2 = 0$; therefore, we have $x^2 = 0$. This shows that A is anticommutative.

Assume now that the condition $\alpha x_1 \cdots x_n = 0$ implies $\alpha = 0$. Let there be given for each strictly increasing sequence σ of indices between 1 and n an element $\alpha(\sigma)$ of R; assume that the elements $\alpha(\sigma)$ are not all 0. Then we shall prove that $x = \Sigma_\sigma\alpha(\sigma)t(\sigma) \neq 0$. There is an integer h with the following properties: $\alpha(\sigma) = 0$ whenever σ is of length $< h$, but there is a σ_0 of length h such that $\alpha(\sigma_0) \neq 0$. Let τ be the strictly increasing sequence formed by the integers between 1 and n which do not occur in σ_0; then we have $xt(\tau) = \Sigma_\sigma\eta(\sigma, \tau)\alpha(\sigma)t(\sigma \vee \tau)$. If σ is of length $< h$, then $\alpha(\sigma) = 0$. If σ is of length $\geqslant h$ but is distinct from σ_0, then we see immediately that there is an index which occurs in both σ and τ, whence $\eta(\sigma, \tau) = 0$. Thus we have

$$xt(\tau) = \eta(\sigma_0, \tau)\alpha(\sigma_0)x_1 \cdots x_n$$

(because $\sigma_0 \vee \tau = (1, \cdots, n)$). The number $\eta(\sigma_0, \tau)$ is ± 1 and $\alpha(\sigma_0) \neq 0$; it follows that $xt(\tau) \neq 0$, whence $x \neq 0$. This shows that the elements $t(\tau)$ form a base of the module A. Theorem 12 is thereby proved.

Corollary. *Let A be a graded algebra admitting $\underline{Z}$ as its group of degrees. Assume that A admits a set S of generators with the following properties: the elements of S are homogeneous of odd degrees; if x, y are in S, then $yx = -xy$ and $x^2 = 0$. The algebra A is then anticommutative.*

Let t, u be homogeneous elements of A of respective degrees e and f. Since each of t, u may be written as a linear combination of products of elements of S, there is a finite subset S' of S such that t, u belong to the subalgebra A' of A generated by S'. The subalgebra A' is homogeneous, and it is anticommutative by theorem 12. Thus we have $ut = (-1)^{ef}tu$, and $t^2 = 0$ if e is odd.

Theorem 13. *Let A be an anticommutative graded algebra. If B is a homogeneous subalgebra of A, then B is anticommutative. If K is a homogeneous ideal in A, then A/K is anticommutative.*

This follows immediately from the definitions.

Theorem 14. *Let $A_1, \cdots, A_n$ be graded anticommutative algebras over a commutative ring R. Then $A_1 \otimes \cdots \otimes A_n$ is an anticommutative algebra.*

If p is any integer, let S_p be the set of elements of the form $a_1 \otimes \cdots \otimes a_n$ where, for each i, a_i is a homogeneous element of degree say k_i of A_i and where $\sum_{i=1}^n k_i = p$. Then it is clear that S_p is a set of module generators of the module T_p of homogeneous elements of degree p of $A_1 \otimes \cdots \otimes A_n$. Let p and q be integers; let $t = a_1 \otimes \cdots \otimes a_n$ and $u = b_1 \otimes \cdots \otimes b_n$ be elements of S_p and S_q respectively, with a_i homogeneous of degree k_i, b_i homogeneous of degree m_i, $\sum_{i=1}^n k_i = p$, $\sum_{i=1}^n m_i = q$. Set $N = \sum_{i>j} k_i m_j$, $N' = \sum_{i>j} m_i k_j$, whence

$$tu = (-1)^N (a_1 b_1) \otimes \cdots \otimes (a_n b_n); \qquad ut = (-1)^{N'} (b_1 a_1) \otimes \cdots \otimes (b_n a_n).$$

We have $b_i a_i = (-1)^{k_i m_i} a_i b_i$, and

$$N + \sum_{i=1}^n k_i m_i + N' = \sum_{i,j=1}^n k_i m_j = pq$$

whence $ut = (-1)^{pq} tu$. It follows immediately that we still have $ut = (-1)^{pq} tu$ whenever $t \in T_p$, $u \in T_q$. Now, assume that $t \in S_p$ and that p is odd. Using the same notation as above, we have $t^2 = (-1)^{N''} a_1^2 \otimes \cdots \otimes a_n^2$, with $N'' = \sum_{i>j} k_i k_j$; since $\sum_{i=1}^n k_i = p$ is odd, one at least of the integers k_i is odd; if k_i is odd, then $a_i^2 = 0$, whence $t^2 = 0$. Now, let $t = \sum_{k=1}^h \alpha_k t_k$ be any element of T_p (p odd), the t_k's being in S_p and the α_k's in R. Then we have

$$t^2 = \sum_{1 \leqslant k < k' \leqslant h} \alpha_k \alpha_{k'} (t_k t_{k'} + t_{k'} t_k) + \sum_{k=1}^h \alpha_k^2 t_k^2 = 0.$$

Theorem 14 is thereby proved.

Theorem 15. *Let A and B be graded algebras over a commutative ring R, admitting $\underline{Z}$ as their group of degrees. Let C be an anticommutative graded algebra over R. Let φ and ψ be homomorphisms of A and B into C; assume that φ and ψ are homogeneous of degree 0. Then there is a uniquely determined homomorphism θ of the algebra $A \otimes B$ into C such that $\theta(a \otimes b) = \varphi(a)\psi(b)$ if $a \in A$, $b \in B$; θ is homogeneous of degree 0.*

The mapping $(a, b) \to \varphi(a)\psi(b)$ of $A \times B$ into C is obviously bilinear. Therefore, there exists a unique linear mapping θ of $A \otimes B$ into C such that $\theta(a \otimes b) = \varphi(a)\psi(b)$ whenever $a \in A$, $b \in B$. Let S be the set of elements of the form $a \otimes b$, with a homogeneous in A and b homogeneous in B. Then S is a set of module generators of $A \otimes B$, and the product of two elements of S is in S. Thus, to prove that θ is an algebra homomorphism, it is sufficient to prove that $\theta(tt') = \theta(t)\theta(t')$ if t, t' are in S (theorem 1, Chapter IV, Sect. 2). Set $t = a \otimes b$, $t' = a' \otimes b'$, with a and a' in A, homogeneous of respective degrees p and p', and b and b' in B, homogeneous of respective degrees q and q'. We have $tt' = (-1)^{p'q} aa' \otimes bb'$, whence $\theta(tt') = (-1)^{p'q}\varphi(a)\varphi(a')\psi(b)\psi(b')$. The elements $\varphi(a')$ and $\psi(b)$ are homogeneous of respective degrees p' and q, whence

$$(-1)^{p'q}\varphi(a')\psi(b) = \psi(b)\varphi(a'),$$

and

$$\theta(tt') = \varphi(a)\psi(b)\varphi(a')\psi(b') = \theta(t)\theta(t').$$

Moreover, $\theta(t)$ is homogeneous of degree $p + q$. Since the module of homogeneous elements of degree r of $A \otimes B$ is generated by the elements $a \otimes b$, where $a \in A$ and $b \in B$ are homogeneous of respective degrees p, q such that $p + q = r$, we see that θ is homogeneous of degree 0.

6. Derivations

In this section, all graded algebras to be considered will be assumed to have the group $\underline{Z}$ of integers as their group of degrees.

Let $A = \sum_{n \in \underline{Z}} A_n$ be a graded algebra, A_n being the module of homogeneous elements of degree n of A. Since the sum $\sum_{n \in \underline{Z}} A_n$ is direct, there is a linear mapping J_A of the module A into itself such that $J_A(x) = (-)^n x$ for any $x \in A_n$. It is clear that $J_A \circ J_A$ is the identity mapping I of A; thus, $\{I, J_A\}$ is a group of automorphisms of the module A, and we may speak of $J_A{}^i$ whenever i is any integer; $J_A{}^i$ is I if i is even, J_A if i is odd. The mapping J_A is an automorphism of the algebra A. For, since the set of homogeneous elements is a set of module generators of A and is stable under multiplication, it will be sufficient to prove that $J_A(xy) = J_A(x)J_A(y)$ if x, y are homogeneous of respective degrees m and n; xy being then homogeneous of degree $m + n$, both sides of our equality are equal to $(-1)^{m+n}xy$. It is clear that J_A is homogeneous of degree 0; J_A is called the *main involution* of A. We shall use the symbol J_A without defining it again each time.

Lemma 1. *Let f be a homogeneous linear mapping of degree i of a graded algebra A into a graded algebra B. Then we have $J_B \circ f = (-1)^i f \circ J_A$.*

Since both sides of the equality are linear mappings, it is sufficient to verify that $J_B(f(x)) = (-1)^i f(J_A(x))$ when x is homogeneous of degree say n; $f(x)$ is then homogeneous of degree $n + i$, and both sides of the equality are equal to $(-1)^{n+i} f(x)$.

Let A and B be graded algebras, and f a homogeneous homomorphism of degree 0 of A into B. A linear mapping d of A into B is called an *f-derivation* (of degree i) of A into B if there exists an integer i such that d is homogeneous of degree i and such that

$$d(xy) = d(x)f(y) + J_B^i(f(x))d(y) \tag{1}$$

for any x, y in A. If $A = B$ and if f is the identity mapping of A, then an f-derivation of degree i of A into A is also called a *derivation of degree i of A.*

Let d and d' be f-derivations of the same degree i of A into B. Then $d + d'$ is still homogeneous of degree i, and it is clear that

$$(d + d')(xy) = (d + d')(x)f(y) + J_B^i(f(x))(d + d')(y)\,;$$

$d + d'$ is therefore an f-derivation of degree i. Similarly, if α is any element of the basic ring R (over which A and B are algebras), then αd is an f-derivation of degree i. Thus, the f-derivations of any given degree i of A into B form a submodule of the module of all linear mappings of A into B.

Theorem 16. *Let A, B, A', B' be graded algebras, g a homogeneous homomorphism of degree 0 of A' into A, h a homogeneous homomorphism of degree 0 of B into B' and f a homogeneous homomorphism of degree 0 of A into B. If d is an f-derivation of degree i of A into B, then $h \circ d \circ g$ is an $(h \circ f \circ g)$-derivation of degree i of A' into B'.*

It is clear that $h \circ d \circ g$ is homogeneous of degree i. Let x', y' be elements of A'. We have, if $x = g(x')$, $y = g(y')$,

$$(h \circ d \circ g)(x'y') = h(d(xy)) = h(d(x))h(f(y)) + h(J_B^i(f(x)))h(d(y)).$$

We have $h \circ J_B^i = J_{B'}^i \circ h$ by lemma 1. It follows that our expression is equal to $(h \circ d \circ g)(x')(h \circ f \circ g)(y') + J_{B'}^i((h \circ f \circ g)(x'))(h \circ d \circ g)(y')$ which proves theorem 16.

Theorem 17. *Let A and B be graded algebras, f a homogeneous homomorphism of degree 0 of A into B and d an f-derivation of degree i of A into B. Let S be a subset of A, A' the subalgebra of A generated by S and B' a homogeneous subalgebra of B. Then*: 1) *if $d(S) \subset B'$ and $f(S) \subset B'$, we have $d(A') \subset B'$* 2) *if $d(S) = \{0\}$, we have $d(A') = \{0\}$.*

First we observe that $d(1) = 0$; for we have

$$d(1) = d(1 \cdot 1) = d(1)f(1) + J_B^i(f(1))d(1) = 2d(1),$$

since $f(1)$ is the unit element of B, and therefore homogeneous of degree 0. Assume that $d(S) \subset B'$, $f(S) \subset B'$. Since f is a homomorphism, $\overset{-1}{f}(B')$ is a subalgebra of A; containing S, it contains A', whence $f(A') \subset B'$. Let A'_1 be the set of elements x of A' such that $d(x) \in B'$; this is a submodule of A', and we have $1 \in A'_1$, $S \subset A'_1$. Since B' is a homogeneous subalgebra of B, it is clear that $J_L(B') \subset B'$, whence $J_B{}^i(f(x)) \in B'$ if $x \in A_1'$. Let x and y be in A_1'; then it follows immediately from (1) that $xy \in A_1'$. This shows that A_1' is a subalgebra of A'; containing S, it is the whole of A', which proves the first assertion. Assume now that $d(S) = \{0\}$, and let A_2' be the kernel of d. It follows immediately from (1) that A_2' is a subalgebra of A (we have seen above that $1 \in A_2'$); containing S, it contains A', and theorem 17 is proved.

Corollary. *The notation being as in theorem* 17, *let d' be another f-derivation of A into B, of the same degree i as d. If d and d' coincide with each other on S, then they coincide with each other on the whole of A'.*

This follows immediately from theorem 17 and from the fact that $d' - d$ is an f-derivation.

Theorem 17 a. *Let A and B be graded algebras, f a homogeneous homomorphism of degree* 0 *of A into B and d an f-derivation of degree i of A into B. Let K be the kernel of f and S a set of ideal generators of K; denote by π the natural mapping of A on A/K, and by g the homomorphism of A/K into B such that $g \circ \pi = f$. If $d(S) = \{0\}$, then d maps K upon $\{0\}$, and there exists a g-derivation $\bar{d}$ of A/K into B, of degree i, such that $\bar{d} \circ \pi = d$; $\bar{d}$ is uniquely determined.*

It will be observed that K, being the kernel of a homogeneous homomorphism f, is itself a homogeneous ideal; thus, A/K has the structure of a graded algebra, and π, g are homogeneous homomorphisms of degree 0. Let K' be the set of elements $x \in K$ such that $d(x) = 0$. If $x \in K'$, $y \in A$, then $d(x) = f(x) = 0$, and it follows immediately from formula (1) that $d(xy) = d(yx) = 0$; since K' is a submodule of K it is an ideal (theorem 2, Chapter IV, Sect. 3); containing S, it is identical to K, whence $d(K) = \{0\}$. It follows that there exists a unique linear mapping $\bar{d}$ of A/K into B such that $\bar{d} \circ \pi = d$. Let $\bar{x}$ be a homogeneous element of degree n of A/K; we may write $\bar{x} = \pi(x)$, where x is homogeneous of degree n in A, whence $\bar{d}(\bar{x}) = d(x)$, which shows that $\bar{d}(\bar{x})$ is homogeneous of degree $n + i$; $\bar{d}$ is therefore homogeneous of degree i. Now, let $\bar{x} = \pi(x)$, $\bar{y} = \pi(y)$ be any elements of A/K (with x, y in A). We have

$$\begin{aligned}\bar{d}(\bar{x}\bar{y}) &= \bar{d}(\pi(xy)) = d(xy) = d(x)f(y) + J_B{}^i(f(x))d(y)\\ &= \bar{d}(\bar{x})g(\bar{y}) + J_B{}^i(g(\bar{x}))\bar{d}(\bar{y}),\end{aligned}$$

which shows that $\bar{d}$ is a g-derivation of degree i.

From now on, we shall consider derivations of a fixed graded algebra A (into itself); the main involution of A will be denoted by J. If $x \in A$, we shall denote by L_x the operator of left multiplication by x in A. It is clear that $x \to L_x$ is a linear mapping of A into the module of linear endomorphisms of A; moreover, since $x(yz) = (xy)z$ if x, y, z are in A, we have

$L_{xy} = L_x \circ L_y$. If x is homogeneous of degree n, then L_x is a homogeneous linear mapping of degree n. Let d be a homogeneous linear mapping of degree i of A into itself; in order for d to be a derivation of degree i, we must have

$$d(xy) = d(x)y + J^i(x)d(y)$$

whenever x and y are in A. This condition may also be formulated as follows: we must have

$$d \circ L_x = L_{d(x)} + L_{J^i(x)} \circ d. \tag{2}$$

Theorem 18. *Let d and e be derivations of respective degrees i and j of A. Then $d \circ e - (-1)^{ij} e \circ d$ is a derivation of degree $i + j$ of A. If i is odd, then $d \circ d$ is a derivation of degree $2i$ of A.*

It is clear that $d \circ e - (-1)^{ij} e \circ d$ is homogeneous of degree $i + j$ and $d \circ d$ homogeneous of degree $2i$. Let x be an element of A. Applying (2), we obtain

$$\begin{aligned} d \circ e \circ L_x &= d \circ L_{e(x)} + d \circ L_{J^j(x)} \circ e \\ &= L_{(d \circ e)(x)} + L_{J^i(e(x))} \circ d + L_{d(J^j(x))} \circ e + L_{J^{i+j}(x)} \circ d \circ e, \end{aligned}$$

and, by interchanging the roles played by d and e,

$$e \circ d \circ L_x = L_{(e \circ d)(x)} + L_{J^j(d(x))} \circ e + L_{e(J^i(x))} \circ d + L_{J^{i+j}(x)} \circ e \circ d.$$

Making use of lemma 1, we have $J^i \circ e = (-1)^{ij} e \circ J^i$, $d \circ J^j = (-)^{ij} J^j \circ d$; it follows that, if we set $\partial = d \circ e - (-1)^{ij} e \circ d$, then we have

$$\partial \circ L_x = L_{\partial(x)} + L_{J^{i+j}(x)} \circ \partial,$$

which shows that ∂ is a derivation. On the other hand, we have

$$J^i \circ d + d \circ J^i = J^i \circ d + (-1)^{i^2} J^i \circ d = 0$$

if i is odd; the first of our formulas then shows that $d \circ d$ is a derivation.

7. Exterior algebras

Let M be a module over a commutative ring R. We shall call an *exterior algebra on M* an object constituted by an algebra E over R and by a linear mapping ψ of M into E with the following properties: *a*) we have $(\psi(x))^2 = 0$ for every $x \in M$; *b*) it φ is any linear mapping of M into an algebra A over R such that $(\varphi(x))^2 = 0$ for every $x \in M$, then there exists a unique homomorphism f of E into A such that $f \circ \psi = \varphi$.

If (E, ψ) and (E', ψ') are exterior algebras on the same module M, then there exists a unique isomorphism J of E with E' such that $J \circ \psi = \psi'$; moreover, $\psi(M)$ is a set of generators of the algebra E. These statements are proved exactly in the same way as the corresponding statements for free monoids, free modules, etc.

We shall now construct an exterior algebra on a module M. Let (T, θ) be a tensor algebra on M. Denote by F the ideal of T which is generated by the elements $(\theta(x))^2$, for $x \in M$, by E the algebra T/F and by π the natural mapping of T on E; set $\psi = \pi \circ \theta$. Then ψ is a linear mapping of M into E; if $x \in M$, we have $(\psi(x))^2 = \pi((\theta(x))^2) = 0$ since $(\theta(x))^2$ belongs to F. Let φ be a linear mapping of M into an algebra A such that $(\varphi(x))^2 = 0$ for all $x \in M$. Since (T, θ) is a tensor algebra on M, there exists a homomorphism g of T into A such that $g \circ \theta = \varphi$. If x is an element of M, then $g((\theta(x))^2) = (\varphi(x))^2 = 0$, which shows that $(\theta(x))^2$ is in the kernel of g. This kernel therefore contains F, and g may be factored in the form $g = f \circ \pi$, where f is a homomorphism of E into A (theorem 3, Chapter IV, Sect. 3). We have $f \circ \psi = f \circ \pi \circ \theta = g \circ \theta = \varphi$. Since $\theta(M)$ is a set of generators of the algebra T, $\pi(\theta(M)) = \psi(M)$ is a set of generators of E, which shows that there cannot exist more than one homomorphism f of E into A such that $f \circ \psi = \varphi$; (E, ψ) is therefore an exterior algebra on M.

The ideal F constructed above is generated by the elements $(\theta(x))^2$, which are homogeneous of degree 2 in T; F is therefore a homogeneous ideal (theorem 4, Sect. 2). It follows that $E = T/F$ has a structure of graded algebra, with $\underline{Z}$ as its group of degrees. The module E_n of homogeneous elements of degree n of E is the image under π of the module T_n of homogeneous elements of degree n of T. We have $T_n = \{0\}$ if $n < 0$; if $n \geqslant 0$, then T_n consists of the linear combinations of the products in T of n elements of $T_1 = \theta(M)$. It follows immediately that $E_n = \{0\}$ if $n < 0$, while, for $n \geqslant 0$, E_n consists of the linear combinations of products in E of n elements of $E_1 = \psi(M)$.

Since F is generated by elements belonging to T_2, E is a regularly graded algebra and π induces an isomorphism of $T_1 = \theta(M)$ with $\psi(M)$ (theorem 5, Sect. 2). Since θ is an isomorphism of M with $\theta(M)$, ψ is an isomorphism of M with $\psi(M)$.

Taking into account the isomorphism theorem for exterior algebras, we obtain the following results:

Theorem 19. *Let (E, ψ) be an exterior algebra on a module M. Then E has the structure of a regularly graded algebra in which the homogeneous elements of degree 1 are those of $\psi(M)$; for any $n \geqslant 0$, the homogeneous elements of degree n are the linear combinations of products of n elements of $\psi(M)$. The mapping ψ is an isomorphism of M with $\psi(M)$.*

Corollary. *If $n \geqslant 0$, then every homogeneous element of degree $n + 1$ of E is a linear combination of products of the form xt, where x is in $\psi(M)$*

and t homogeneous of degree n; it is also a linear combination of products of the form tx (with the same specifications on x and t).

This follows immediately from theorem 19.

An element of E which is a product of a certain number of elements of $\psi(M)$ is called *decomposable.*

Theorem 20. *An exterior algebra (E, ψ) on a module M is anticommutative.*

It is clear that $\psi(M)$ is a set of generators of E. If x and y are in M, then we have $(\psi(x))^2 = 0$, $(\psi(y))^2 = 0$ and

$$0 = (\psi(x + y))^2 = (\psi(x))^2 + (\psi(y))^2 + \psi(x)\psi(y) + \psi(y)\psi(x),$$

whence $\psi(x)\psi(y) + \psi(y)\psi(x) = 0$. The elements of $\psi(M)$ being homogeneous of degree 1, theorem 20 follows from the corollary to theorem 12, Sect. 5.

Corollary. *Let a, b, c be elements of E and x an element of $\psi(M)$; then we have $axbxc = 0$.*

For, let $b = \Sigma_{n \in \underline{Z}} b_n$ be the decomposition of b into its homogeneous components. Then $xbx = \Sigma_{n \in \underline{Z}} xb_n x = \Sigma_{n \in \underline{Z}} (-1)^n x^2 b_n = 0$.

Let (E, ψ) be an exterior algebra on a module M and f a linear mapping of M into a module M'; let (E', ψ') be an exterior algebra on M'. Then $\psi' \circ f$ is a linear mapping of M into E', and we have $((\psi' \circ f)(x))^2 = 0$ for every $x \in$ M; it follows that there exists a unique homomorphism $\bar{f}$ of E into E' such that $\bar{f} \circ \psi = \psi' \circ f$; $\bar{f}$ is called the *prolongation of f* ($\bar{f}$ depends of course on the choices of the exterior algebras (E, ψ) and (E', ψ')). Since $\bar{f}$ maps $\psi(M)$ into $\psi'(M')$, it is homogeneous of degree 0 (as follows from theorem 19). Let g be a linear mapping of M' into a third module M'', (E'', ψ'') an exterior algebra on M$''$ and $\bar{g}$ the prolongation of g to E'. Then $\bar{g} \circ \bar{f}$ is a homomorphism of E into E'', and we have

$$g \circ \bar{f} \circ \psi = \bar{g} \circ \psi' \circ f = \psi'' \circ g \circ f,$$

which proves that $\bar{g} \circ \bar{f}$ is the prolongation of $g \circ f$.

Theorem 21. *Let f be an epimorphism of a module M on a module M', and let N be the kernel of f. Let (E, ψ) and (E', ψ') be exterior algebras on M and M' respectively, and $\bar{f}$ the prolongation of f. Then $\bar{f}$ is an epimorphism, and its kernel is the ideal generated by $\psi(N)$ in E.*

The algebra $\bar{f}(E)$ contains $\bar{f}(\psi(M)) = \psi'(f(M)) = \psi'(M')$, which is a set of generators of E'; it follows that $\bar{f}(E) = E'$. If $x \in$ N, then

$$\bar{f}(\psi(x)) = \psi'(f(x)) = 0;$$

therefore, the kernel of $\bar{f}$ contains $\psi(N)$, and also the ideal K generated by $\psi(N)$. Let π be the natural homomorphism of E on E/K; the kernel of $\pi \circ \psi$ contains N since $\psi(N) \subset K$. It follows that there exists

One may presume that this (type of) theorem "motivates" the definition of tensor product of graded algebras (p. 156).

a linear mapping h of M' into E/K such that $h \circ f = \pi \circ \psi$; if $x' \in M'$, and if $x \in M$ is such that $f(x) = x'$, then $h(x') = \pi(\psi(x))$, whence

$$(h(x'))^2 = \pi((\psi(x))^2) = 0.$$

This shows that there exists a homomorphism $\bar{h}$ of E' into E/K such that $\bar{h} \circ \psi' = h$. The mapping $\bar{h} \circ \bar{f}$ is a homomorphism of E into E/K; if $x \in M$, then $(\bar{h} \circ \bar{f})(\psi(x)) = \bar{h}(\psi'(f(x))) = h(f(x)) = \pi(\psi(x))$. Since $\bar{h} \circ \bar{f}$ coincides with π on the set of generators $\psi(M)$ of E, we have $\bar{h} \circ \bar{f} = \pi$. If t is an element of the kernel of $\bar{f}$, then we have $\pi(t) = \bar{h}(\bar{f}(t)) = 0$, whence $t \in K$; this shows that K is the kernel of $\bar{f}$.

Theorem 22. *Let M be a module which is the direct sum of two submodules N and P; let (E, ψ) be an exterior algebra on M. Denote by ψ_N and ψ_P the restrictions of ψ to N and P, and by E_N and E_P the subalgebras of E generated by $\psi(N)$ and $\psi(P)$ respectively. Then (E_N, ψ_N) and (E_P, ψ_P) are exterior algebras on N and on P. There is an isomorphism f of E with the algebra $E_N \otimes E_P$ such that $f(\psi(y + z)) = \psi_N(y) \otimes 1 + 1 \otimes \psi_P(z)$ if $y \in N$, $z \in P$; f is homogeneous of degree 0 when we consider $E_N \otimes E_P$ as graded by the total degree. We have $f(t) = t \otimes 1$ if $t \in E_N$, $f(u) = 1 \otimes u$ if $u \in E_P$.*

Since $M = N + P$ is a direct sum, there is a linear mapping f_1 of M into $E_N \otimes E_P$ such that $f_1(y + z) = \psi_N(y) \otimes 1 + 1 \otimes \psi_P(z)$ if $y \in N$, $z \in P$. We have

$$(f_1(y + z))^2 = (\psi_N(y))^2 \otimes 1 + \psi_N(y) \otimes \psi_P(z) - \psi_N(y) \otimes \psi_P(z) + 1 \otimes (\psi_P(z))^2 = 0,$$

because $(1 \otimes \psi_P(z))(\psi_N(y) \otimes 1) = -\psi_N(y) \otimes \psi_P(z)$, since $\psi_N(y)$ and $\psi_P(z)$ are homogeneous of degree 1. It follows that there exists a homomorphism f of E into $E_N \otimes E_P$ such that $f \circ \psi = f_1$. The elements of $f(\psi(M))$ are homogeneous of total degree 1 in $E_N \otimes E_P$; since $\psi(M)$ generates E, f is homogeneous of degree 0. The mapping $t \to t \otimes 1$ is obviously a homomorphism of E_N into $E_N \otimes E_P$. Since $f(\psi_N(y)) = \psi_N(y) \otimes 1$ when $y \in N$ and since $\psi_N(N)$ generates E_N, we have $f(t) = t \otimes 1$ for every $t \in E_N$; we see in the same way that $f(u) = 1 \otimes u$ if $u \in E_P$.

Since E_N, E_P and E are anticommutative, there is a homomorphism g of $E_N \otimes E_P$ into E such that $g(t \otimes u) = tu$ if $t \in E_N$, $u \in E_P$ (theorem 15, Sect. 5). The mapping $g \circ f$ is a homomorphism of E into itself, which maps every element of either E_N or E_P upon itself; since $E_N \cup E_P$ contains $\psi(N) \cup \psi(P)$, which is a set of generators of E (because $\psi(M) = \psi(N) + \psi(P)$), $g \circ f$ is the identity mapping of E on itself. It follows immediately that f is a monomorphism. On the other hand, if $t \in E_N$, $u \in E_P$, then $t \otimes u = (t \otimes 1)(1 \otimes u) = f(t)f(u) = f(tu)$; it follows that $f(E)$ contains every element of the form $t \otimes u$, whence $f(E) = E_N \otimes E_P$; f is therefore an isomorphism. The mapping g is homogeneous of degree 0 if $E_N \otimes E_P$ is graded by the total degree (theorem 15, Sect. 5); it follows that f is homogeneous of degree 0. There remains only to prove that (E_N, ψ_N) and (E_P, ψ_P) are exterior algebras on N and P respectively. Let φ be any linear mapping of N into an algebra A, such that $(\varphi(y))^2 = 0$ for every $y \in N$. Let p_N be the projector of M on N relative to the direct sum decomposition $M = N + P$; then $\varphi' = \varphi \circ p_N$ is a linear mapping of M into A, and we have $(\varphi'(x))^2 = 0$ for every $x \in M$. It follows that there exists a homomorphism h of E into A such that $h \circ \psi = \varphi'$. If h_N is the restriction of h to E_N, then it is clear that $h_N \circ \psi_N = \varphi$. This property characterizes entirely the homomorphism h_N, since $\psi_N(N)$ generates E_N; thus, (E_N, ψ_N) is an exterior algebra on N. We would see in the same way that (E_P, ψ_P) is an exterior algebra on P.

Corollary 1. *Let M and M' be modules over the same commutative ring, (E, ψ) an exterior algebra on M and (E', ψ') an exterior algebra on M'. Let ψ'' be the mapping of $M \times M'$ into $E \otimes E'$ defined by the formula*

$$\psi''(x, x') = \psi(x) \otimes 1 + 1 \otimes \psi'(x') \qquad (x \in M, \quad x' \in M').$$

Then $(E \otimes E', \psi'')$ is an exterior algebra on $M \times M'$.

The sets $M_1 = M \times \{0\}$ and $M_2 = \{0\} \times M'$ are submodules of $M \times M'$, and $M \times M'$ is their direct sum. Let (F, θ) be an exterior algebra on $M \times M'$; let F_i be the subalgebra of F generated by M_i $(i = 1, 2)$, and θ_i the restriction of θ to M_i. Then (F_i, θ_i) is an exterior algebra on M_i (theorem 22); therefore, there exist isomorphisms j of E with F_1 and j' of E' with F_2 such that

$$j(\psi(x)) = \theta_1(x, 0) \ (x \in M), \qquad j'(\psi'(x')) = \theta_2(0, x') \ (x' \in M'),$$

On the other hand, there is an isomorphism f of F with $F_1 \otimes F_2$ which maps $\theta(x, x')$ upon $\theta_1(x, 0) \otimes 1 + 1 \otimes \theta_2(0, x')$. Thus $\overset{-1}{f} \circ (j_1 \otimes j_2)$ is an isomorphism of $E \otimes E'$ with F; if $x \in M$, $x' \in M'$, our isomorphism maps $\psi(x) \otimes 1 + 1 \otimes \psi'(x')$ upon $\theta(x, x')$, which proves the corollary.

Corollary 2. *Let M be a module over a commutative ring, (E, ψ) an exterior algebra on M, N a submodule of M and (F, ψ_N) an exterior algebra on N. If N is a direct summand in M, then the prolongation of the identity mapping of N into M is an isomorphism of F with the subalgebra of E generated by $\psi(N)$.*

This follows immediately from theorem 22.

A remark on terminology.

Let M be a module over a commutative ring. Then there exists an exterior algebra (E, ψ) on M such that M is a subset of E and ψ the identity mapping of M into E. For, let (E_1, ψ_1) be any exterior algebra on M. Let E_1' be the set of elements of E_1 which do not belong to $\psi_1(M)$. It is easily seen that there exists a set E' which is equipotent to E'_1 and which has no element in common with M. Let then E be the set $M \cup E'$. If f' is a bijection of E' on E'_1, there is a bijection f of E on E_1 which extends ψ_1 and f'. We may define an algebra structure on the set E by the condition that f be an isomorphism of this algebra with E_1. If ψ is the identity mapping of M into E, then we have $f \circ \psi = \psi_1$. It follows immediately that (E, ψ) is an exterior algebra on M.

In the future, when we shall speak of an exterior algebra E on M without specifying any mapping of M into E, we shall mean that M is a subset of E and that, if ψ_0 is the identity mapping of M into E, then (E, ψ_0) is an exterior algebra on M in the sense previously defined. This clearly implies that M is a submodule of E. If (E, ψ) is any exterior algebra on M, then E is an exterior algebra on $\psi(M)$.

8. Grassmann algebras

Let M be a module over a commutative ring R and E an exterior algebra on M. Let ι be the linear mapping of the module $M \times M$ into $E \otimes E$ defined by $\iota(x, y) = x \otimes 1 + 1 \otimes y$ (x, y in M). Then we know that $(E \otimes E, \iota)$ is an exterior algebra on $M \times M$ (corollary 1 to theorem 22, Sect. 7). Let υ be the linear mapping of M into $M \times M$ defined by $\upsilon(x) = (x, x)$ ($x \in M$); denote by U the prolongation of υ to E. This homomorphism of E into $E \otimes E$, which plays an important role in the theory of exterior algebras, is called the *analyzing mapping.* It is homogeneous of degree 0 if $E \otimes E$ is graded by the total degree.

Lemma 1. *Let f be a linear mapping of M into a module N, F an exterior algebra on N, $\bar{f}$ the prolongation of f to E, U and V the analyzing mappings of E and F. Then we have $(\bar{f} \otimes \bar{f}) \circ U = V \circ \bar{f}$.*

The mapping $\bar{f} \otimes \bar{f}$ is an algebra homomorphism (theorem 11, Sect. 4). Thus, both sides of the formula to be proved are homomorphisms of E into $F \otimes F$; it will be sufficient to show that $(\bar{f} \otimes \bar{f})(U(x)) = V(\bar{f}(x))$ if $x \in M$. The left side is equal to $(\bar{f} \otimes \bar{f})(x \otimes 1 + 1 \otimes x) = \bar{f}(x) \otimes 1 + 1 \otimes \bar{f}(x)$; this is also the value of the right side, and lemma 1 is proved.

Let I be the identity mapping of E onto itself. Then $(U \otimes I) \circ U$ is a homomorphism of E into $(E \otimes E) \otimes E$, while $(I \otimes U) \circ U$ is a homomorphism of E into $E \otimes (E \otimes E)$. Let ω_E be the canonical isomorphism of $(E \otimes E) \otimes E$ with $E \otimes (E \otimes E)$; then we have

$$\omega_E \circ (U \otimes I) \circ U = (I \otimes U) \circ U. \tag{1}$$

For, both sides are homomorphisms of E into $E \otimes (E \otimes E)$; it will therefore be sufficient to show that they have the same effect on an element x of M.

We have $((U \otimes I) \circ U)(x) = (x \otimes 1 + 1 \otimes x) \otimes 1 + (1 \otimes 1) \otimes x$; the image of this element by ω_E is $x \otimes (1 \otimes 1) + 1 \otimes (x \otimes 1 + 1 \otimes x)$; this is also the value of $((I \otimes U) \circ U)(x)$, which proves formula (1).

Let $x_1, \cdots, x_n$ be elements of M; if σ is a strictly increasing sequence of indices between 1 and n, set

$$t(\sigma) = x_{i_1} \cdots x_{i_h}$$

if $\sigma = (i_1, \cdots, i_h)$. Using the same notation for sequences as in Sect. 5, we shall prove the formula

$$(2) \qquad \boxed{U(x_1 \cdots x_n) = \Sigma_\sigma \eta(\sigma, \sigma^*) t(\sigma) \otimes t(\sigma^*)},$$

where the summation is extended to all strictly increasing sequences σ of indices between 1 and n, and where σ^* denotes the sequence whose terms are the indices which do not occur in σ, arranged by order of magnitude. Set $y_{i1} = x_i \otimes 1$, $y_{i2} = 1 \otimes x_i$; then we have

$$U(x_1 \cdots x_n) = \Pi_{i=1}^n (y_{i1} + y_{i2}) = \Sigma_p (\Pi_{i=1}^n y_{i,p(i)})$$

where the summation is extended to all mappings p of $\{1, \cdots, n\}$ into $\{1, 2\}$. Let p be one of these mappings; assume that $p(i) = 1$ when $i = i_1, \cdots, i_h$ (with $i_1 < \cdots < i_h$), while $p(i) = 2$ for the other values of i. Set $\sigma_p = (i_1, \cdots, i_h)$; applying formula (2), Sect. 5 to the anticommutative algebra $E \otimes E$, we obtain

$$\Pi_{i=1}^n y_{i,p(i)} = \eta(\sigma_p, \sigma_p^*)(y_{i_1,1} \cdots y_{i_h,1})(y_{k_1,2} \cdots y_{k_{n-h},2}),$$

where we have set $\sigma_p^* = (k_1, \cdots, k_{n-h})$. The mapping $t \to t \otimes 1$ being a homomorphism of E into $E \otimes E$, we have $y_{i_1,1} \cdots y_{i_h,1} = t(\sigma_p) \otimes 1$; we see in the same way that $y_{k_1,2} \cdots y_{k_{n-h},2} = 1 \otimes t(\sigma^*)$. Moreover, it is clear that $p \to \sigma_p$ is a bijection of the set of mappings of $\{1, \cdots, n\}$ into $\{1, 2\}$ on the set of strictly increasing sequences of indices between 1 and n; formula (2) is thereby proved.

Denote by E_n the module of homogeneous elements of degree n of E; then E is the direct sum of E_0 and of $\Sigma_{n \neq 0} E_n$, and $\{1\}$ is a base of E_0. It follows that there exists a linear form ε on E which maps 1 upon the unit element 1_R of R and E_n upon $\{0\}$ if $n \neq 0$. In the notation of formula (2), we have $\varepsilon(t(\sigma)) = 1$ if σ is the empty sequence, $\varepsilon(t(\sigma)) = 0$ otherwise. If I is the identity mapping of E, then $\varepsilon \otimes I$ and $I \otimes \varepsilon$ are linear mappings of $E \otimes E$ into $R \otimes E = E$ and $E \otimes R = E$ respectively. It follows from formula (2) that we have $(\varepsilon \otimes 1)(U(x_1 \cdots x_n)) = (I \otimes \varepsilon)(U(x_1 \cdots x_n)) = x_1 \cdots x_n$ whence

$$(3) \qquad (\varepsilon \otimes I) \circ U = I, \qquad (I \otimes \varepsilon) \circ U = I.$$

Let ζ be the canonical automorphism of the *module* $E \otimes E$ (not of the *algebra* $E \otimes E$!) which maps $t \otimes u$ upon $u \otimes t$ whenever $t, u \in E$. The notation being as in formula (2), we have $\eta(\sigma, \sigma^*) = (-1)^{h(n-h)}\eta(\sigma^*, \sigma)$ if σ is a sequence of length h. For, denote by N the number of pairs (i, j) such that i occurs in σ, j in σ^* and $i > j$, and by N^* the number of pairs (i, j) such that i occurs in σ^*, j in σ and $i > j$; then we have $\eta(\sigma, \sigma^*) = (-1)^N$, $\eta(\sigma^*, \sigma) = (-1)^{N^*}$, and $N + N^*$ is the number of all pairs (i, j) such that i occurs in σ and j in σ^*, i. e., it is $h(n-h)$. Thus we have

$$\zeta(U(x_1 \cdots x_n)) = \Sigma_\sigma(-1)^{h(\sigma)(n-h(\sigma))}\eta(\sigma^*, \sigma)t(\sigma^*) \otimes t(\sigma),$$

where $h(\sigma)$ denotes the length of σ. The module $E \otimes E$ is the direct sum of the modules $E_m \otimes E_n$, for all $(m, n) \in \underline{Z} \times \underline{Z}$; denote by K the automorphism of the module $E \otimes E$ which maps every element w of $E_m \otimes E_n$ upon $(-1)^{mn}w$. Then we obtain the formula

$$\zeta \circ U = K \circ U. \tag{4}$$

If $t \in E$, we set

$$U(t) = \Sigma_{m,n} U_{m,n}(t), \qquad U_{m,n}(t) \varepsilon E_m \otimes E_n;$$

$U_{m,n}(t)$ is therefore the homogeneous component of degree (m, n) of $U(t)$ in the gradation of $E \otimes E$ by the bidegree. If t is homogeneous of degree p, then $U_{m,n}(t) = 0$ if $m + n \neq p$, since U is homogeneous of degree 0 relative to the gradation of $E \otimes E$ by the total degree. *If m is odd, then, for any $t \in E$, $U_{m,m}(t)$ belongs to the submodule of $E_m \otimes E_m$ generated by the elements of the form $u \otimes v - v \otimes u$* (with u and v in E_m). It is sufficient to prove this in the case where $t = x_1 \cdots x_{2m}$, with $x_i \in M$ $(1 \leqslant i \leqslant 2m)$; in that case, we may decompose the set of strictly increasing sequences of length m of indices between 1 and $2m$ into two mutually disjoint sets S, S^* such that the conditions $\sigma \in S$, $\sigma^* \in S^*$ are equivalent to each other. Since $\eta(\sigma^*, \sigma) = -\eta(\sigma, \sigma^*)$ when σ is of length m, we have

$$U_{m,m}(t) = \Sigma_{\sigma \in S}\eta(\sigma, \sigma^*)(t(\sigma) \otimes t(\sigma^*) - t(\sigma^*) \otimes t(\sigma)),$$

which proves our assertion. We see in the same way that, if m is even and > 0, then $U_{m,m}(t)$ is a linear combination of elements of the form $u \otimes v + v \otimes u$, with u, v in E_m.

Now, let A and B be modules over R. Let φ and ψ be linear mappings of E into A and B respectively; then we set

$$\varphi \wedge \psi = (\varphi \otimes \psi) \circ U;$$

$\varphi \wedge \psi$ is therefore a linear mapping of E into $A \otimes B$. It is clear that $(\varphi, \psi) \to \varphi \wedge \psi$ is a bilinear mapping of $\mathrm{Hom}(E, A) \times \mathrm{Hom}(E, B)$ into $\mathrm{Hom}(E, A \otimes B)$.

Let C be a third module over R, and θ an element of $\mathrm{Hom}(E, C)$. Denote by $\omega_{A,B,C}$ the canonical mapping of $(A \otimes B) \otimes C$ into $A \otimes (B \otimes C)$. Then we have

$$\omega_{A,B,C} \circ ((\varphi \wedge \psi) \wedge \theta) = \varphi \wedge (\psi \wedge \theta). \tag{5}$$

In fact, the left side is

$$\omega_{A,B,C} \circ ((((\varphi \otimes \psi) \circ U) \otimes \theta) \circ U) = \omega_{A,B,C} \circ ((\varphi \otimes \psi) \otimes \theta) \circ (U \otimes I) \circ U.$$

We have $\omega_{A,B,C} \circ ((\varphi \otimes \psi) \otimes \theta) = (\varphi \otimes (\psi \otimes \theta)) \circ \omega_E$, where ω_E is the canonical isomorphism of $(E \otimes E) \otimes E$ with $E \otimes (E \otimes E)$ (cf. formula (3), Chapter III, Sect. 10), and $\omega_E \circ (U \otimes I) \circ U = (I \otimes U) \circ U$ by formula (1). Thus the left side is $(\varphi \otimes (\psi \otimes \theta)) \circ (I \otimes U) \circ U$, which can also be written as $(\varphi \otimes ((\psi \otimes \theta) \circ U)) \circ U = \varphi \wedge (\psi \wedge \theta)$, and our formula is proved.

For any module A, we take $A \otimes R = R \otimes A = A$; then, if A, B, C are three modules over R of which one is R itself, $\omega_{A,B,C}$ is the identity mapping. Taking $A = B = R$, we see that $(\varphi, \psi) \to \varphi \wedge \psi$ is a law of composition in Hom (E, R), which is the dual module E^* of E. It follows from (5) that this law of composition is associative. The linear form ε being defined as above, it follows from (3) that

$$\varepsilon \wedge \varphi = (\varepsilon \otimes \varphi) \circ U = (I_R \otimes \varphi) \circ (\varepsilon \otimes I) \circ U = I_R \otimes \varphi = \varphi,$$

if φ is any linear mapping of E into a module (where I_R is the identity mapping of R); and we see in the same way that $\varphi \wedge \varepsilon = \varphi$. In particular, ε is a unit element for the law of composition $(\varphi, \psi) \to \varphi \wedge \psi$ in E^*. Thus, E^*, with this law of composition, is an algebra over R; we say that it is a *Grassmann algebra* for the module M, and that $\varphi \wedge \psi$ is the *Grassmann product* of φ and ψ. Moreover, if A is any module over R, then the mappings $(\varphi, \psi) \to \varphi \wedge \psi$ and $(\varphi, \psi) \to \psi \wedge \varphi$ are scalar multiplications for structures of left and right modules over E^* on the additive group Hom (E, A); thus, Hom (E, A) may be considered as an (E^*, E^*)-module.

If $\varphi \in$ Hom (E, A), $\psi \in$ Hom (E, B) and $x_1, \cdots, x_n$ are elements of M, then we have

$$(\varphi \wedge \psi)(x_1 \cdots x_n) = \Sigma_\sigma \eta(\sigma, \sigma^*) \varphi(t(\sigma)) \otimes \psi(t(\sigma^*)),$$

with the same notation as in formula (2); this follows immediately from formula (2).

Let E_n be the module of homogeneous elements of degree n of E. Denote by E_n^* the module of linear forms on E which map $E_{n'}$ upon $\{0\}$ whenever $n' \neq n$. Since $E = \Sigma_{n \in \underline{Z}} E_n$, the operation of restriction to E_n on linear forms on E induces an isomorphism of E_n^* with the dual module of E_n; let χ_n be this isomorphism. Moreover, there is an isomorphism of E^* with $\Pi_{n \in \underline{Z}} E_n^*$ which maps any element of E_n^* upon its image under the natural injection of E_n^* into $\Pi_{n \in \underline{Z}} E_n^*$ (cf. corollary 2 to theorem 20, Chapter III,

Sect. 6). The sum $G = \sum_{n \in Z} E_n^*$ is direct; G is a submodule of E^* and is identical to E^* in the case where there is an n_0 such that $E_n = \{0\}$ for $n > n_0$. (This is always the case if M has a finite set of generators, as follows from theorem 19, Sect. 7.) The decomposition $G = \sum_{n \in Z} E_n^*$ defines on G the structure of a graded module. We have $E_n^* = \{0\}$ if $n < 0$; E_0^* has a base $\{\varepsilon\}$, where ε is the unit element of E^*.

Theorem 23. *The notation being as above, G is a subalgebra of E^*; it is a regularly graded anticommutative algebra.*

If $\varphi \in E_m^*$, $\psi \in E_n^*$, then $(\varphi \otimes \psi)(E_{m'} \otimes E_{n'}) = \{0\}$ if $(m', n') \neq (m, n)$. Since $U(E_p) \subset \sum_{m'+n'=p} E_{m'} \otimes E_{n'}$, we have $(\varphi \wedge \psi)(E_p) = \{0\}$ if $p \neq m + n$, whence $\varphi \wedge \psi \in E_{m+n}^*$. This shows that G is a subalgebra of E^* and that G is a graded algebra. It is clearly regularly graded. Denote by ζ the automorphism of the module $E \otimes E$ which maps $t \otimes u$ upon $u \otimes t$ if t, $u \in E$; then we have $\psi \otimes \varphi = (\varphi \otimes \psi) \circ \zeta$, whence

$$\psi \wedge \varphi = (\varphi \otimes \psi) \circ \zeta \circ U = (\varphi \otimes \psi) \circ K \circ U$$

by virtue of formula (4). Thus, if $\varphi \in E_m^*$, $\psi \in E_n^*$, then we have $\psi \wedge \varphi = (-1)^{mn} \varphi \wedge \psi$, since $\varphi \otimes \psi$ maps $E_{m'} \otimes E_{n'}$ upon $\{0\}$ whenever $(m', n') \neq (m, n)$. Let φ be homogeneous of odd degree m; then it follows from what we have established above that, if $t \in E$, then

$$(\varphi \wedge \varphi)(t) = (\varphi \otimes \varphi)(U(t))$$

is a sum of elements of the form $(\varphi \otimes \varphi)(u \otimes v - v \otimes u)$ with u and v in E_m. Since $(\varphi \otimes \varphi)(u \otimes v - v \otimes u) = \varphi(u)\varphi(v) - \varphi(v)\varphi(u) = 0$, we have $\varphi \wedge \varphi = 0$.

Let N be another module over R, and let γ be a bilinear form on $N \times M$. Then γ defines a linear mapping λ of N into the dual module M^* of M: if $y \in N$, then $\lambda(y)$ is the linear form $x \to \gamma(y, x)$ on M. The form $\lambda(y)$ may be extended to a linear form $\Lambda_1(y)$ on E which maps E_n upon $\{0\}$ whenever $n \neq 1$; Λ_1 is a linear mapping of N into E^*. It follows from theorem 23 that $\Lambda_1(y) \wedge \Lambda_1(y) = 0$ for all $y \in N$. Therefore, if F is an exterior algebra on N, there is a homomorphism Λ of F into E^* which extends Λ_1; Λ is called the *homomorphism of F into E^* associated to the bilinear form* γ. Since $\Lambda(N)$ is contained in the algebra G of theorem 23, we have $\Lambda(F) \subset G$; Λ is homogeneous of degree 0. If $u \in F$ and $t \in E$, set

$$\Gamma(u, t) = (\Lambda(u))(t);$$

it is clear that Γ is a bilinear form on $F \times E$, and that its restriction to $N \times M$ is γ; Γ is called the *prolongation to $F \times E$* of the bilinear form γ.

In particular, if we take $M = N^*$ and γ to be the canonical bilinear form $(x^*, x) \to x^*(x)$ on $M^* \times M$, then Λ is a homomorphism of an exterior algebra $E(M^*)$ on M^* into E^*; this homomorphism is called the *canonical homomorphism* of $E(M^*)$ into E^*; it is in general neither a monomorphism nor an epimorphism.

Theorem 24. *Let M and P be modules over the same commutative ring R and f a linear mapping of M into P. Let E and F be exterior algebras on M and P respectively, and $\bar{f}$ the prolongation of f to E. Let A and B be modules over R, φ an element of* Hom (F, A) *and ψ an element of* Hom (F, B). *Then we have $(\varphi \circ \bar{f}) \wedge (\psi \circ \bar{f}) = (\varphi \wedge \psi) \circ \bar{f}$.*

Let U and V be the analyzing mappings of E and F. Then we have

$$\begin{aligned}(\varphi \circ \bar{f}) \wedge (\psi \circ \bar{f}) &= ((\varphi \circ \bar{f}) \otimes (\psi \circ \bar{f})) \circ U = (\varphi \otimes \psi) \circ (\bar{f} \otimes \bar{f}) \circ U \\ &= (\varphi \otimes \psi) \circ V \circ \bar{f} = (\varphi \wedge \psi) \circ \bar{f}\end{aligned}$$

by virtue of lemma 1.

Corollary. *The notation being as in theorem 24, the transpose mapping ${}^t\bar{f}$ of $\bar{f}$ is a homomorphism of the algebra F^* dual to F into E^*.*

This is the special case of theorem 24 where $A = B = R$.

Theorem 25. *Let M be a module over a commutative ring R, E an exterior algebra on M and E^* the dual algebra of E. If A is a subset of E, denote by A^0 the set of linear forms on E which map A upon $\{0\}$. Let N be a submodule of M. Denote by π the natural mapping of M on M/N, by $E(M/N)$ an exterior algebra on M/N, and by $\bar{\pi}$ the prolongation of π to E; let $E^*(M/N)$ be the dual algebra of $E(M/N)$. Then, if A is the ideal of E generated by N, A^0 is the subalgebra of E^* which is the image of $E^*(M/N)$ by the transpose mapping of $\bar{\pi}$. Let $E(N)$ be an exterior algebra on N, K the identity mapping of N into M, $E^*(N)$ the dual algebra of $E(N)$, $\bar{K}$ the prolongation of K to $E(N)$ and ${}^t\bar{K}$ the transpose mapping of $\bar{K}$. Then, if A is the subalgebra of E generated by N, A^0 is the ideal of E^* which is the kernel of the mapping ${}^t\bar{K}$.*

Assume first that A is the ideal generated by N; then A is the kernel of $\bar{\pi}$ (theorem 21, Sect. 7). If $\varphi \in A^0$, then the kernel of φ contains the kernel A of $\bar{\pi}$, and φ may be written in the form $\psi \circ \bar{\pi}$, with $\psi \in E^*(M/N)$; thus $\varphi = {}^t\bar{\pi}(\psi)$ belongs to ${}^t\bar{\pi}(E^*(M/N))$, which is a subalgebra of E^* by the corollary to theorem 24. Conversely, if $\varphi = {}^t\bar{\pi}(\psi)$ for some $\psi \in E^*(M/N)$, then $\varphi = \psi \circ \bar{\pi}$ clearly maps A upon $\{0\}$.

Assume now that A is the subalgebra generated by N. Since N is a set of generators of $E(N)$, we have $A = \bar{K}(E(N))$. In order for an element φ of E^* to belong to A^0, it is necessary and sufficient that $\varphi \circ \bar{K} = 0$, i. e., that ${}^t\bar{K}(\varphi) = 0$; A^0 is therefore the kernel of ${}^t\bar{K}$. This is an ideal by virtue of the corollary to theorem 24.

Theorem 26. *Let N, N' and M be modules over a commutative ring R, f a linear mapping of N into N', γ' a bilinear form on $N' \times M$ and γ the bilinear form on $N \times M$ defined by $\gamma(y, x) = \gamma'(f(y), x)$ $(x \in M, y \in N)$. Let E, F and F' be exterior algebras on M, N and N', $\bar{f}$ the prolongation of f, Γ the prolongation of γ to $F \times E$ and Γ' the prolongation of γ' to $F' \times E$. Then we have $\Gamma(u, t) = \Gamma'(\bar{f}(u), t)$ if $t \in E$, $u \in F$.*

Let Λ and Λ' be the homomorphisms of F and F' into E^* associated with the bilinear forms γ and γ'. We shall prove that $\Lambda = \Lambda' \circ \bar{f}$. It is sufficient to prove that $\Lambda(y) = \Lambda'(f(y))$ if $y \in N$. But $\Lambda(y)$ is the element of E_1^* which maps any $x \in M$ upon $\gamma(y, x) = \gamma'(f(y), x)$, and is therefore identical to $\Lambda'(f(y))$. If $t \in E$ and $u \in F$, then $\Gamma(u, t) = (\Lambda(u))(t) = (\Lambda'(\bar{f}(u)))(t) = \Gamma'(\bar{f}(u), t)$, which proves theorem 26.

Theorem 27. *Let M, M' and N be modules over a commutative ring R, f a linear mapping of M into M', γ' a bilinear form on $N \times M'$ and γ the bilinear form on $N \times M$ defined by $\gamma(y, x) = \gamma'(y, f(x))$ $(x \in M, y \in N)$. Let E, E', F be exterior algebras on M, M', N, $\bar{f}$ the prolongation of f, Γ the prolongation of γ to $F \times E$ and Γ' the prolongation of γ' to $F \times E'$. Then we have $\Gamma(u, t) = \Gamma'(u, \bar{f}(t))$ if $u \in F$, $t \in E$.*

Let Λ and Λ' be the homomorphisms of F into the dual algebras E^* of E and E'^* of E' which are associated to the bilinear forms γ, γ', and let ${}^t\bar{f}$ be the transpose mapping of $\bar{f}$. We shall prove that $\Lambda = {}^t\bar{f} \circ \Lambda'$. Since ${}^t\bar{f}$ is an algebra homomorphism (corollary to theorem 24), so is ${}^t\bar{f} \circ \Lambda'$, and it will be sufficient to prove that ${}^t\bar{f}(\Lambda'(y)) = \Lambda(y)$ if $y \in N$. Now, $\Lambda'(y)$ is the linear form on E' which maps any $x' \in M'$ upon $\gamma'(y, x')$ and which maps upon $\{0\}$ the module of homogeneous elements of degree n of E' if $n \neq 1$. The image of this linear form under ${}^t\bar{f}$, which is $\Lambda'(y) \circ \bar{f}$, maps any $x \in M$ upon $\gamma'(y, f(x)) = \gamma(y, x)$ and maps E_n upon $\{0\}$ if $n \neq 1$; this image is therefore $\Lambda(y)$, which proves our assertion. If $t \in E$, $u \in F$, we have

$$\Gamma(u, t) = (\Lambda(u))(t) = {}^t\bar{f}(\Lambda'(u))(t) = (\Lambda'(u))(\bar{f}(t)),$$

which is equal to $\Gamma'(u, \bar{f}(t))$; this proves theorem 27.

9. The determinant of a matrix

In this section, we shall adopt the following terminological conventions. The letter R will denote a commutative ring. If M is any module over R, we shall denote by $E(M)$ an exterior algebra on M and by $E^*(M)$ the dual of $E(M)$, with its structure as a Grassmann algebra. If λ is a linear form on M, the value $\lambda(x)$ taken by λ at an element $x \in M$ will also be denoted by $\langle \lambda, x \rangle$. If $u \in E(M^*)$, $t \in E(M)$, the value at (u, t) of the prolongation to $E(M^*) \times E(M)$ of the bilinear form $(\lambda, x) \to < \lambda, x >$ on $M^* \times M$ will be denoted by $< u, t >$. If n is an integer > 0, we shall denote by R^n the module product of n modules identical to R, and by $(e_{n1}, \cdots, e_{nn})$ the canonical base of R^n, e_{ni} being the element whose i-th coordinate is 1 and whose other coordinates are 0.

Let $A = (a_{ij})$ be a square matrix of degree n; let $\lambda_1, \cdots, \lambda_n$ be the linear forms on R^n which are represented by the rows of A relative to the base $(e_{n1}, \cdots, e_{nn})$, whence $\lambda_i(e_{nj}) = a_{ij}$ $(1 \leqslant i, j \leqslant n)$. We set

$$\det A = < \lambda_1 \cdots \lambda_n, e_{n1} \cdots e_{nn} >;$$

this element of R is called the *determinant* of A.

Theorem 28. *Let $R_1, \cdots, R_n$ be n rows of type $(1, n)$ with elements in R; denote by $(R_1, \cdots, R_n)$ the square matrix of degree n whose rows are $R_1, \cdots, R_n$. Then $(R_1, \cdots, R_n) \to \det (R_1, \cdots, R_n)$ is an n-linear form on the product of n modules identical to the module of rows of type $(1, n)$. If there are indices i, j such that $R_i = R_j$, $i \neq j$, then we have $\det(R_1, \cdots, R_n) = 0$.*

This follows immediately from the definition and from the fact that $\lambda_1 \cdots \lambda_n = 0$ if $\lambda_i = \lambda_j$ with $i \neq j$.

Another immediate corollary of the definition is that the determinant of a square matrix (a) of degree 1 is the element a.

Theorem 29. *Let N and M be modules on R, γ a bilinear form on $N \times M$ and Γ its prolongation to $E(N) \times E(M)$. If $y_1, \cdots, y_n$ are in N and $x_1, \cdots, x_n$ in M, we have*

$$\Gamma(y_1 \cdots y_n, x_1 \cdots x_n) = \det (\gamma(y_i, x_j))_{1 \leqslant i, j \leqslant n}.$$

There is a linear mapping f of R^n into M such that $f(e_{nj}) = x_j$ $(1 \leqslant j \leqslant n)$. If $y \in N$, let λ_y be the linear form $z \to \gamma(y, f(z))$ on R^n, whence

$$< \lambda_y, z > = \gamma(y, f(z)).$$

Applying theorem 26, Sect. 9 to the linear mapping $y \to \lambda_y$ of N into the dual of R^n and theorem 27, Sect. 9 to the mapping f, we obtain

$$\Gamma(y_1 \cdots y_n, x_1 \cdots x_n) = < \lambda_{y_1} \cdots \lambda_{y_n}, e_{n1} \cdots e_{nn} >.$$

Since $< \lambda_{y_i}, e_{nj} > = \gamma(y_i, x_j)$, theorem 29 follows from the definition of a determinant.

Let $A = (a_{ij})$ be any matrix with elements in R, of type (m, n). Let h be an integer $\leqslant \min (m, n)$; let $\sigma = (i_1, \cdots, i_h)$ and $\tau = (j_1, \cdots, j_h)$ be strictly increasing sequences of length h of integers between 1 and m and between 1 and n respectively. Then the determinant of the matrix $(a_{i_p j_q})_{1 \leqslant p, q \leqslant h}$ is called the *subdeterminant of type* (σ, τ) of A; the subdeterminants of type (σ, τ) are also called the *subdeterminants of order* h of A.

Let now $A = (a_{ij})$ be a square matrix of degree n with elements in R, and let h be an integer $\leqslant n$. If σ, τ are strictly increasing sequences of length h of integers between 1 and n, we shall denote by $D(\sigma, \tau; A)$ the subdeterminant of type (σ, τ) of A. Let σ_0 and σ_1 be two *distinct* strictly increasing sequences of length h of indices between 1 and n; for any strictly increasing sequence σ of indices between 1 and n, denote by σ^* the strictly increasing sequence formed by the integers between 1 and n not occuring in σ. Let the numbers $\eta(\sigma, \tau)$ be defined as in Sect. 5, formula (1). Then we shall prove the formulas

$$(1) \qquad \det A = \eta(\sigma_0, \sigma_0^*)\Sigma_\sigma \eta(\sigma, \sigma^*)D(\sigma_0, \sigma; A)D(\sigma_0^*, \sigma^*; A)$$

$$(2) \qquad 0 = \Sigma_\sigma \eta(\sigma, \sigma^*)D(\sigma_0, \sigma; A)D(\sigma_1^*, \sigma^*; A)$$

where the summation is extended to all strictly increasing sequences of length h; these formulas are due to Laplace.

Let $\lambda_1, \cdots, \lambda_n$ be the linear forms on R^n such that $\lambda_i(e_{nj}) = a_{ij}$. Set $\sigma_0 = (i_1, \cdots, i_h)$, $\sigma_0^* = (j_1, \cdots, j_{n-h})$; then we have, by formula (2), Sect. 5,

$$\det A = \eta(\sigma_0, \sigma_0^*) < \lambda_{i_1} \cdots \lambda_{i_h}\lambda_{j_1} \cdots \lambda_{j_{n-h}}, e_{n1} \cdots e_{nn} >.$$

Let $\overline{\lambda}_i$ be the linear form on $E(R^n)$ which extends λ_i and which maps upon 0 every homogeneous element of degree $\neq 1$; set $\varphi = \overline{\lambda}_{i_1} \wedge \cdots \wedge \overline{\lambda}_{i_h}$, $\psi = \overline{\lambda}_{j_1} \wedge \cdots \wedge \overline{\lambda}_{j_{n-h}}$. Then we have, by the definition of the prolongation of a bilinear form,

$$\det A = \eta(\sigma_0, \sigma_0^*)(\varphi \wedge \psi)(e_{n1} \cdots e_{nn}).$$

If $\tau = (k_1, \cdots, k_r)$ is any strictly increasing sequence of indices between 1 and n, set $t(\tau) = e_{nk_1} \cdots e_{nk_r}$. Then we have, by formula (2), Sect. 8,

$$\det A = \eta(\sigma_0, \sigma_0^*)\Sigma_\sigma \eta(\sigma, \sigma^*)\varphi(t(\sigma))\psi(t(\sigma^*)).$$

We have $\varphi(t(\sigma)) = < \lambda_{i_1} \cdots \lambda_{i_h}, t(\sigma) > = D(\sigma_0, \sigma; A)$ by virtue of theorem 29, and similarly $\psi(t(\sigma^*)) = D(\sigma_0^*, \sigma^*; A)$. The first formula of Laplace is thereby proved. In order to prove the second, observe that, since σ_0 and σ_1 are distinct, there is an index which occurs both in σ_0 and σ_1^*. Set $\sigma_1^* = (j'_1, \cdots, j'_{n-h})$. Let A' be the square matrix defined as follows: if i occurs in σ_0, the row of index i of A' is the same as that of A; if $i = j_k$ $(1 \leqslant k \leqslant n-h)$, then the row of index i of A' is the row of index j'_k of A. Then A' has two identical rows, whence $\det A' = 0$ (theorem 28). On the other hand, we have $D(\sigma_0, \sigma; A') = D(\sigma_0, \sigma; A)$, $D(\sigma_0^*, \sigma^*; A') = D(\sigma_1^*, \sigma^*; A')$ for every σ; the second formula therefore follows from the first, applied to A'.

Assume that $a_{1j} = 0$ for $2 \leqslant j \leqslant n$; applying the Laplace formula with $\sigma_0 = (1)$, we have $\eta(\sigma_0, \sigma_0^*) = 1$ and $D(\sigma_0, \sigma; A) = 0$ whenever $\sigma = (j)$, $j \neq 1$. Thus we obtain $\det A = a_{11}D((1)^*, (1)^*; A)$; $D((1)^*, (1)^*; A)$ is the determinant of the matrix $(a_{i+1,j+1})_{1 \leqslant i,j \leqslant n-1}$. A matrix A is called *lower* *triangular* if $a_{ij} = 0$ whenever $i < j$. If this condition is satisfied, then we have

$$\det A = \prod_{i=1}^{n} a_{ii}.$$

This is obviously true if $n = 0$ or 1. Assume that $n > 1$ and that our formula is true for matrices of degrees $< n$. The matrix $A' = (a_{i+1, j+1})_{1 \leqslant i, j \leqslant n-1}$ is lower triangular, and it follows from what we have just proved that $\det A = a_{11} (\det A')$; it follows that our formula is true for matrices of degree n.

In particular, if $A = (a_{ij})$ is a diagonal matrix (i. e., $a_{ij} = 0$ whenever $i \neq j$), then we have $\det A = \prod_{i=1}^{n} a_{ii}$. Even more particularly, we see that the determinant of the unit matrix of any degree is 1.

Theorem 30. *Let M be a module with a finite base $(x_1, \cdots, x_n)$; denote by $(x_1^*, \cdots, x_n^*)$ the dual base of the dual module M^* of M. If σ is any strictly increasing sequence of indices between 1 and n, say $\sigma = (i_1, \cdots, i_h)$, set $t(\sigma) = x_{i_1} \cdots x_{i_h}$, $t^*(\sigma) = x_{i_1}^* \cdots x_{i_h}^*$, these products being constructed in $E(M)$ and $E(M^*)$ respectively. Then the elements $t(\sigma)$, for all σ of length h, form a base of the module E_h of homogeneous elements of degree h of $E(M)$. The canonical homomorphism Λ of $E(M^*)$ into $E^*(M)$ is an isomorphism; we have $(\Lambda(t^*(\sigma)))(t(\tau)) = 1$ if $\sigma = \tau$,* 0 *if $\sigma \neq \tau$.*

We first prove these last formulas. If σ is of length h, then $t^*(\sigma)$ is homogeneous of degree h in $E(M^*)$, and $\Lambda(t^*(\sigma))$ homogeneous of degree h in $E^*(M)$, whence $(\Lambda(t^*(\sigma)))(t(\tau)) = 0$ if τ is of length $\neq h$. Assume that τ is of length h; set $\sigma = (i_1, \cdots, i_h)$, $\tau = (j_1, \cdots, j_h)$. Then, by definition, $(\Lambda(t^*(\sigma)))(t(\tau))$ is equal to $< x_{i_1}^* \cdots x_{i_h}^*, x_{j_1} \cdots x_{j_h} >$, or also to $\det (< x_{i_p}^*, x_{j_q} >)_{1 \leqslant p, q \leqslant h}$, by theorem 29. If $\sigma \neq \tau$, then there is an index p such that i_p does not occur in τ, whence $< x_{i_p}^*, x_{j_q} > = 0$ for $1 \leqslant q \leqslant h$, and therefore $(\Lambda(t^*(\sigma)))(t(\tau)) = 0$. If $\sigma = \tau$, then $(< x_{i_p}^*, x_{j_q} >)_{1 \leqslant p, q \leqslant h}$ is the unit matrix of degree h, whence $(\Lambda(t^*(\sigma)))(t(\tau)) = 1$.

In particular, we have $< x_1^* \cdots x_n^*, x_1 \cdots x_n > = 1$. Thus, if α is an element of R such that $\alpha x_1 \cdots x_n = 0$, then $\alpha = < x_1^* \cdots x_n^*, \alpha x_1 \cdots x_n > = 0$. Making use of theorem 12, Sect. 5, we conclude that, for any h, the elements $t(\sigma)$, for all σ of length h, form a base of E_h. The elements $t(\sigma)$, for all strictly increasing sequences σ, therefore form a base of the module $E(M)$; by the formulas established above, the elements $\Lambda(t^*(\sigma))$ form the dual base of $E^*(M)$. It follows immediately that Λ is a module isomorphism, and therefore also an algebra isomorphism.

Theorem 31. *Let $x_1, \cdots, x_n$ be elements of a module M over R. Let $A = (a_{ij})$ be a matrix of type (n, m) with elements in R, m being $\leqslant n$. If σ is a strictly increasing sequence of integers between 1 and m, let $D(\sigma)$ be the subdeterminant of type $(\sigma, (1, \cdots, m))$ of A. Set $y_i = \sum_{j=1}^{n} a_{ji} x_j$; then we have*

$$y_1 \cdots y_m = \Sigma_{\sigma} D(\sigma) t(\sigma),$$

with $t(\sigma) = x_{j_1} \cdots x_{j_m}$ if $\sigma = (j_1, \cdots, j_m)$.

Consider first the case where $x_1, \cdots, x_n$ form a base of M; in that case, we use the notation of the proof of theorem 30. Since $y_1 \cdots y_m \in E_m$, it may be written in the form $\Sigma_\sigma a(\sigma)t(\sigma)$, the summation being extended to all strictly increasing sequences σ of length m of integers between 1 and n, and the $a(\sigma)$'s being in R. It follows from theorem 30 that $a(\sigma) = (\Lambda(t^*(\sigma)))(y_1 \cdots y_m)$; if $\sigma = (j_1, \cdots, j_m)$, this is equal by definition to $< x^*_{j_1} \cdots x^*_{j_m}, y_1 \cdots y_m >$, i. e., to $\det (< x^*_{j_p}, y_q >)_{1 \leqslant p, q \leqslant m}$ (theorem 29). But we have $< x^*_{j_p}, y_q > = a_{j_p, q}$, whence $< x^*_{j_1} \cdots x^*_{j_p}, y_1 \cdots y_m > = D(\sigma)$, and the formula is proved in that case. To go over to the general case, we observe that there exists a linear mapping f of R^n into M such that $f(e_{nj}) = x_j$ $(1 \leqslant j \leqslant n)$; let $\bar{f}$ be its prolongation to $E(R^n)$. Set $z_i = \Sigma^n_{j=1} a_{ji} e_{nj}$; then

$$y_1 \cdots y_m = \bar{f}(z_1 \cdots z_m) = \Sigma_\sigma D((j_1, \cdots, j_m))\bar{f}(e_{nj_1} \cdots e_{nj_m}) = \Sigma_\sigma D(\sigma)t(\sigma).$$

In particular, if A is a square matrix $(m = n)$, then we have, in the notation of theorem 31,

$$y_1 \cdots y_n = (\det A)(x_1 \cdots x_n).$$

Let M be a free module over R with a finite base $(x_1, \cdots, x_n)$. Denote by $E_h(M)$ the module of homogeneous elements of degree h of $E(M)$. Then it follows immediately from theorem 30 that $E_n(M) \neq \{0\}$, while $E_h(M) = \{0\}$ for any $h > n$. This shows that any other finite base of the module M also has n elements. Moreover, every base of M is actually finite. For, let $(x'_i)_{i \in I}$ be any base of M, and let $i_1 \cdots, i_h$ be any distinct h indices of I. The submodule M' of M generated by the elements $x'_{i_1}, \cdots, x'_{i_h}$ is clearly a direct summand in M and has a base composed of the elements x'_{i_k} $(1 \leqslant k \leqslant h)$. The product of these elements in $E(M')$ is $\neq 0$ by theorem 30. On the other hand, the prolongation of the identity mapping of M' into M is a monomorphism of $E(M')$ into $E(M)$ by corollary 2 to theorem 22, Sect. 7; this shows that $x'_{i_1} \cdots x'_{i_h} \neq 0$. This last element being homogeneous of degree h, we have $h \leqslant n$. This proves that I cannot contain more than n elements.

Let f be an endomorphism of M, and $\bar{f}$ its prolongation to $E(M)$. The one element set $\{x_1 \cdots x_n\}$ is a base of $E_n(M)$; it follows immediately that, if d is the element of R such that $\bar{f}(x_1 \cdots x_n) = dx_1 \cdots x_n$, then we have $\bar{f}(t) = dt$ for every $t \in E_n(M)$. If $f(x_i) = \Sigma^n_{j=1} a_{ji} x_j$, $a_{ji} \in R$, then we have

$$\bar{f}(x_1 \cdots x_n) = (\det (a_{ij}))x_1 \cdots x_n$$

by theorem 31, whence $d = \det (a_{ij})$. The element d is called the *determinant of the endomorphism* f and is denoted by $\det f$. It follows from what we have said that $\det f$ is equal to the determinant of the matrix which represents f with respect to a base of M.

Theorem 32. *If f, g are endomorphisms of a free module M over R with a finite base, then* $\det(f \circ g) = (\det f)(\det g)$. *If A, B are square matrices of degree n with elements in R, then* $\det AB = (\det A)(\det B)$.

Let $E_n(M)$ be the module of homogeneous elements of degree n of $E(M)$. Let $\bar{f}$ and $\bar{g}$ be the prolongations of f and g. Then we have, for $t \in E_n(M)$, $\bar{f}(\bar{g}(t)) = \bar{f}((\det g)t) = (\det g)\bar{f}(t) = (\det g)(\det f)t$, whence

$$\det(f \circ g) = (\det f)(\det g).$$

If f, g are the endomorphisms of R^n which are represented by A, B relative to the base $(e_{n1}, \cdots, e_{nn})$, then $f \circ g$ is represented by AB, whence $\det f \circ g = AB = (\det A)(\det B)$.

Theorem 33. *Let A be a square matrix of degree n with elements in R. Then we have* $\det {}^tA = \det A$.

Set $A = (a_{ij})$; denote by $(e_{n1}^*, \cdots, e_{nn}^*)$ the base of the dual of R^n which is dual to the base $(e_{n1}, \cdots, e_{nn})$. Set $x_i^* = \sum_{j=1}^n a_{ij} e_{nj}^*$, whence $x_i^*(e_{nj}) = a_{ij}$; then we have $\det A = < x_1^* \cdots x_n^*, e_{n1} \cdots e_{nn} >$ by definition of the determinant of a matrix. On the other hand, we have $x_1^* \cdots x_n^* = (\det {}^tA) e_{n1}^* \cdots e_{nn}^*$ by theorem 31, whence

$$\det A = (\det {}^tA) < e_{n1}^* \cdots e_{nn}^*, e_{n1} \cdots e_{nn} > = \det {}^tA.$$

Theorem 34. *Let M and N be modules over R and γ a bilinear form on $N \times M$; denote by $\bar{\gamma}$ the bilinear form on $M \times N$ defined by $\bar{\gamma}(x, y) = \gamma(y, x)$ $(x \in M, y \in N)$. Let Γ and $\bar{\Gamma}$ be the prolongations of γ and $\bar{\gamma}$ to $E(N) \times E(M)$ and $E(M) \times E(N)$ respectively. Then we have $\Gamma(t, u) = \bar{\Gamma}(u, t)$ if $t \in E(M)$, $u \in E(N)$.*

Since Γ and $\bar{\Gamma}$ are bilinear forms and $E(M)$ (resp.: $E(N)$) is generated as a module by elements of the form $x_1 \cdots x_m$, with $x_i \in M$ (resp.: $y_1 \cdots y_n$, with $y_j \in N$), it will be sufficient to prove our formula in the case where $t = x_1 \cdots x_m$, $u = y_1 \cdots y_n$, with $x_i \in M$, $y_j \in N$. If $m \neq n$, then $\bar{\Gamma}(t, u)$ and $\Gamma(u, t)$ are both 0. If $m = n$, the equality $\bar{\Gamma}(t, u) = \Gamma(u, t)$ follows immediately from theorems 29 and 33.

Theorem 35. *If $\underline{C}_1, \cdots \underline{C}_n$ are n columns of type $(n, 1)$ with elements in R, denote by $(\underline{C}_1, \cdots, \underline{C}_n)$ the square matrix of degree n whose i-th column is $\underline{C}_i$ $(1 \leqslant i \leqslant n)$. Then $(\underline{C}_1, \cdots, \underline{C}_n) \to \det(\underline{C}_1, \cdots, \underline{C}_n)$ is an n-linear form on the product of n modules identical to the module of all columns of type $(n, 1)$ with elements in R. If there exist indices i and j such that $i \neq j$, $\underline{C}_i = \underline{C}_j$, then* $\det(\underline{C}_1, \cdots, \underline{C}_n) = 0$.

This follows immediately from theorems 28 and 33.

Using the same notation as in the Laplace formulas, we observe that $D(\sigma, \tau; {}^tA) = D(\tau, \sigma; A)$ by virtue of theorem 33. Thus, if we write the Laplace formulas for ${}^tA$ and take into account the equality $\det {}^tA = \det A$, we obtain the formulas

$$\det A = \eta(\sigma_0, \sigma_0^*)\ \Sigma_\sigma \eta(\sigma, \sigma^*)D(\sigma, \sigma_0; A)D(\sigma^*, \sigma_0^*; A)$$
$$0 = \Sigma_\sigma \eta(\sigma, \sigma^*)D(\sigma, \sigma_0; A)D(\sigma^*, \sigma_1^*; A) \text{ if } \sigma_1 \neq \sigma_0.$$

These formulas are also due to Laplace.

A matrix $A = (a_{ij})$ is called *upper triangular* if $a_{ij} = 0$ whenever $i > j$. The transpose of such a matrix is lower triangular; therefore, it follows from theorem 33 and from a result established earlier that $\det A = \Pi_{i=1}^n a_{ii}$ if $A = (a_{ij})$ is an upper triangular matrix.

Theorem 36. *Let h and n be integers such that $1 \leqslant h \leqslant n$; let B be a square matrix of degree h, C a matrix of type $(h, n-h)$, C' a matrix of type $(n-h, h)$ and D a square matrix of degree $n-h$, all these matrices having their elements in R. Set*

$$A = \begin{pmatrix} B & C \\ 0 & D \end{pmatrix} \qquad A' = \begin{pmatrix} B & 0 \\ C' & D \end{pmatrix};$$

then we have $\det A = \det A' = (\det B)\,(\det D)$.

We compute $\det A$ by means of the Laplace formula, taking $\sigma_0 = (1, \cdots, h)$, whence $\eta(\sigma_0, \sigma_0^*) = 1$. If σ is a strictly increasing sequence of length h different from $(1, \cdots, h)$, then there is at least one index $\leqslant h$ which occurs in σ^*; $D(\sigma_0^*, \sigma^*; A)$ is therefore the determinant of a matrix one column of which is the zero column, whence $D(\sigma_0^*, \sigma^*; A) = 0$ by theorem 35. Thus we have $\det A = D(\sigma_0, \sigma_0; A)D(\sigma_0^*, \sigma_0^*; A) = (\det B)\,(\det D)$. Applying this result to ${}^tA'$, we obtain $\det A' = (\det B)(\det D)$.

10. Some applications of determinants

1. *The signature of a permutation.*

Let S be a finite set, and P the group of permutations of S. An operation $s \in P$ is called a *transposition* if there exist two elements a, b of S such that $a \neq b$, $s(a) = b$, $s(b) = a$, $s(c) = c$ for every element c of S distinct from a and b.

Lemma 1. *The transpositions of a finite set S generate the group of permutations of S.*

We prove this by induction on the number n of elements of S. The lemma is obvious for $n = 0$. Assume that $n > 0$ and that the lemma is proved for sets of $n-1$ elements. Let a be any element of S, and P_a the stability group of a. Let P' be the subgroup of P generated by the transpositions. The operation of restriction to the complementary set S' of $\{a\}$ induces an isomorphism of P_a with the group of permutations of S', and any operation of P_a whose restriction to S' is a transposition is itself a transposition. Therefore, it follows from the inductive assumption that $P_a \subset P'$. On the other hand, it is obvious that P' operates transitively on S; therefore, the index of P_a in P' is equal to n (theorem 15, Chapter II, Sect. 4), which is also the index of P_a in P. It follows that $P' = P$.

Now, let p be any permutation of S. Construct the module $\underline{Z}^n$ over $\underline{Z}$, the product of n modules indentical to $\underline{Z}$ (where n is the number of elements of S), and let $(e_{n1}, \cdots, e_{nn})$ be the canonical base of $\underline{Z}^n$. Let j be any bijection of S on $\{1, \cdots, n\}$, and let $p' = j \circ p \circ \overset{-1}{j}$; p' is a permutation of $\{1, \cdots, n\}$, and $p \to p'$ is an isomorphism of P with the group of permutations of $\{1, \cdots, n\}$. Associate with p the endomorphism f_p of $\underline{Z}^n$ defined by $f_p(e_{nj}) = e_{n,\, p'(j)}$. We see immediately that $f_{p \circ q} = f_p \circ f_q$ if p, q are permutations of S; if p is the identity permutation of S, then f_p is the identity mapping. Set

$$\chi(p) = \det f_p;$$

then χ is a homomorphism of the group P into the multiplicative monoid of elements of $\underline{Z}$. If p is a transposition, we have $\chi(p) = -1$. For we have in general $e_{np'(1)} \cdots e_{np'(n)} = \chi(p) e_{n1} \cdots e_{nn}$; it will therefore be sufficient to prove that, if x, y are elements of a module M over any commutative ring R, and a, b, c elements of an exterior algebra on M, then $aybxc = -axbyc$; this, however, follows immediately from the relations

$$axbxc = aybyc = a(x+y)b(x+y)c = 0$$

(cf. corollary to theorem 20, Sect. 7). Since the transpositions form a set of generators of P, this shows that $\chi(p)$ does not depend on the choice of the bijection j; $\chi(p)$ is called the *signature* of the permutation p.

Let M be any module over a commutative ring R, and $x_1, \cdots, x_n$ elements of M. If p is a permutation of $\{1, \cdots, n\}$, then we have

$$x_{p(1)} \cdots x_{p(n)} = \chi(p) x_1 \cdots x_n. \tag{1}$$

For, by virtue of what was proved a few lines above, this formula is true if p is a transposition. On the other hand, if it is true for permutations p and q, it is also true for $p \circ q$, as follows immediately from the fact that χ is a homomorphism. Since the transpositions generate the group of permutations of $\{1, \cdots, n\}$, our formula is true for any permutation. It follows that, if $\sigma = (i_1, \cdots, i_h)$ is any strictly increasing sequence of indices between 1 and n and $\sigma^* = (j_1, \cdots, j_{n-h})$ the strictly increasing sequence whose terms are the indices which do not occur in σ, then the number $\eta(\sigma, \sigma^*)$ introduced in Sect. 5, formula (1), is equal to the signature of the permutation which maps k upon i_k if $k \leqslant h$, upon j_{k-h} if $k > h$ (cf. theorem 12, Sect. 5).

If p is the permutation defined by $p(i) = i + 1$ if $i < n$, $p(n) = 1$, then $\chi(p) = (-1)^{n+1}$. For, using the same notation as above, we have $e_{n2} \cdots e_{nn} e_{n1} = (-1)^{n-1} e_{n1} \cdots e_{nn}$, by the anticommutativity of exterior algebras.

Let $A = (a_{ij})$ be any square matrix of degree n with elements in a commutative ring R. Let M be a free module over R with a finite base $(x_1, \cdots, x_n)$, and E an exterior algebra on M. Set $y_i = \sum_{j=1}^{n} a_{ji} x_j$; then we have $y_1 \cdots y_n = (\det A) x_1 \cdots x_n$ (theorem 31, Sect. 9). If we expand the product $y_1 \cdots y_n$, we find

$$y_1 \cdots y_n = \Sigma_f (\Pi_{i=1}^{n} a_{f(i),i}) x_{f(1)} \cdots x_{f(n)},$$

the summation being extended to all mappings f of the set $\{1, \cdots, n\}$ into itself. If f is not a permutation, then there are two distinct indices i, j such that $f(i) = f(j)$, whence $x_{f(1)} \cdots x_{f(n)} = 0$ (corollary to theorem 20, Sect. 7). If f is a permutation, then $x_{f(1)} \cdots x_{f(n)} = \chi(f) x_1 \cdots x_n$ (formula (1)). Thus we find the following expression of a determinant :

$$\det A = \Sigma_p \chi(p) \Pi_{i=1}^{n} a_{p(i),i} \tag{2}$$

the summation being extended to all permutations p of the set $\{1, \cdots, n\}$.

If $\underline{R}_1, \cdots, \underline{R}_n$ are n rows of type $(1, n)$ with elements in a commutative ring R, denote by $\det(\underline{R}_1, \cdots, \underline{R}_n)$ the determinant of the matrix whose i-th row is $\underline{R}_i$ $(1 \leqslant i \leqslant n)$. Let p be any permutation of $\{1, \cdots, n\}$; then we have

$$\det(\underline{R}_{p(1)}, \cdots, \underline{R}_{p(n)}) = \chi(p) \det(\underline{R}_1, \cdots, \underline{R}_n). \tag{3}$$

For, let M be a free module over R with a finite base $(x_1, \cdots, x_n)$, and let $y_1, \cdots, y_n$ be the linear forms on M which are representend by $\underline{R}_1, \cdots, \underline{R}_n$ relative to the base $(x_1, \cdots, x_n)$. Using the same conventions of notation as in Sect. 9 (cf. the beginning of that section), we have

$$\det(\underline{R}_1, \cdots, \underline{R}_n) = \langle y_1 \cdots y_n, x_1 \cdots x_n \rangle$$
$$\det(\underline{R}_{p(1)}, \cdots, \underline{R}_{p(n)}) = \langle y_{p(1)} \cdots y_{p(n)}, x_1 \cdots x_n \rangle$$

and our formula follows from formula (1). We have an entirely similar statement relative to the operation of permuting among themselves the columns of a matrix; this statement follows from the preceding one by the relation $\det {}^tA = \det A$.

2. *Invertible matrices.*

Let $A = (a_{ij})$ be a square matrix of degree n with elements in a commutative ring R. If i is any integer between 1 and n, denote by $(i)^*$ the strictly increasing sequence formed by the integers $\neq i$ between 1 and n. We have $\eta((i), (i)^*) = (-1)^{i-1}$; if i, j are any two indices between 1 and n, we denote by M_{ij} the product by $(-1)^{i+j}$ of the subdeterminant of type $((i)^*, (j)^*)$ of A. Application of the Laplace formulas then gives the following relations:

$$\sum_{j=1}^{n} a_{ij}M_{ij} = \det A, \quad \sum_{j=1}^{n} a_{ij}M_{i'j} = 0 \text{ if } i \neq i'$$

$$\sum_{j=1}^{n} a_{ji}M_{ji} = \det A, \quad \sum_{j=1}^{n} a_{ji}M_{ji'} = 0 \text{ if } i \neq i'.$$

The element M_{ij} is called the *minor* of indices i and j of A; the matrix $\bar{A} = (M_{ij})$ is called the *adjoint matrix* of A. Denote by I_n the unit matrix of degree n; then the preceding relations may be written in the form

$$A({}^t\bar{A}) = (\det A)I_n, \quad ({}^t\bar{A})A = (\det A)I_n. \tag{4}$$

Theorem 37. *Let A be a square matrix of degree n with elements in a commutative ring R; denote by I_n the unit matrix of degree n. Then the following conditions are all equivalent: a) there exists a matrix A' such that $AA' = I_n$; b) there exists a matrix A'' such that $A''A = I_n$; c) A is invertible in the ring of all square matrices of degree n with elements in R; d)* $\det A$ *is invertible in the ring R. If these conditions are satisfied, the inverse matrix of A is* $(\det A)^{-1}({}^t\bar{A})$, *where $\bar{A}$ is the adjoint matrix of A.*

If *a*) is satisfied, then we have $(\det A)(\det A') = \det I_n = 1$; if *b*) is satisfied, then $(\det A'')(\det A) = 1$. Since R is commutative, we see that either one of *a*) or *b*) implies *d*). If *d*) is satisfied, then the formulas written above give $A((\det A)^{-1}({}^t\bar{A})) = ((\det A)^{-1})({}^t\bar{A}))A = I_n$; this shows that A is invertible and that $A^{-1} = (\det A)^{-1}({}^t\bar{A})$; since *c*) obviously implies *a*) and *b*), theorem 37 is proved.

Corollary. *Let M and N be modules over a commutative ring; assume that M and N have finite bases $(x_1, \cdots, x_n)$ and $(y_1, \cdots, y_n)$ with the same number of elements. Any epimorphism f of M on N is then an isomorphism.*

Let z_i be an element of M such that $f(z_i) = y_i$ $(1 \leqslant i \leqslant n)$. Since $(y_1, \cdots, y_n)$ is a base of N, there exists a linear mapping g of N into M such that $g(y_i) = z_i$ $(i = 1, \cdots, n)$; it is then clear that $f \circ g$ is the identity mapping of N. Let A be the matrix which represents f with respect to the bases $(x_1, \cdots, x_n)$ and $(y_1, \cdots, y_n)$, and B the matrix which represents g with respect to the bases $(y_1, \cdots, y_n)$ and $(x_1, \cdots, x_n)$; then AB is the unit matrix. Therefore, it follows from theorem 37 that A is invertible and that $BA = I_n$; $g \circ f$ is the identity mapping of M, from which it follows that f is an isomorphism.

Theorem 38. *Let M and N be modules over a commutative ring R and f a linear mapping of M into N. Let $x_1, \cdots, x_n$ be elements of M and $y_1, \cdots, y_n$ elements of N; assume that $f(x_i) = \sum_{j=1}^{n} a_{ji}y_j$, with $a_{ij} \in R$. Denote by A the matrix (a_{ij}); then the elements* $(\det A)y_i$ $(i = 1, \cdots, n)$ *belong to $f(M)$.*

Let $\bar{A} = (M_{ij})$ be the adjoint matrix of A; set $x'_i = \sum_{j=1}^{n} M_{ji} x_j$. Then it follows from the formulas (4) above that $f(x'_i) = (\det A) y_i$.

Theorem 39. *Let $A = (a_{ij})$ be a matrix of type (m, n) with elements in a field R. Then the rank r of A is equal to the largest integer h such that some subdeterminant of order h of A is $\neq 0$.*

Let M be a vector space over R with a base $(x_1, \cdots, x_m)$ of n elements. Let $S(p)$ (resp.: $S'(p)$) be the set of strictly increasing sequences of length p of integers between 1 and m (resp.: between 1 and n). Set

$$y_i = \sum_{j=1}^{m} a_{ji} x_j \ (i = 1, \cdots, n);$$

if $\sigma = (i_1, \cdots, i_p) \in S(p)$ set $t(\sigma) = x_{i_1} \cdots x_{i_p}$ (the product being constructed in an exterior algebra E on M); if $\tau = (j_1, \cdots, j_p) \in S'(p)$, set $u(\tau) = y_{j_1} \cdots y_{j_p}$. Then we have $u(\sigma) = \sum_{\tau \in S(p)} D(\sigma, \tau) t(\tau)$ (theorem 31, Sect. 9), where $D(\sigma, \tau)$ is the subdeterminant of type (σ, τ) of A. On the other hand, the elements $t(\sigma)$ form a base of E (theorem 30, Sect. 9). If $y_{i_1}, \cdots, y_{i_p}$ are linearly independent, then they may be included in a base of M, and $y_{i_1} \cdots y_{i_p}$ is $\neq 0$ (theorem 30, Sect. 9); if not, then one of them is a linear combination of the others, and we have $y_{i_1} \cdots y_{i_p} = 0$ because $y_{i_1} \cdots y_{i_p}$ is a homogeneous element of degree p in an exterior algebra over a vector space of dimension $< p$. It follows immediately that h is equal to the largest number r' such that the set $\{y_1, \cdots, y_m\}$ contains r' linearly independent elements, i. e., to the dimension of the subspace of M generated by $y_1, \cdots, y_m$. This number is equal to the rank of A by virtue of the corollary to theorem 66, Chapter III, Sect. 15.

Corollary. *Let R be a domain of integrity with at least 2 elements and let $A = (a_{ij})$ be a square matrix of degree n with elements in R. In order for the system of equations $\sum_{j=1}^{n} a_{ij} X_j = 0$ $(1 \leqslant i \leqslant n)$ to have a solution composed of elements not all equal to 0 in R, it is necessary and sufficient that* $\det A = 0$.

We may consider R as a subring of a field of quotients K of R. It follows from theorem 39 and from the corollary to theorem 70, Chapter III, Sect. 16, that $\det A = 0$ is a necessary and sufficient condition for our system of equations to have a solution composed of elements not all zero of K. If this condition is satisfied, let $b_1, \cdots, b_n$ be elements not all zero of K such that $\sum_{j=1}^{n} a_{ij} b_j = 0$ $(1 \leqslant i \leqslant n)$; then we may write $b_j = d^{-1} c_j$, with $c_1, \cdots, c_n, d$ in R; $c_1, \cdots, c_n$ are not all zero, and we have $\sum_{j=1}^{n} a_{ij} c_j = 0$ $(1 \leqslant i \leqslant n)$.

3. *Discriminants.*

Let K be a field, and let V and W be vector spaces of the same finite dimension n over K. Let β be a bilinear form on $V \times W$. If $B = (x_1, \cdots, x_n)$ and $C = (y_1, \cdots, y_n)$ are bases of V and W respectively, then the element

$\det(\beta(x_i, y_j))_{1 \leqslant i,j \leqslant n}$ is called the *discriminant* of β with respect to the bases B and C. If $V = W$, $C = B$, then the discriminant of β with respect to B and B is also called the discriminant of β with respect to B.

Let $B' = (x'_1, \cdots, x'_n)$ be some other base of V and $C' = (y'_1, \cdots, y'_n)$ some other base of W. Let T be the transition matrix from B to B' and U the transition matrix from C to C'. Then, if D is the discriminant of β with respect to B and C, its discriminant with respect to B' and C' is $(\det T)D(\det U)$. For, let $T = (t_{ij})$, $U = (u_{ij})$; then we have $x'_i = \sum_{k=1}^n t_{ki}x_k$, $y'_j = \sum_{m=1}^n u_{mj}y_m$, whence

$$\beta(x'_i, y'_j) = \sum_{k=1}^n \sum_{m=1}^n t_{ki}\beta(x_k, y_m)u_{mj}.$$

This shows that the matrix $(\beta(x'_i, y'_i))$ is equal to ${}^tT(\beta(x_i, y_j))U$; since $\det {}^tT = \det T$, our formula is established.

Theorem 40. *Let V and W be vector spaces of the same finite dimension n over a field K; let β be a bilinear form on $V \times W$. Let B be a base of V and C a base of W. A necessary and sufficient condition for β to be nondegenerate is for its discriminant with respect to B and C to be $\neq 0$.*

Set $B = (x_1, \cdots, x_n)$, $C = (y_1, \cdots, y_n)$, $\beta(x_i, y_j) = b_{ij}$. If $x = \sum_{i=1}^n c_i x_i$ is an element of V, a necessary and sufficient condition for $\beta(x, y)$ to be 0 for all y in W is that $\sum_{i=1}^n c_i b_{ij} = 0$ $(j = 1, \cdots, n)$. For this system of equations in $c_1, \cdots, c_n$ to have no solution other than $(0, \cdots, 0)$, it is necessary and sufficient that $\det(b_{ij}) = \det(b_{ji})$ should be $\neq 0$. We see in the same way that, if this condition is satisfied, then there does not exist any element $y \neq 0$ of W such that $\beta(x, y) = 0$ for every $x \in V$; theorem 40 is thereby proved.

11. Existence of certain derivations

In this section, we shall use the following notation. We shall denote by M a module over a commutative ring R, by E an exterior algebra on M, by E_n the module of homogeneous elements of E, by E^* the dual of E, with its structure as a Grassmann algebra. The multiplication in E is a bilinear mapping of $E \times E$ into E; we shall denote by μ the linearization of this mapping, which is a linear mapping of $E \otimes E$ into E. If g is any linear mapping of E into itself, and I the identity mapping of E into itself, $g \wedge I$ is a linear mapping of E into $E \otimes E$; we shall set

$$(1) \qquad h_g = \mu \circ (g \wedge I);$$

h_g is therefore a linear mapping of E into itself. We shall denote by U the analyzing mapping of E.

It is clear that $g \to h_g$ is an endomorphism of the module Hom (E, E) of all linear mappings of E into itself.

Theorem 41. *Assume that $g(E_p) = \{0\}$ if $p \neq 1$ and that g maps E_1 into E_n, for some $n \geqslant 0$. Then h_g is a homogeneous derivation of degree $n-1$ of E whose restriction to E_1 coincides with the restriction of g.*

Let x be in $E_1 = M$; then $h_g(x) = \mu((g \otimes I)(U(x)) = \mu(g(x) \otimes 1) = g(x)$, since $g(1) = 0$; this shows that g and h_g have the same restriction to E_1. Let t and u be any elements of E. Then $(g \wedge I)(tu) = (g \otimes I)(U(t)U(u))$. We have $E \otimes E = \Sigma_p E_p \otimes E$ (direct); we shall set, for any $v \in E$, $U(v) = \Sigma_p U_p(v)$, $U_p(v) \in E_p \otimes E$; $U_p(v)$ is therefore the homogeneous component of degree p of $U(v)$ in the gradation by the first partial degree. Since $g \otimes I$ maps $E_p \otimes E$ upon $\{0\}$ if $p \neq 1$, we have

$$(g \otimes I)(U(t)U(u)) = (g \otimes I)(U_1(t)U_0(u) + U_0(t)U_1(u)).$$

Since 1 is a basic element of E_0, $U_0(v)$ may be written in the form $1 \otimes w$, with some $w \in E$. Let ε be the linear form on E which maps 1 upon the unit element 1_R of R and E_m upon $\{0\}$ if $m > 1$; then we know that $(\varepsilon \otimes I) \circ U = I$ (formula (3), Sect. 8); it follows immediately that $v = (\varepsilon \otimes I)(U(v)) = w$. This being said, let us first compute $(g \otimes I)(U_1(t)U_0(u))$. Set

$$U_1(t) = \Sigma_{i=1}^h t'_i \otimes t''_i,$$

with $t'_i \in E_1$, $t''_i \in E$; then $U_1(t)U_0(u) = \Sigma_{i=1}^h t'_i \otimes t''_i u$; the image of this element under $g \otimes I$ is $\Sigma_{i=1}^h g(t'_i) \otimes t''_i u$. Next, consider $(g \otimes I)(U_0(t)U_1(u))$; set $U_1(u) = \Sigma_{j=1}^k u'_j \otimes u''_j$, $u'_j \in E_1$, $u''_j \in E$. Denote by J the main involution of E. If z is in E_q, then $(1 \otimes z)(u'_j \otimes u''_j) = (-1)^q u'_j \otimes z u''_j = u'_j \otimes J(z) u''_j$; it follows that $U_0(t)U_1(u) = \Sigma_{j=1}^k u'_j \otimes J(t) u''_j$, whose image under $g \otimes I$ is $\Sigma_{j=1}^k g(u'_j) \otimes J(t) u''_j$. Since $\mu(a \otimes b) = ab$ if a, b are in E, we have

$$h_g(tu) = \Sigma_{i=1}^h g(t'_i) t''_i u + \Sigma_{j=1}^k g(u'_j) J(t) u''_j.$$

If n is even, then $g(u'_j)$, which is in E_n, is in the center of E. If n is odd, then we have $g(u'_j)z = (-1)^q z g(u'_j)$ if $z \in E_q$, whence $g(u'_j)J(t) = t g(u'_j)$ Since $\Sigma_{i=1}^h g(t'_i) t''_i = h_g(t)$, $\Sigma_{j=1}^k g(u'_j) u''_j = h_g(u)$, we have

$$h_g(tu) = h_g(t)u + J^{n-1}(t) h_g(u).$$

It is clear that μ is homogeneous of degree 0 (relative to the gradation of $E \otimes E$ by the total degree). The image of $E_p \otimes E_q$ under $g \otimes I$ is $\{0\}$ if $p \neq 1$ and is contained in $E_n \otimes E_q$ if $p = 1$; it follows that $g \otimes I$ is homogeneous of degree $n-1$, and therefore that h_g is homogeneous of degree $n-1$. Theorem 41 is thereby proved.

Corollary. *Any linear mapping of M into E_n may be extended, in one and only one way, to a derivation of E; this derivation is homogeneous of degree $n-1$.*

The existence follows immediately from theorem 41. The uniqueness follows from the fact that M is a set of generators of E (corollary to theorem 17, Sect. 6).

Applying this in particular to the case where $n=0$, we see that, if λ is any linear form on M, there is a unique derivation d_λ of E such that $d_\lambda(x)=\lambda(x)\cdot 1$ for every $x \in M$; d_λ is homogeneous of degree -1. The mapping $\lambda \to d_\lambda$ is a linear mapping of the dual M^* of M into the module of derivations of E. We shall see that

$$d_\lambda \circ d_\lambda = 0. \tag{2}$$

The operation $d_\lambda \circ d_\lambda$ is a homogeneous derivation of degree -2 of E (theorem 18, Sect. 6); therefore it maps E_1 into $E_{-1}=\{0\}$. Since E_1 is a set of generators of E, it follows that $d_\lambda \circ d_\lambda = 0$. Applying formula (2) to $d_{\lambda'}$, d_λ, and $d_{\lambda+\lambda'}$, where λ, λ' are linear forms on M, we obtain

$$d_\lambda \circ d_{\lambda'} + d_{\lambda'} \circ d_\lambda = 0. \tag{3}$$

Theorem 42. *Let λ be a linear form on M and d_λ the derivation of E which maps any $x \in M$ upon $\lambda(x)\cdot 1$. Let $\overline{\lambda}$ be the linear form on E which extends λ and maps E_p upon $\{0\}$ if $p \neq 1$. Then the transpose ${}^t d_\lambda$ of d is the operation of left multiplication by $\overline{\lambda}$ in the algebra E^*.*

If we denote by g the mapping $t \to \overline{\lambda}(t)\cdot 1$ of E into iteslf, we have $d_\lambda = \mu \circ (g \otimes I) \circ U$. Now, $\overline{\lambda} \otimes I$ is a mapping of $E \otimes E$ into $R \otimes E = E$; if t, u are in E, then $(\mu \circ (g \otimes I))(t \otimes u) = g(t)u = \overline{\lambda}(t)u$, whence $\mu \circ (g \otimes I) = \overline{\lambda} \otimes I$. Let φ be any element of E^*; then

$${}^t d_\lambda(\varphi) = \varphi \circ d_\lambda = \varphi \circ (\overline{\lambda} \otimes I) \circ U.$$

Since $\varphi = I_R \otimes \varphi$ if I_R is the identity mapping of R, we have

$${}^t d_\lambda(\varphi) = (\overline{\lambda} \otimes \varphi) \circ U = \overline{\lambda} \wedge \varphi,$$

which proves theorem 42.

We have considered the case where g maps any E_p, $p \neq 1$, upon $\{0\}$. Now, we shall consider the case where $g(E) \subset E_1$, and we shall furthermore assume that there is an $n \geqslant 0$ such that $g(E_p) = \{0\}$ when $p \neq n$. Under these assumptions, we shall prove the formula

$$U \circ h_g = (h_g \otimes I) \circ U + (J^{n-1} \otimes h_g) \circ U, \tag{4}$$

where J is the main involution of E.

We have $U \circ h_g = U \circ \mu \circ (g \otimes I) \circ U$. The multiplication in the algebra $E \otimes E$ is a bilinear mapping of $(E \otimes E) \times (E \otimes E)$ into $E \otimes E$; the linearization of this bilinear mapping is a linear mapping of $(E \otimes E) \otimes (E \otimes E)$ into $E \otimes E$, which we shall denote by μ_2. If t, u are in E, we have $U(\mu(t \otimes u)) = U(tu) = U(t)U(u) = \mu_2(U(t) \otimes U(u))$, whence

$$U \circ \mu = \mu_2 \circ (U \otimes U).$$

We have

$$(U \otimes U) \circ (g \otimes I) = (U \circ g) \otimes U = ((U \circ g) \otimes (I \otimes I)) \circ (I \otimes U).$$

If $t \in E$, then $g(t) \in E_1$, whence $U(g(t)) = g(t) \otimes 1 + 1 \otimes g(t)$. Denote by θ_1 and θ_2 respectively the linear mappings $v \to v \otimes 1$ and $v \to 1 \otimes v$ of E into $E \otimes E$; then we have $U \circ g = \theta_1 \circ g + \theta_2 \circ g$, whence

$$\begin{aligned} &(U \otimes U) \circ (g \otimes I) \\ &= ((\theta_1 \circ g) \otimes (I \otimes I)) \circ (I \otimes U) + ((\theta_2 \circ g) \otimes (I \otimes I)) \circ (I \otimes U). \end{aligned}$$

Let t, u, v be in E. Then we have

$$\begin{aligned} &\mu_2(((\theta_1 \circ g) \otimes (I \otimes I))(t \otimes (u \otimes v))) \\ &= \mu_2((g(t) \otimes 1) \otimes (u \otimes v)) = g(t)u \otimes v = ((\mu \circ (g \otimes I))(t \otimes u)) \otimes v \\ &= ((\mu \circ (g \otimes I)) \otimes I)((t \otimes u) \otimes v). \end{aligned}$$

Denote by ω_E the canonical isomorphism of $E \otimes (E \otimes E)$ with $(E \otimes E) \otimes E$ which maps $t \otimes (u \otimes v)$ upon $(t \otimes u) \otimes v$ (if $t, u, v \in E$). Then we have

$$\mu_2 \circ ((\theta_1 \circ g) \otimes (I \otimes I)) \circ (I \otimes U) \circ U = ((\mu \circ (g \otimes I)) \otimes I) \circ \omega_E \circ (I \otimes U) \circ U.$$

But we know that $\omega_E \circ (I \otimes U) \circ U = (U \otimes I) \circ U$ (formula (1), Sect. 8), whence

$$\begin{aligned} &\mu_2 \circ ((\theta_1 \otimes g) \otimes (I \otimes I)) \circ (I \otimes U) \circ U \\ &= ((\mu \circ (g \otimes I)) \otimes I) \circ (U \otimes I) \circ U = ((\mu \circ (g \otimes I) \circ U) \otimes I) \circ U \\ &= (h_g \otimes I) \circ U. \end{aligned}$$

We have

$$\begin{aligned} \mu_2(((\theta_2 \circ g) \otimes (I \otimes I))(t \otimes (u \otimes v)) &= \mu_2((1 \otimes g(t)) \otimes (u \otimes v)) \\ &= (1 \otimes g(t))(u \otimes v). \end{aligned}$$

Since $g(t) \in E_1$, we have $(1 \otimes g(t))(z \otimes v) = (-1)^q z \otimes g(t)v = J(z) \otimes g(t)v$ if $z \in E_q$, whence $(1 \otimes g(t))(u \otimes v) = J(u) \otimes g(t)v$. Denote by ω'_E the automorphism of the module $E \otimes (E \otimes E)$ which maps $t \otimes (u \otimes v)$ upon $u \otimes (t \otimes v)$ if t, u, v are in E. Then we obtain

$$\mu_2 \circ ((\theta_2 \circ g) \otimes (I \otimes I)) = (J \otimes (\mu \circ (g \otimes I))) \circ \omega'_E.$$

Denote by ζ the automorphism of the module $E \otimes E$ which maps $t \otimes u$ upon $u \otimes t$ if $t, u \in E$; then it is clear that $\omega'_E = \overset{-1}{\omega}_E \circ (\zeta \otimes I) \circ \omega_E$. Since $\omega_E \circ (I \otimes U) \circ U = (U \otimes I) \circ U$, we have

$$\begin{aligned}&\mu_2 \circ ((\theta_2 \circ g) \otimes (I \otimes I)) \circ (I \otimes U) \circ U \\ &= (J \otimes (\mu \circ (g \otimes I))) \circ \overset{-1}{\omega}_E \circ ((\zeta \circ U) \otimes I) \circ U.\end{aligned}$$

Let K be the automorphism of the module $E \otimes E$ which maps any $w \in E_p \otimes E_q$ upon $(-1)^{pq} w$; then we have $\zeta \circ U = K \circ U$ (formula (4), Sect. 8). The mapping $\mu \circ (g \otimes I)$ maps $E_q \otimes E$ upon $\{0\}$ if $q \neq n$; thus, $(J \otimes (\mu \circ (g \otimes I)) \circ \overset{-1}{\omega}_E$ maps $(E \otimes E_q) \otimes E$ upon $\{0\}$ if $q \neq n$. On the other hand, if $t \in E_p$, $u \in E_n$, then $K(t \otimes u) = (-1)^{pn} t \otimes u = J^n(t) \otimes u$; it follows that $K \otimes I$ coincides with $(J^n \otimes I) \otimes I$ on $(E \otimes E_n) \otimes E$. Therefore, we have

$$\begin{aligned}&(J \otimes (\mu \circ (g \otimes I))) \circ \overset{-1}{\omega}_E \circ ((K \circ U) \otimes I) \circ U \\ &= (J \otimes (\mu \circ (g \otimes I))) \circ \overset{-1}{\omega}_E \circ ((J^n \otimes I) \otimes I) \circ (U \otimes I) \circ U.\end{aligned}$$

It is clear that $\overset{-1}{\omega}_E \circ ((J^n \otimes I) \otimes I) = (J^n \otimes (I \otimes I)) \circ \overset{-1}{\omega}_E$; since

$$\overset{-1}{\omega}_E \circ (U \otimes I) \circ U = (I \otimes U) \circ U,$$

we obtain

$$\begin{aligned}&(J \otimes (\mu \circ (g \otimes I))) \circ \overset{-1}{\omega}_E \circ ((\zeta \circ U) \otimes I) \circ U \\ &= (J \otimes (\mu \circ (g \otimes I))) \circ (J^n \otimes (I \otimes I)) \circ (I \otimes U) \circ U \\ &= (J^{n+1} \otimes (\mu \circ (g \otimes I) \circ U)) \circ U = (J^{n+1} \circ h_g) \circ U.\end{aligned}$$

Since J^2 is the identity, we have $J^{n+1} = J^{n-1}$, and formula (4) is proved.

Theorem 43. *Assume that g maps E_n into E_1 and E_p upon $\{0\}$ if $p \neq n$ (where n is some integer $\geqslant 0$). Denote by E^*_m the set of linear forms on E which map $E_{m'}$ upon $\{0\}$ whenever $m' \neq m$, and by G the subalgebra $G = \Sigma_{m \geqslant 0} E^*_m$ of E^*. Then the transpose mapping ${}^t h_g$ of h_g induces a homogeneous derivation of degree $n - 1$ of the graded algebra G.*

The mapping $g \otimes I$ maps $E_p \otimes E_q$ into $E_{p+1-n} \otimes E_q$; on the other hand, U and μ are homogeneous of degree 0 relative to the gradation of $E \otimes E$ by the total degree. It follows immediately that h_g is homogeneous of degree $1 - n$. Let φ be in E^*_m; then ${}^t h_g(\varphi) = \varphi \circ h_g$ maps E_p upon $\{0\}$ if $p + 1 - n \neq m$, whence ${}^t h_g(\varphi) \in E^*_{m+n-1}$; this shows that ${}^t h_g$ maps G into itself, and induces a homogeneous endomorphism of degree $n - 1$ of the graded module G. Let φ and ψ be elements of G. Then we have, by formula (4),

$$\begin{aligned}{}^t h_g(\varphi \wedge \psi) &= (\varphi \otimes \psi) \circ U \circ h_g \\ &= (\varphi \otimes \psi) \circ (h_g \otimes I) \circ U + (\varphi \otimes \psi) \circ (J^{n-1} \otimes h_g) \circ U \\ &= ((\varphi \circ h_g) \otimes \psi) \circ U + ((\varphi \circ J^{n-1}) \otimes (\psi \circ h_g)) \circ U.\end{aligned}$$

Let J^* be the main involution of the graded algebra G. If $\varphi \in E_m^*$, $t \in E_p$, then $(\varphi \circ J^{n-1})(t) = (-1)^{p(n-1)}\varphi(t) = (-1)^{m(n-1)}\varphi(t) = (((J^*)^{n-1})(\varphi))(t)$ since $\varphi(t) = 0$ if $p \neq m$. Thus we have $\varphi \circ J^{n-1} = (J^*)^{n-1}(\varphi)$, and therefore

$$^t h_g(\varphi \wedge \psi) = (^t h_g(\varphi)) \wedge \psi + (J^*)^{n-1}(\varphi) \wedge {}^t h_g(\psi).$$

Theorem 43 is thereby proved.

Consider the special case where $n = 0$. A linear mapping g of E_0 into E_1 is uniquely determined by the value $x = g(1)$ of 1, and x may be an arbitrary element of E_1. The mapping U_p being defined as in the proof of theorem 42, we have $(g \otimes I) \circ U_p = 0$ if $p > 0$. On the other hand, we have, for any $t \in E$, $(g \otimes I)(U_0(t)) = (g \otimes I)(1 \otimes t) = x \otimes t$, and the image of this element under μ is xt. Thus, in that case, h_g is the operation of left multiplication by x in E. This shows that, if $x \in M$, then the transpose of the operation of left multiplication by x in E induces a homogeneous derivation of degree -1 of G.

12. The trace of a matrix

Let $A = (a_{ij})$ be a square matrix of degree n with elements in a commutative ring R. Let R^n be the product of n modules identical to R, and $(e_1, \cdots, e_n)$ the canonical base of R^n. Relative to this base, A represents an endomorphism f of R^n which maps e_i upon $\sum_{j=1}^n a_{ji}e_j$. Let E be an exterior algebra on R^n. Since f is a linear mapping of M into $M = E_1$, f may be extended, in one and only one way, to a derivation d_f of degree 0 of E (corollary to theorem 41, Sect. 11). The mapping d_f maps into itself the module E_n of homogeneous elements of degree n of E; since E_n has a base composed of one element, there is a uniquely determined element s of E_n such that $d_f(t) = st$ for every $t \in E_n$. This element is called the *trace* of the matrix A and is denoted by Tr A.

If f and f' are endomorphisms of R^n, then $d_f + d_{f'}$ is a derivation of E which extends $f + f'$; it follows that $d_f + d_{f'} = d_{f+f'}$. We see in the same way that $d_{af} = ad_f$ if $a \in R$. Let A, A' be the matrices which represent f and f' with respect to the base $(e_1, \cdots, e_n)$; then we have, for $t \in E_n$, $d(t_f) = (\mathrm{Tr}\, A)t$, $d_{f'}(t) = (\mathrm{Tr}\, A')t$, $d_{f+f'}(t) = (\mathrm{Tr}\,(A + A'))t$, $d_{af}(t) = (\mathrm{Tr}\, aA)t$. It follows that the mapping $A \to$ Tr A is a linear form on the module of square matrices of degree n with elements in R. On the other hand, since d_f and $d_{f'}$ are derivations of degree 0, so is $d'' = d_f \circ d_{f'} - d_{f'} \circ d_f$ (theorem 18, Sect. 6); this derivation extends the mapping $f \circ f' - f' \circ f = f''$ of M into itself, whence $d'' = d_{f''}$. On the other hand, we have, for $t \in E_n$, $d''(t) = ((\mathrm{Tr}\, A)(\mathrm{Tr}\, A') - (\mathrm{Tr}\, A')(\mathrm{Tr}\, A))t = 0$. Since the matrix which represents f'' is $AA' - A'A$, we obtain $\mathrm{Tr}\,(AA' - A'A) = 0$, or

$$\mathrm{Tr}\, AA' = \mathrm{Tr}\, A'A. \tag{1}$$

In order to compute Tr A, we first establish the following formula. Let d be any derivation of degree 0 of a graded algebra E, and let $u_1, \cdots, u_n$ be elements of E; then we have

$$d(u_1 \cdots u_n) = \sum_{i=1}^{n} u_{1i} \cdots u_{ni} \tag{2}$$

where $u_{ji} = u_j$ if $j \neq i$, $u_{ii} = d(u_i)$. We proceed by induction on n. Formula (2) is obviously true if $n = 0$ or 1. Assume that $n > 1$ and that formula (2) is true for products of $n-1$ factors. Since d is a derivation of degree 0, we have

$$\begin{aligned} d(u_1 \cdots u_n) &= d(u_1 \cdots u_{n-1})u_n + u_1 \cdots u_{n-1}d(u_n) \\ &= (\textstyle\sum_{i=1}^{n-1} u_{1i} \cdots u_{n-1,i})u_n + u_1 \cdots u_{n-1}d(u_n), \end{aligned}$$

which proves that the formula is true for products of n factors.

This being said, let f be an endomorphism of R^n such that $f(e_i) = \sum_{j=1}^{n} a_{ji}e_j$, and let d_f be the derivation of an exterior algebra E on R^n which extends f. We have

$$(\Pi_{k<i}e_k)d_f(e_i)(\Pi_{k>i}e_k) = \sum_{j=1}^{n} a_{ji}(\Pi_{k<i}e_k)e_j(\Pi_{k>i}e_k) = a_{ii}e_1 \cdots e_n,$$

whence, by formula (2), $d_f(e_1 \cdots e_n) = (\sum_{i=1}^{n} a_{ii})e_1 \cdots e_n$, and therefore

$$\text{Tr } (a_{ij}) = \sum_{i=1}^{n} a_{ii}. \tag{3}$$

13. Alternating mutilinear mappings

Let M and P be modules over a commutative ring R, and n an integer $\geqslant 0$. Denote by M^n the product of n modules identical to M. A multilinear mapping φ of M^n into P is called *alternating* if we have $\varphi(x_1, \cdots, x_n) = 0$ whenever there exists an index $i < n$ such that $x_i = x_{i+1}$. Let E be an exterior algebra on M and E_n the module of homogeneous elements of degree n of E; if Λ is any linear mapping of E_n into P, then it is clear that the formula

$$\varphi(x_1, \cdots, x_n) = \Lambda(x_1 \cdots x_n) \qquad (x_i \in M, 1 \leqslant i \leqslant n)$$

defines an alternating n-linear mapping of M^n into P. We shall see that conversely, any alternating n-linear mapping may be defined in this manner.

Theorem 44. *The notation being as above, let φ be an n-linear alternating mapping of M^n into P. Then there exists a uniquely determined linear mapping Λ of E_n into P such that $\varphi(x_1, \cdots, x_n) = \Lambda(x_1 \cdots x_n)$ for all $x_1, \cdots, x_n$ in M.*

Let (T, θ) be a tensor algebra on M. It results from our construction of an exterior algebra that there exists a homomorphism f of T into E

such that $f \circ \theta$ is the identity mapping of M, and that the kernel of f is the ideal K generated in T by the elements $(\theta(x))^2$, for $x \in M$. Let T_n be the module of homogeneous elements of degree n of T; then f induces an epimorphism f_n of T_n on E_n whose kernel is $T_n \cap K$. The elements of K are the sums of elements of the form $a(\theta(x))^2b$, with a and b in T (theorem 2, Sect. 1). Moreover, any element of T may be written as a sum of decomposable elements; every element z of K is therefore a sum of elements of the form $a(\theta(x))^2b$, where the elements a and b are decomposable. Assume now that $z \in T_n$. Any decomposable element is homogeneous; if a and b are homogeneous of respective degrees p and q, then $a(\theta(x))^2b$ is homogeneous of degree $p + 2 + q$. Thus, any $z \in K \cap T_n$ may be written in the form $\sum_{i=1}^h a_i(\theta(x_i))^2b_i$, where a_i, b_i are decomposable elements of respective degrees p_i and q_i such that $p_i + q_i + 2 = n$. It follows immediately that $K \cap T_n$ is generated as a module by the elements of the form $\theta(y_1) \cdots \theta(y_n)$ where $y_1, \cdots, y_n$ are elements of M such that $y_i = y_{i+1}$ for at least one index $i < n$.

On the other hand, if τ_n is the mapping $(z_1, \cdots, z_n) \to \theta(z_1) \cdots \theta(z_n)$ of M^n into T_n, then we know that (T_n, τ_n) is a tensor product of n modules identical with M. Therefore, there exists a linear mapping Φ of T_n into P such that $\varphi = \Phi \circ \tau_n$. If $y_1, \cdots, y_n$ are elements of M such that $y_i = y_{i+1}$ for some index $i < n$, then we have $\Phi(\theta(y_1) \cdots \theta(y_n)) = \varphi(y_1, \cdots, y_n) = 0$; this shows that the kernel of Φ contains the kernel $K \cap T_n$ of f_n, and therefore that there exists a linear mapping Λ of E_n into P such that $\Phi = \Lambda \circ f_n$. If $x_1, \cdots, x_n$ are in M, we have

$$\varphi(x_1, \cdots, x_n) = \Phi(\tau_n(x_1, \cdots, x_n)) = \Lambda(f_n(\theta(x_1) \cdots \theta(x_n))) = \Lambda(x_1 \cdots x_n).$$

The uniqueness of the mapping Λ follows from the fact that E_n is generated as a module by the products in E of n elements of M. Theorem 44 is thereby proved.

Corollary. *Let the notation be as in theorem 44. Let $x_1, \cdots, x_n$ be elements of M and $A = (a_{ij})$ a square matrix of degree n. Set $y_i = \sum_{j=1}^n a_{ji}x_j$; then we have $\varphi(y_1, \cdots, y_n) = (\det A)\varphi(x_1, \cdots, x_n)$.*

For, we know that $y_1 \cdots y_n = (\det A)x_1 \cdots x_n$.

14. The Pfaffian of an alternating bilinear form

Let M be a module over a commutative ring R, and let γ be an alternating bilinear form on $M \times M$ (i. e., an alternating bilinear mapping of $M \times M$ into R). The form γ defines a linear mapping of M into its dual module, which assigns to every $x \in M$ the linear form $\gamma_x : y \to \gamma(x, y)$ on M. Let E be an exterior algebra on M. We know that, to every linear form λ

on M, there is associated a derivation d_λ of E which maps any $y \in M$ upon $\lambda(y)\cdot 1$ (corollary to theorem 41, Sect. 11). We shall denote by d_x the derivation which is associated to γ_x; thus, we have $d_x(y) = \gamma(x, y)$ for any $y \in M$. Let also L_x be the operation of left multiplication by x in E, i. e., the mapping $t \to xt$ of E into itself. We set

$$\Lambda_x = L_x + d_x;$$

$x \to \Lambda_x$ is therefore a linear mapping of M into the module Hom (E, E) of endomorphisms of the module E. We know that the module Hom (E, E) is the underlying module of an algebra, in which the multiplication is the mapping $(f, g) \to f \circ g$: we shall denote this algebra by A. We shall prove that $\Lambda_x \circ \Lambda_x = 0$ for every $x \in M$. We have

$$\Lambda_x \circ \Lambda_x = L_x \circ L_x + L_x \circ d_x + d_x \circ L_x + d_x \circ d_x.$$

We have, for $t \in E$, $L_x(L_x(t)) = x(xt) = 0$, whence $L_x \circ L_x = 0$. We have $d_x(L_x(t)) = d_x(xt) = d_x(x)t - xd_x(t)$; but $d_x(x) = \gamma(x, x) = 0$, and $xd_x(t) = (L_x \circ d_x)(t)$, whence $L_x \circ d_x + d_x \circ L_x = 0$. Finally, we have $d_x \circ d_x = 0$ by formula (2), Sect. 11. This shows that $\Lambda_x \circ \Lambda_x = 0$. It follows that the mapping $x \to \Lambda_x$ may be extended to a homomorphism $t \to \Lambda_t$ of E into A.

Let A_k be the set of homogeneous linear mappings of degree k of the graded module E into itself (where k is any integer). We know that $\sum_{k \in \underline{Z}} A_k = A'$ is a subalgebra of A; furthermore, the decomposition $A' = \sum_{k \in \underline{Z}} A_k$ defines on A' the structure of a graded algebra. If $x \in M$, then Λ_x is in A', since L_x is homogeneous of degree 1 and d_x homogeneous of degree -1; it follows that the image of E under the mapping $t \to \Lambda_t$ is contained in A'. If $t \in E$, we set

$$\Lambda_t = \sum_{k \in \underline{Z}} \Lambda_{k,t}, \qquad \Lambda_{k,t} \in A_k.$$

Concurrently with the mapping $t \to \Lambda_t$, we shall also consider the homomorphism $t \to \overline{\Lambda}_t$ which is defined in the same manner as the preceding one, but using the bilinear form $-\gamma$ instead of γ; we set $\overline{\Lambda}_t = \sum_{k \in \underline{Z}} \overline{\Lambda}_{k,t}$, $\overline{\Lambda}_{k,t} \in A_k$.

Lemma 1. *If $t \in E_n$, then $\Lambda_{k,t}$ and $\overline{\Lambda}_{k,t}$ are the zero mapping unless k is of the form $n - 2h$, with $0 \leqslant h \leqslant n$; furthermore, we have $\Lambda_{n-2h,t} = (-1)^h \overline{\Lambda}_{n-2h,t}$, and $\Lambda_{n,t}$ is the operator of left multiplication by t* (i. e., *the mapping $u \to tu$*). *If $t = x_1 \cdots x_n$, with $x_i \in M$ $(1 \leqslant i \leqslant n)$, then $\Lambda_{-n,t}$ is $d_{x_1} \circ \cdots \circ d_{x_n}$.*

The mappings $t \to \Lambda_{h,t}$ and $t \to \overline{\Lambda}_{h,t}$ being linear, it will be sufficient to prove our assertions in the case where $t = x_1 \cdots x_n$ is the product of n elements of M. The derivation of E which maps any $y \in M$ upon $-\gamma(x, y)$ is obviously $-d_x$; thus we have

$$\Lambda_t = (L_{x_1} + d_{x_1}) \circ \cdots \circ (L_{x_n} + d_{x_n}), \qquad \overline{\Lambda}_t = (L_{x_1} - d_{x_1}) \circ \cdots \circ (L_{x_n} - d_{x_n}).$$

Set $G_{i,1} = L_{x_i}$, $G_{i,2} = d_{x_i}$; denote by H_m the sum of the elements $G_{1,f(1)} \circ \cdots \circ G_{n,f(n)}$, for all mappings f of $\{1, \cdots, n\}$ into $\{1, 2\}$ with the property that there are exactly m indices i for which $f(i) = 2$; then we have $\Lambda_t = \sum_{m=0}^{n} H_m$, $\overline{\Lambda}_t = \sum_{m=0}^{n} (-1)^m H_m$; moreover, H_m is clearly homogeneous of degree $(n - m) - m = n - 2m$. We have $H_0 = L_{x_1} \circ \cdots \circ L_{x_n}$. If we denote by L_u the operator of left multiplication by an element u of E, then, clearly, $L_{uv} = L_u \circ L_v$ for any u, v in E; it follows that $H_0 = L_t$. Since $H_n = d_{x_1} \circ \cdots \circ d_{x_n}$, lemma 1 is proved.

We set

$$\Omega(t) = \Lambda_t(1), \qquad \overline{\Omega}(t) = \overline{\Lambda}_t(1).$$

Lemma 2. *If λ is any linear form on M, then Ω commutes with the derivation d_λ of E which maps any $x \in M$ upon $\lambda(x) \cdot 1$. The mappings Ω and $\overline{\Omega}$ are automorphisms of the module E, and each one is the inverse of the other.*

We shall prove by induction on n that, if $t \in E_n$, then

$$\Omega(d\ (t)) = d_\lambda(\Omega(t)), \qquad \overline{\Omega}(d_\lambda(t)) = d_\lambda(\overline{\Omega}(t)), \qquad \overline{\Omega}(\Omega(t)) = \Omega(\overline{\Omega}(t)) = t$$

Our formulas are true if $n = 0$. For, Λ_1 is the unit element of A, i. e., the identity mapping, whence $\Omega(1) = 1$, and, similarly, $\overline{\Omega}(1) = 1$; since $d_\lambda(1) = 0$, our formulas are true for $t = 1$, and therefore also for any $t \in E_0$. Assume that $n > 0$ and that our formulas are true when $t \in E_m$, for any $m < n$. Since every element of E_n is a linear combination of products of elements of M by elements of E_{n-1}, it will be sufficient, to prove our formulas in the case where $t \in E_n$, to consider the case of an element t of the form xu, with $x \in M$, $u \in E_{n-1}$. We have

$$\Omega(d_\lambda(xu)) = \Omega(\lambda(x)u - xd_\lambda(u)) = \lambda(x)\Omega(u) - \Omega(xd_\lambda(u)).$$

Now, we observe that, if v is any element of E, we have

$$(1) \qquad \Omega(xv) = \Lambda_{xv}(1) = \Lambda_x(\Lambda_v(1)) = \Lambda_x(\Omega(v)) = x\Omega(v) + d_x(\Omega(v)).$$

Thus we obtain

$$\Omega(d_\lambda(xu)) = \lambda(x)\Omega(u) - x\Omega(d_\lambda(u)) - d_x(\Omega(d_\lambda(u))).$$

Since $d_\lambda(u) \in E_{n-2}$, it follows from our inductive assumption that

$$\Omega(d_\lambda(u)) = d_\lambda(\Omega(u)).$$

On the other hand, we have $d_x \circ d_\lambda + d_\lambda \circ d_x = 0$ (formula (3), Sect. 11). It follows that

$$\Omega(d_\lambda(xu)) = d_\lambda(x\Omega(u)) + d_\lambda(d_x(\Omega(u))) = d_\lambda(\Omega(xu)),$$

by virtue of formula (1). We see in the same way that $\overline{\Omega}(d_\lambda(xu)) = d_\lambda(\overline{\Omega}(xu))$ We have

$$\overline{\Omega}(\Omega(xu)) = \overline{\Omega}(x\Omega(u) + d_x(\Omega(u))) = x\overline{\Omega}(\Omega(u)) - d_x(\overline{\Omega}(\Omega(u))) + \overline{\Omega}(d_x(\Omega(u))),$$

by application of the formula analogous to (1) for $\overline{\Omega}$. Since $u \in E_{n-1}$, we have $\overline{\Omega}(\Omega(u)) = u$ by our inductive assumption. On the other hand, it follows immediately from lemma 1 that $\Omega(u)$ belongs to $\sum_{m \leqslant n-1} E_m$, and therefore that $\overline{\Omega}(d_x(\Omega(u))) = d_x(\overline{\Omega}(\Omega(u)))$ by our inductive assumption. Thus we have $\overline{\Omega}(\Omega(xu)) = xu$. We would see in the same way that $\Omega(\overline{\Omega}(xu)) = xu$.

Lemma 3. *Let Γ be the prolongation of the bilinear form γ to $E \times E$. Denote by ε the linear form on E which maps 1 upon the unit element of R and E_p upon $\{0\}$ when $p > 0$. If t and u are elements of E_n, then we have* $\Gamma(t, u) = (-1)^{n(n-1)/2}\varepsilon(\Lambda_t(u))$.

The mappings $t \to \Gamma(t, u)$ and $t \to \Lambda_t(u)$ being linear, it will be sufficient to prove this in the case where $t = x_1 \cdots x_n$, $x_1, \cdots, x_n$ being elements of M. The homogeneous component of degree 0 of $\Lambda_t(u)$ is $\Lambda_{-n,t}(u)$, since $u \in E_n$, and we have $\Lambda_{-n,t} = d_{x_1} \circ \cdots \circ d_{x_n}$. Let $\overline{\lambda}_i$ be the linear form on E which maps any $y \in M$ upon $\gamma(x_i, y)$ and E_p upon $\{0\}$ if $p \neq 1$. Then the transpose mapping of d_{x_i} is the operation of left multiplication by $\overline{\lambda}_i$ in the dual algebra E^* of E (theorem 42, Sect. 11). Therefore, the transpose mapping of $\Lambda_{-n,t}$ is the operation of left multiplication by $\varphi = \overline{\lambda}_n \circ \cdots \circ \overline{\lambda}_1$ in E^*, and we have $\varepsilon(\Lambda_{-n,t}(u)) = (\varphi \wedge \varepsilon)(u) = \varphi(u)$, since ε is the unit element of E^*. Let θ be the homomorphism of E into E^* associated with γ; then we have $\varphi = \theta(x_n \cdots x_1)$. It is easily seen that the signature of the permutation of $\{1, \cdots, n\}$ which maps k upon $n - k + 1$ $(1 \leqslant k \leqslant n)$ is $(-1)^{n(n-1)/2}$; thus we have $x_n \cdots x_1 = (-1)^{n(n-1)/2} x_1 \cdots x_n$. On the other hand, we have by definition $\Gamma(t, u) = (\theta(t))(u)$; lemma 3 is thereby proved.

Lemma 4. *Let t be an element of the form $x_1 \cdots x_n$, with $x_i \in M$ $(1 \leqslant i \leqslant n)$. The notation being as in lemma 3, we have*

$$\Gamma(t, t) = (\varepsilon(\Omega(t)))^2.$$

The left side is $(-1)^{n(n-1)/2}\varepsilon(\Lambda_t(t))$. Set $\overline{\Omega}(t) = \overline{t}$; then $\Lambda_t(t) = \Lambda_t(\Omega(\overline{t}))$, by lemma 2, and this is equal to $\Lambda_t(\Lambda_{\overline{t}}(1)) = \Lambda_{t\overline{t}}(1) = \Omega(t\overline{t})$. Let F be the subalgebra of E generated by $x_1, \cdots, x_n$; if $1 \leqslant i \leqslant n$, then L_{x_i} obviously maps F into itself, and so does d_{x_i} because d_{x_i} is a derivation and maps the generators x_j of F upon the elements $\gamma(x_i, x_j)\cdot 1$, which belong to F (cf. theorem 17, Sect. 6). Since $\overline{\Lambda}_t = (L_{x_1} - d_{x_1}) \circ \cdots \circ (L_{x_n} - d_{x_n})$, $\overline{\Lambda}_t$ maps F into itself, whence $\overline{t} = \overline{\Lambda}_t(1) \in F$. We conclude that $\overline{t}$ is a linear combination of the products $x_{i_1} \cdots x_{i_h}$ for all strictly increasing sequences $(i_1, \cdots, i_h)$ of integers between 1 and n. Since $t = x_1 \cdots x_n$, we have $tx_{i_1} \cdots x_{i_h} = 0$ whenever $h > 0$; it follows immediately that $t\overline{t} = \varepsilon(\overline{t})t$, whence $\Omega(t\overline{t}) = \varepsilon(\overline{t})\Omega(t)$ and we have $\Gamma(t, t) = (-1)^{n(n-1)/2}\varepsilon(\overline{\Omega}(t))\varepsilon(\Omega(t))$. It will therefore be sufficient to prove that $\varepsilon(\overline{\Omega}(t)) = (-1)^{n(n-1)/2}\varepsilon(\Omega(t))$. Using the notation of lemma 1 we have

$$\Omega(t) = \Sigma_{h=0}^{n} \Lambda_{n-2h,t}(1), \qquad \overline{\Omega}(t) = \Sigma_{h=0}^{n} (-1)^h \Lambda_{n-2h,t}(1).$$

The element $\Lambda_{n-2h,t}(1)$ is homogeneous of degree $n-2h$. Thus, if n is odd, then $\varepsilon(\Omega(t))$ and $\varepsilon(\overline{\Omega}(t))$ are both equal to 0. Assume that $n = 2n'$ is even; then $\varepsilon(\Omega(t)) = (-1)^{n'}\varepsilon(\overline{\Omega}(t))$, and we have $(-1)^{n'} = (-1)^{n(n-1)/2}$; lemma 4 is thereby proved.

It will be observed that the proof has shown that $\varepsilon(\Omega(t)) = 0$ when n is odd.

Lemma 5. *Let φ be a linear mapping of a module M' over R into M. Let γ' be the bilinear form on $M' \times M'$ defined by $\gamma'(x', y') = \gamma(\varphi(x'), \varphi(y'))$. Let E' be an exterior algebra on M', Φ the prolongation of φ to E' and Ω' the automorphism of the module E' which is associated with γ' in the same way as Ω is associated with γ. Then we have $\Phi \circ \Omega' = \Omega \circ \Phi$.*

If $x' \in M'$, denote by $L'_{x'}$ the operator of left multiplication by x' in E' and by $d'_{x'}$ the derivation of E' which maps any $y' \in M'$ upon $\gamma'(x', y')\cdot 1$; set $\Lambda'_{x'} = L'_{x'} + d'_{x'}$. Since $\Phi(x't') = \Phi(x')\Phi(t')$ if $x' \in M'$, $t' \in E'$, we have $\Phi \circ L'_{x'} = L_{\Phi(x')} \circ \Phi$. The operations $\Phi \circ d'_{x'}$ and $d_{\Phi(x')} \circ \Phi$ are both Φ-derivations of E' into E (theorem 16, Sect. 6); if $y' \in M'$, they both map y' upon $\gamma'(x', y') = \gamma(\Phi(x'), \Phi(y'))$. These operations are therefore identical to each other (corollary to theorem 17, Sect. 6). It follows that $\Phi \circ \Lambda'_{x'} = \Lambda_{\Phi(x')} \circ \Phi$ for any $x' \in M'$. Let $t' \to \Lambda'_{t'}$ be the homomorphism of E' into the algebra of endomorphisms of E' which extends the mapping $x' \to \Lambda'_{x'}$. If $t' = x'_1 \cdots x'_n$ with $x'_i \in M'$ $(1 \leqslant i \leqslant n)$, then

$$\Lambda'_{t'} = \Lambda'_{x'_1} \circ \cdots \circ \Lambda'_{x'_n}, \quad \Lambda_{\Phi(t')} = \Lambda_{\Phi(x'_1)} \circ \cdots \circ \Lambda_{\Phi(x'_n)},$$

and it follows that $\Phi \circ \Lambda'_{t'} = \Lambda_{\Phi(t')} \circ \Phi$; it follows immediately that this last formula is true for any $t' \in E'$. Applying both sides to the unit element, we obtain $\Phi(\Omega'(t)) = \Omega(\Phi(t))$.

We may define a new multiplication on the module E, say $(t, u) \to t \,\square\, u$, by the condition that $\Omega(tu) = \Omega(t) \,\square\, \Omega(u)$ for any t and u in E: this is accomplished by taking $t \,\square\, u$ to be $\Omega(\overline{\Omega}(t)\overline{\Omega}(u))$. With this new multiplication, E becomes an algebra $\overline{E}$ over R, and Ω is an isomorphism of E with $\overline{E}$. Since Ω coincides with the identity on M, $\overline{E}$ is again an exterior algebra on M.

Let $A = (a_{ij})$ be a square matrix of degree n with elements in a commutative ring R. Let R^n be the product of n modules over R identical to R, and let $(e_{n1}, \cdots, e_{nn})$ be the canonical base of R^n, e_{ni} being the element whose i-th coordinate is 1 and whose other coordinates are 0. We may associate with A the bilinear form γ_A on $R^n \times R^n$ which is defined by the condition that $\gamma_A(e_{ni}, e_{nj}) = a_{ij}$ $(1 \leqslant i, j \leqslant n)$. We have, if $\alpha_1, \cdots, \alpha_n \in R$,

$$\gamma_A(\Sigma_{i=1}^{n} \alpha_i e_{ni}, \Sigma_{i=1}^{n} \alpha_i e_{ni}) = \Sigma_{1 \leqslant i < j \leqslant n} \alpha_i \alpha_j (a_{ij} + a_{ji}) + \Sigma_{i=1}^{n} \alpha_i^2 a_{ii}.$$

The matrix A is called *alternating* if the bilinear form γ_A is alternating. If this is so, then, computing $\gamma_A(e_i + e_j, e_i + e_j)$ and $\gamma_A(e_i, e_i)$ by the preceding formula, we see that $a_{ij} + a_{ji} = 0$, $a_{ii} = 0$. Conversely, our formula shows that these conditions are also sufficient to make A an alternating matrix. Assume that A is alternating; let E be an exterior algebra on R^n, and denote by Ω the automorphism of the module E associated with the alternating bilinear form γ_A; set $t = e_{n1} \cdots e_{nn}$, denote by ε the unit element of the dual algebra E^* of E and set $\pi = \varepsilon(\Omega(t))$. The element π of R depends only on the matrix A, not on the choice of the exterior algebra E on R^n. For, let E' be some other exterior algebra on R^n. Then there is an isomorphism Φ of E with E' which coincides with the identity mapping on R^n: Φ is the prolongation to E of the identity mapping of R^n into itself. The transpose mapping ${}^t\Phi$ of Φ is an isomorphism of the dual algebra E'^* of E' with E^* (corollary to theorem 24, Sect. 8) and consequently maps the unit element ε' of E'^* upon ε, whence $\varepsilon' \circ \Phi = \varepsilon$. On the other hand, $t' = \Phi(t)$ is the product of $e_{n1}, \cdots, e_{nn}$ in the algebra E' and we have $\Omega'(t') = \Phi(\Omega(t))$ by lemma 5, whence $\varepsilon'(\Omega'(t')) = \varepsilon(\Omega(t))$, which proves our assertion. The element π is called the *Pfaffian* of the alternating matrix A, and is denoted by Pf A.

Theorem 45. *Let A be an alternating matrix of degree n with elements in a commutative ring R. Then we have* $\det A = (\mathrm{Pf}\ A)^2$; *if n is odd, then* $\mathrm{Pf}\ A = 0$.

We use the same notation as above. If Γ is the prolongation to $E \times E$ of the bilinear form γ_A, then we have $\det A = \Gamma(t, t)$ by theorem 29, Sect. 9. The first assertion therefore follows from lemma 4. The second follows from the remark which comes after the proof of lemma 4.

Theorem 46. *Let A be an alternating matrix of degree n with elements in a commutative ring R, and let B be any square matrix of degree n with elements in R. Then ${}^tB \cdot A \cdot B$ is alternating and we have* $\mathrm{Pf}\ ({}^tB \cdot A \cdot B) = (\det B)(\mathrm{Pf}\ A)$.

We set $A' = {}^tB \cdot A \cdot B = (a'_{ij})$, and we denote by $\gamma_{A'}$ the bilinear form on $R^n \times R^n$ such that $\gamma_{A'}(e_{ni}, e_{nj}) = a'_{ij}$. Let φ be the endomorphism of R^n which is represented by B relative to the base $(e_{n1}, \cdots e_{nn})$, whence $\varphi(e_{ni}) = \sum_{k=1}^n b_{ki}e_{nk}$ if $B = (b_{ij})$. We see easily that $\gamma_A(\varphi(e_{ni}), \varphi(e_{nj})) = a'_{ij}$; $\gamma_{A'}$ is therefore the bilinear form $(x, y) \to \gamma_A(\varphi(x), \varphi(y))$, which shows that $\gamma_{A'}$, and therefore also A', is alternating. Let Ω and Ω' be the automorphisms of the module E which are associated with the bilinear forms γ_A and $\gamma_{A'}$; if Φ is the prolongation of φ to E, then we have $\Phi \circ \Omega' = \Omega \circ \Phi$ by lemma 5, whence, if $t = e_{n1} \cdots e_{nn}$, $\varepsilon(\Omega'(t)) = \varepsilon(\Omega(\Phi(t)))$. But we have $\Phi(t) = (\det B)t$ by theorem 31, Sect. 9; therefore, $\varepsilon(\Omega'(t)) = (\det B)\varepsilon(\Omega(t))$, and theorem 46 is proved.

15. Exterior algebras on vector spaces

In this section, we shall denote by K a field. Let V be a finite dimensional vector space over K; set $\dim V = n$. Let E be an exterior algebra on V; denote by E_p the space of homogeneous elements of degree p of E. Let $(x_1, \cdots, x_n)$ be a base of V. For any strictly increasing sequence $\sigma = (i_1, \cdots, i_h)$ of integers between 1 and n, set $t(\sigma) = x_{i_1} \cdots x_{i_h}$. Then the elements $t(\sigma)$, for all strictly increasing sequences of length p, form a base of E_p (theorem 30, Sect. 9). The number of these sequences is obviously equal to the number of the subsets with p elements of $\{1, \cdots, n\}$; this is also the dimension of E_p. The vector space E is of dimension 2^n which is equal to the number of all subsets of $\{1, \cdots, n\}$.

Denote by V^* the dual space of V and by $E(V^*)$ an exterior algebra on V^*. Then the canonical homomorphism of $E(V^*)$ into the dual E^* of the vector space E (with its structure of a Grassmann algebra) is an isomorphism (theorem 30, Sect. 9). Another way of saying this is the following: the prolongation to $E \times E(V^*)$ of the canonical bilinear form $(x, x^*) \to x^*(x)$ on $V \times V^*$ is a nondegenerate bilinear form on $E \times E(V^*)$.

Let z be any basic element of the one dimensional space E_n (for instance $z = x_1 \cdots x_n$). Let p be any integer between 0 and n; if $t \in E_p$, $u \in E_{n-p}$, we may write

$$tu = \beta_p(t, u)z, \quad \beta_p(t, u) \in K.$$

It is clear that β_p is a bilinear form on $E_p \times E_{n-p}$. This bilinear form is nondegenerate. For, let $t = \Sigma_\sigma a(\sigma)t(\sigma)$ $(a(\sigma) \in K$, the summation being extended to all strictly increasing sequences σ of length $p)$ be an element of E_p such that $\beta_p(t, u) = 0$ for all $u \in E_{n-p}$. Let τ be any strictly increasing sequence of length $n - p$, and let τ^* be the strictly increasing sequence of length p formed by the indices which do not occur in τ. If σ is any strictly increasing sequence of length p distinct from τ^*, then σ and τ have one term in common, whence $t(\sigma)t(\tau) = 0$. It follows that $a(\tau^*)\eta(\tau^*, \tau)x_1 \cdots x_n = 0$; since $\eta(\tau^*, \tau) = \pm 1$, we have $a(\tau^*) = 0$; this being true for every strictly increasing sequence τ of length $n - p$, we conclude that $t = 0$. We would see in the same way that the conditions $u \in E_{n-p}$, $\beta_p(t, u) = 0$ for all $t \in E_p$ imply $u = 0$.

The bilinear form β_p depends on the choice of the basic element z of E_n; if z is replaced by az, a being an element $\neq 0$ of K, then β_p is replaced by $a^{-1}\beta_p$.

Now, let W be any p-dimensional subspace of V Then the subalgebra F of E generated by W is an exterior algebra on W (corollary 2 to theorem 22, Sect. 7). The space F_p of homogeneous elements of degree p of F is of dimension 1 and contained in E_p; any basic element of this space is called a *representative p-vector* of W. If $(y_1, \cdots, y_p)$ is a base of W, then $y_1 \cdots y_p$ is a representative p-vector of W. Conversely, if $p > 0$, any representative p-vector of W is the product of the elements of some base of W; for, if a is an element $\neq 0$ of K, $ay_1 \cdots y_p$ may be written in the form $(ay_1) \cdots y_p$, and $(ay_1, \cdots, y_p)$ is a base of W. If we put a representative p-vector t of W in the form $\Sigma_\sigma a(\sigma)t(\sigma)$ (the summation being extended to all strictly increasing sequences σ of length p, and the elements $t(\sigma)$ being defined as above), then the elements $a(\sigma)$ are said to constitute a system of *Plücker coordinates of the first kind of the space* W with respect to the base $(x_1, \cdots, x_n)$. Once the base $(x_1, \cdots, x_n)$ is determined, any other system of Plücker coordinates of the first kind of W with respect to this base is of the form $(ba(\sigma))$, b being an element $\neq 0$ in K.

Theorem 47. *Let V be a vector space of finite dimension n, E an exterior algebra on V and W a p-dimensional subspace of V; let t be a representative p-vector of W. Then W is the set of elements y of V such that $yt = 0$.*

We use the same notation as above. If $y \in W$, then yt is a homogeneous element of degree $p + 1$ of F, whence $yt = 0$. If y is an element of V not in W, then $y, y_1, \cdots, y_p$ are linearly independent and may therefore be included in a base of V. It follows that $yy_1 \cdots y_p \neq 0$, whence $yt \neq 0$.

It follows in particular from theorem 47 that a subspace of V is uniquely determined once a representative p-vector of this subspace is given. However, in general, not every element $t \neq 0$ of E_p is the representative p-vector of a subspace of W: if $p > 0$, t must be the product of p elements of V, i. e., it must be decomposable.

Theorem 48. *Let V be a vector space of finite dimension n, E an exterior algebra on V and W, W' subspaces of V of respective dimensions p, p'; let t (resp.: t') be a representative p-vector (resp.: p'-vector) of W (resp.: W'). If $W \cap W' \neq \{0\}$, then we have $tt' = 0$; if $W \cap W' = \{0\}$ then tt' is a representative $(p + p')$-vector of $W + W'$.*

If W, W' have an element $y \neq 0$ in common, there are bases $(y_1, \cdots, y_p)$ of W and $(y'_1, \cdots, y'_{p'})$ of W' such that $y_1 = y'_1 = y$, whence $y_1 \cdots y_p y'_1 \cdots y'_{p'} = 0$ and $tt' = 0$. If not, let $(y_1, \cdots, y_p)$ be any base of W and $(y'_1, \cdots, y'_{p'})$ any base of W'. Then $(y_1, \cdots, y_p, y'_1, \cdots, y'_{p'})$ is a base of $W + W'$, and $y_1 \cdots y_p y'_1 \cdots y'_{p'}$ is a representative $(p + p')$-vector of $W + W'$; the same is therefore true of tt'.

Let V^* be the dual of the space V. If W is a subspace of V, we shall call the orthogonal space of W the subspace of V^* composed of the elements x^* such that $x^*(W) = \{0\}$. Let E^* be the dual space of E; if A is a subspace of E, we shall call the orthogonal space of A the subspace of E^* composed of the elements φ such that $\varphi(A) = \{0\}$.

Theorem 49. *Let V be a vector space of finite dimension over K, W a subspace of V, V^* the dual space of V, W^0 the orthogonal space of W. Let $E(V)$ and $E(V^*)$ be exterior algebras on V and V^* and Λ the canonical isomorphism of $E(V^*)$ with the dual algebra $E^*(V)$ of $E(V)$. The orthogonal space of the ideal generated by W in $E(V)$ is the image under Λ of the subalgebra of $E(V^*)$ generated by W^0. The orthogonal space of the subalgebra of $E(V)$ generated by W is the image under Λ of the ideal generated by W^0 in $E(V^*)$.*

Let π be the natural mapping of V on V/W, $E(V/W)$ an exterior algebra on V/W, $\bar{\pi}$ the prolongation of π to E, $E^*(V/W)$ the dual algebra of $E(V/W)$, and ${}^t\bar{\pi}$ the transpose mapping of $\bar{\pi}$. Then the orthogonal space of the ideal $\mathfrak{K}$ generated by W is ${}^t\bar{\pi}(E^*(V/W))$ (theorem 25, Sect. 8). The algebra $E^*(V/W)$ is isomorphic to an exterior algebra on the dual of V/W, and is therefore generated by its homogeneous elements of degree 1; thus the orthogonal space of $\mathfrak{K}$ is a subalgebra of E^* generated by its homogeneous elements of degree 1. But the homogeneous elements of degree 1 of the orthogonal space of $\mathfrak{K}$ are obviously the elements of $\Lambda(W^0)$, which proves the first assertion. Let K be the identity mapping of W into V, $E(W)$ an exterior algebra on W, $\bar{K}$ the prolongation of K to $E(W)$, $E^*(W)$ the dual algebra of $E(W)$ and ${}^t\bar{K}$ the transpose mapping of $\bar{K}$. Then the orthogonal space of the subalgebra F of $E(V)$ generated by W is the kernel of ${}^t\bar{K}$ (theorem 25, Sect. 8). If we denote by $E_1^*(V)$ and $E_1^*(W)$ the spaces of homogeneous elements of degree 1 of $E^*(V)$ and $E^*(W)$, then $E^*(V)$ (resp.: $E^*(W)$) is an exterior algebra on $E_1^*(V)$ (resp.: $E_1^*(W)$) (because of the fact that Λ is an isomorphism, and of the similar statement for W). The restriction of ${}^t\bar{K}$ to $E_1^*(V)$ is an epimorphism of this space on $E_1^*(W)$ whose kernel is $\Lambda(W^0)$; the kernel of ${}^t\bar{K}$ is therefore the ideal generated by $\Lambda(W^0)$ (theorem 21, Sect. 7), which proves the second assertion.

The notation being as in theorem 49, denote by G the subalgebra of $E^*(V)$ generated by $\Lambda(W^0)$. Then, since Λ is an isomorphism of $E(V^*)$ with $E^*(V)$, G is an exterior algebra on $\Lambda(W^0)$. If p is the dimension of W, then the dimension of W^0 is $n-p$, and the space G_{n-p} of homogeneous elements of degree $n-p$ of G is of dimension 1. Any basic element of this space is called a *representative* $(n-p)$*-form* of the space W. If $(\lambda_1, \cdots, \lambda_{n-p})$ is a base of W^0, then $\Lambda(\lambda_1) \wedge \cdots \wedge \Lambda(\lambda_{n-p})$ is a representative form of W. Let $(x_1, \cdots, x_n)$ be a base of V; for any strictly increasing sequence $\sigma = (i_1, \cdots, i_h)$ of integers between 1 and n, set $t(\sigma) = x_{i_1} \cdots x_{i_h}$, $t^*(\sigma) = \Lambda(x^*_{i_1} \cdots x^*_{i_h})$, $(x^*_1, \cdots, x^*_n)$ being the base of V^* dual to the base $(x_1, \cdots, x_n)$ of V. Then the elements $t(\sigma)$ form a base of $E(V)$, and the elements $t^*(\sigma)$ a base of $E^*(V)$; we have

$$(t^*(\sigma))(t(\sigma')) = \begin{cases} 1 \text{ if } \sigma = \sigma' \\ 0 \text{ if } \sigma \neq \sigma'. \end{cases} \tag{1}$$

If φ is a representative $(n-p)$-form of W, then φ may be written in the form $\Sigma_\sigma a'(\sigma)t^*(\sigma)$, the summation being extended to the strictly increasing sequences of length $n-p$; we then say that the elements $a'(\sigma)$ form a *system of Plücker coordinates of the second kind* of the space W.

We shall now study the relationship between representative p-vectors and $(n-p)$-forms of a space W. We have defined above a bilinear form β_p on $E_p \times E_{n-p}$, which depends on the choice of a basic element in E_n; we shall suppose that we have taken this basic element to be $x_1 \cdots x_n$ (where $(x_1, \cdots, x_n)$ is a base of V). We have seen that β_p is nondegenerate; thus, it defines an isomorphism of E_p with the dual of E_{n-p} which maps any $t \in E_p$ upon the linear form $u \to \beta_p(t, u)$ on E_{n-p}. On the other hand, if E^*_{n-p} is the space of homogeneous elements of degree $n-p$ of E^*, then E^*_{n-p} is also isomorphic to the dual of E_{n-p}. It follows that there exists an isomorphism Q_p of E_p with E^*_{n-p} which maps any $t \in E$ upon the linear form ζ on E defined by $\zeta(u) = \beta_p(t, u)$ if $u \in E_{n-p}$, $\zeta(u) = 0$ if $u \in E_q$ for some $q \neq n-p$. We may explicit this isomorphism as follows. For any strictly increasing sequence σ of indices between 1 and n, we denote by σ^* the strictly increasing sequence formed by the indices which do not occur in σ. If σ and τ are strictly increasing sequences of respective lengths p and $n-p$, then $t(\sigma)t(\tau)$ is 0 if $\tau \neq \sigma^*$, while, if $\tau = \sigma^*$, then $t(\sigma)t(\tau) = \eta(\sigma, \sigma^*)x_1 \cdots x_n$. It follows that $\beta_p(t(\sigma), t(\tau)) = 0$ if $\tau \neq \sigma^*$, $\beta_p(t(\sigma), t(\sigma^*)) = \eta(\sigma, \sigma^*)$. Comparing with the formulas (1), we obtain

$$Q_p(t(\sigma)) = \eta(\sigma, \sigma^*)t^*(\sigma^*).$$

Now, we shall see that Q_p maps the representative p-vectors of W upon its representative $(n-p)$-forms. In order to prove this, we may assume without loss of generality that $\{x_1, \cdots, x_n\}$ contains a base $\{x_1, \cdots, x_p\}$ of W; if $\sigma_1 = (1, \cdots, p)$, the representative p-vectors of W are then the elements $at(\sigma_1)$, with $a \neq 0$ in K. On the other hand, $\{x^*_{p+1}, \cdots, x^*_n\}$ is a base of W^0 and the representative $(n-p)$-forms of W are therefore the elements $at^*(\sigma_1^*)$, $a \neq 0$ in K, which proves our assertion. Returning to the general case, where the base $(x_1, \cdots, x_n)$ is not related in any particular way to W, we see that, if

$$t = \Sigma_\sigma a(\sigma)t(\sigma)$$

is a representative p-vector of W, then

$$t^* = \Sigma_\sigma \eta(\sigma, \sigma^*)a(\sigma)t^*(\sigma^*)$$

is a representative $(n-p)$-form of W.

Theorem 50. *Let V be a vector space of finite dimension over K, and let W and W' be subspaces of V, of respective dimensions p and p'; let φ be a representative $(n-p)$-form of W and φ' a representative $(n-p')$-form of W'.*

If $W \cap W'$ is of dimension $> p + p' - n$, then $\varphi \wedge \varphi' = 0$; if $W \cap W'$ is of dimension $p + p' - n$, then $\varphi \wedge \varphi'$ is a representative $(2n - p - p')$-form of $W \cap W'$.

Let W^0 (resp. : W'^0) be the space of linear forms on V which map W (resp.: W') upon $\{0\}$; then the space of linear forms which map $W \cap W'$ upon $\{0\}$ is $W^0 + W'^0$ (theorem 61, Chapter III, Sect. 13). The spaces W^0 and W'^0 are of dimensions $n - p$ and $n - p'$. A necessary and sufficient condition for $W^0 \cap W'^0$ to be $\{0\}$ is that the sum $W^0 + W'^0$ be direct, *i. e.*, that the dimension of $W^0 + W'^0$ be $2n - p - p'$, or also that the dimension of $W \cap W'$ be $n\text{-}(2n - p - p') = p + p' - n$. Let V^* be the dual space of V, $E(V^*)$ an exterior algebra on V^* and Λ the canonical isomorphism of $E(V^*)$ with E^*. Then φ and φ' are the images under Λ of a representative $(n - p)$ -vector of W^0 and of a $(n - p')$-representative vector of W'^0 respectively. Theorem 50 therefore follows from theorem 48.

16. Transfer of the basic ring

In this section, we shall denote by R a commutative ring and by ρ a homomorphism of R into a commutative ring S. If M is any module over R, we shall denote by M^S a module over S which is deduced from M by inverse transfer of the basic ring to S. It will be remembered that the additive group of M^S is the same as that of $S \otimes M$, S being regarded as a module over R in which the scalar multiplication is defined by $\alpha\beta = \rho(\alpha)\beta$ $(\alpha \in R,\ \beta \in S)$. The scalar multiplication of M^S is defined by the condition that $\beta(\beta' \otimes x) = \beta\beta' \otimes x$ if β, β' are in S and x in M.

We have on S the structure of a module over R, and the structure of a ring; these two structures combine with each other to give the structure of an algebra over R on S. In order to show this, we have to establish that the mapping $(\beta, \beta') \rightarrow \beta\beta'$ of $S \times S$ into S is bilinear with respect to the module structure of S over R. We know already that this mapping is biadditive. Let α be an element of R; then we have

$$(\alpha\beta)\beta' = \rho(\alpha)\beta\beta' = \alpha(\beta\beta'), \qquad \beta(\alpha\beta') = \beta\rho(\alpha)\beta' = \rho(\alpha)\beta\beta' = \alpha(\beta\beta'),$$

since S is a commutative ring; this proves our assertion. We may consider S as a graded algebra over R in which every element is homogeneous of degree 0.

Let A be any graded algebra over R. Then the tensor product $S \otimes A$ has the structure of a graded algebra over R. On the other hand, $S \otimes A$ is the set of elements of the module A^S; thus we have a multiplication on A^S (the multiplication of $S \otimes A$) relative to which A^S is a ring. We shall see that the module structure of A^S over S and its ring structure combine with each other to make A^S an algebra over S. We have to show that the multiplication is a bilinear mapping of $A^S \times A^S$ into A^S. It is clear that the multiplication is biadditive. We have therefore only to show that $(\beta x)y = x(\beta y) = \beta(xy)$ if x, y are in A^S and β in S. We may write $x = \sum_{i=1}^h \beta_i \otimes t_i$, $y = \sum_{j=1}^k \gamma_j \otimes u_j$, the elements β_i, γ_j being in S and t_i, u_j being in K. The elements of S being considered as homogeneous of degree 0, we have

$$(\beta x)y = \sum_{i=1}^h \sum_{j=1}^k (\beta\beta_i \otimes t_i)(\gamma_j \otimes u_j) = \sum_{i=1}^h \sum_{j=1}^k \beta\beta_i\gamma_j \otimes t_i u_j$$
$$= \beta \sum_{i=1}^h \sum_{j=1}^k \beta_j\gamma_j \otimes t_i u_j = \beta(xy)$$
$$x(\beta y) = \sum_{i=1}^h \sum_{j=1}^k (\beta_i \otimes t_i)(\beta\gamma_j \otimes u_j) = \sum_{i=1}^h \sum_{j=1}^k \beta_i\beta\gamma_j \otimes t_i u_j$$
$$= \beta \sum_{i=1}^h \sum_{j=1}^k \beta_i\gamma_j \otimes t_i u_j = \beta(xy),$$

with proves our assertion.

Let A_n be the module of homogeneous elements of degree n of A; since A is the direct sum of the modules A_n, A^S is the direct sum of the modules A_n^S (which may be regarded as submodules of A^S) (cf. theorem 40, Chapter III, Sect. 10). We have $A_n^S = S \otimes A_n$; this is the module of homogeneous elements of degree n of the graded algebra $S \otimes A$ (graded by the total degree). It follows that the formula $A^S = \sum_{n \in \underline{Z}} A_n^S$ defines on A^S the structure of a graded algebra; this graded algebra is called the *algebra deduced from A by inverse transfer of the basic ring to S*. It is clear that the elements $1 \otimes a$ $(a \in A)$ form a set of modules generators of A^S, and that $(1 \otimes a)(1 \otimes a') = 1 \otimes aa'$ if a, a' are in A.

Theorem 51. *Let A and B be graded algebras over R and f a homogeneous homomorphism of degree 0 of A into B. Then the linear mapping f^S of A^S into B^S deduced from f by transfer of the basic ring to S is a homogeneous homomorphism of degree 0 of the graded algebra A^S into B^S.*

We have $f^S = I \otimes f$, where I is the identity mapping of S; theorem 51 therefore follows from theorem 11, Sect. 4.

Theorem 52. *Let M be a module over R, (T, θ) a tensor algebra on M and (E, ψ) an exterior algebra on M. Then (T^S, θ^S) is a tensor algebra on M^S and (E^S, ψ^S) an exterior algebra on M^S.*

Let T_n and T_n^S be the modules of homogeneous elements of degree n of T and T^S, where n is any integer $\geqslant 0$. If we denote by τ_n the mapping $(x_1, \cdots, x_n) \to \theta(x_1) \cdots \theta(x_n)$ of M^n (the product of n modules identical with M) into T_n, then (T_n, τ_n) is a tensor product of n modules identical with M. Making use of theorem 45, Chapter III, Sect. 11, we see that there exists a mapping τ'_n of $(M^S)^n$ into T_n^S such that (T_n^S, τ'_n) is a tensor product of n modules identical with M^S and

$$\tau'_n(1 \otimes x_1, \cdots, 1 \otimes x_n) = 1 \otimes \theta(x_1) \cdots \theta(x_n) \ (x_1, \cdots, x_n \in M).$$

We have $1 \otimes \theta(x_1) \cdots \theta(x_n) = \theta^S(1 \otimes x_1) \cdots \theta^S(1 \otimes x_n)$. The mappings $(y_1, \cdots, y_n) \to \tau'_n(y_1, \cdots, y_n)$ and $(y_1, \cdots, y_n) \to \theta^S(y_1) \cdots \theta^S(y_n)$ of $(M^S)^n$ into T^S_n being multilinear, and the elements $1 \otimes x$ ($x \in M$) constituting a set of module generators of M^S, it follows that

$$\tau'_n(y_1, \cdots, y_n) = \theta^S(y_1) \cdots \theta^S(y_n) \quad (y_i \in M^S, 1 \leqslant i \leqslant n).$$

Referring to the construction of a tensor algebra on a module, we see that there exists a tensor algebra $(\overline{T}, \overline{\theta})$ on M^S with the following properties: for any $n \geqslant 0$, the module $\overline{T}_n$ of homogeneous elements of degree n of $\overline{T}$ is T^S_n; $\overline{\theta}$ is the mapping θ^S; if we denote by $\square$ the multiplication in $\overline{T}$, then we have, for $y_1, \cdots, y_n$ in M^S,

$$\overline{\theta}(y_1) \square \cdots \square \overline{\theta}(y_n) = \tau'_n(y_1, \cdots, y_n) = \theta^S(y_1) \cdots \theta^S(y_n).$$

Since T^S and $\overline{T}$ are both direct sums of the modules T^S_n for all $n \geqslant 0$, there is an isomorphism ι of the module T^S with $\overline{T}$ which coincides with the identity on each T^S_n. If $y_1, \cdots, y_m, z_1, \cdots, z_n$ are in M^S, then

$$\begin{aligned} &\iota((\theta^S(y_1) \cdots \theta^S(y_m))(\theta^S(z_1) \cdots \theta^S(z_n))) \\ &= (\overline{\theta}(y_1) \square \cdots \square \overline{\theta}(y_m)) \square (\overline{\theta}(z_1) \square \cdots \square \overline{\theta}(z_n)). \end{aligned}$$

It follows immediately that $\iota(tu) = \iota(t) \square \iota(u)$ if $t \in T^S_m$, $u \in T^S_n$, and therefore that ι is an algebra isomorphism. Since $\iota \circ \theta^S = \overline{\theta}$, (T^S, θ^S) is a tensor algebra on M^S.

There is an epimorphism f of T on E such that $f \circ \theta = \psi$, and the kernel F of f is the ideal generated in T by the elements $(\theta(x))^2$, with $x \in M$. The mapping f^S is a homomorphism of T^S into E^S (theorem 51), and we have $f^S \circ \theta^S = \psi^S$ (cf. Chapter III, Sect. 11). The subalgebra $f^S(T^S)$ of E^S contains the elements $1 \otimes f(t)$, $t \in T$; since f is an epimorphism, it follows that the same is true of f^S. Since $f^S = I \otimes f$, where I is the identity mapping of S, the kernel of f^S is the module generated by the elements $1 \otimes t$, $t \in F$ (theorem 29, Chapter III, Sect. 8). Any element of F is a sum of elements of the form $a(\theta(x))^2 b$, with a, b in T and $x \in M$. We have

$$1 \otimes a(\theta(x))^2 b = (1 \otimes a)(1 \otimes \theta(x))^2(1 \otimes b);$$

it follows that the kernel of f^S is the ideal generated by the elements $(1 \otimes \theta(x))^2 = (\theta^S(1 \otimes x))^2$ for all $x \in M$. If x, y are in M, then the kernel of f^S contains $(\theta^S(1 \otimes x))^2$, $(\theta^S(1 \otimes y))^2$ and $(\theta^S(1 \otimes (x + y)))^2$; it follows immediately that it contains the element

$$\theta^S(1 \otimes x)\theta^S(1 \otimes y) + \theta^S(1 \otimes y)\theta^S(1 \otimes x).$$

Now, every element z of M^S may be written in the form $\sum_{i=1}^n \beta_i(1 \otimes x_i)$ with $\beta_1, \cdots, \beta_n$ in S and $x_1, \cdots, x_n$ in M. We have

$$\begin{aligned} (\theta^S(z))^2 = &\textstyle\sum_{i<j} \beta_i\beta_j(\theta^S(1 \otimes x_i)\theta^S(1 \otimes x_j) + \theta^S(1 \otimes x_j)\theta^S(1 \otimes x_i)) \\ &+ \textstyle\sum_i \beta_i^2(\theta^S(1 \otimes x_i))^2, \end{aligned}$$

which proves that $(\theta^S(z))^2$ belongs to the kernel of f^S. Referring to the construction of an exterior algebra (Sect. 7), we conclude that (E^S, ψ^S) is an exterior algebra on M^S.

Theorem 53. *Let M and N be modules over R and f a linear mapping of M into N. Let E and F be exterior algebras on M and on N, and $\bar{f}$ the prolongation of f to E. Then $\bar{f}^S$ is the prolongation of f^S to E^S.*

In this statement, it is understood that we take M^S to be a submodule of E^S, which is possible since M is a direct summand in E; E^S is then an exterior algebra on M^S. The mapping $\bar{f}^S$ is a homomorphism and clearly extends f^S, which proves the theorem.

Let A and B be graded algebras over R, admitting $\underline{Z}$ as their group of degrees. Then $(A \otimes B)^S$ is a graded algebra over S. As a module, $(A \otimes B)^S$ may be regarded as a tensor product $A^S \otimes B^S$ of the modules A^S and B^S (theorem 45, Chapter III, Sect. 11). On the other hand, $A^S \otimes B^S$ has the structure of an algebra, as a tensor product of the graded algebras A^S and B^S. Thus, we have on $(A \otimes B)^S = A^S \otimes B^S$ two algebra structures, one resulting from $A \otimes B$ by transfer of the basic ring to S, the other being the tensor product of the algebras A^S and B^S. These two structures are actually identical. For, let Z be the set of elements of the form

$$1 \otimes (a \otimes b) = (1 \otimes a) \otimes (1 \otimes b),$$

where a and b are homogeneous elements of A and B respectively; then Z is a set of module generators of the module $(A \otimes B)^S$, and the product of two elements of Z (in either one of the two algebra structures on $(A \otimes B)^S$) is in Z. It will therefore be sufficient to prove that the product of two elements $a \otimes b$ (a homogeneous of degree d and b homogeneous of degree e) and $a' \otimes b'$ (a' homogeneous of degree d' and b' homogeneous of degree e') is the same in both our algebra structures; since $1 \otimes b$ is homogeneous of degree e in B^S and $1 \otimes a'$ homogeneous of degree d' in A^S, both products are equal to $(-1)^{d'e}(1 \otimes aa') \otimes (1 \otimes bb')$, and our assertion is proved.

Let M be a module over R, E an exterior algebra on M and U the analyzing mapping of E; U is therefore a homomorphism of E into $E \otimes E$, which extends the mapping $x \to x \otimes 1_E + 1_E \otimes x$ of M into $E \otimes E$ (where 1_E is the unit element of E). The mapping U^S is a homomorphism of E^S into $E^S \otimes E^S$ and maps $1_S \otimes x$ (where 1_S is the unit element of S and $x \in M$) upon $1_S \otimes (x \otimes 1_E) + 1_S \otimes (1_E \otimes x) = (1_S \otimes x) \otimes 1_{E^S} + 1_{E^S} \otimes (1_S \otimes x)$ (where $1_{E^S} = 1_S \otimes 1_E$ is the unit element of E^S). It follows immediately that, for any $y \in M^S$, $U^S(y)$ is $y \otimes 1_{E^S} + 1_{E^S} \otimes y$, and therefore that U^S is the analyzing mapping of E^S.

Let A and B be modules over R, φ a linear mapping of E into A and ψ a linear mapping of E into B. Then we have

$$(\varphi \wedge \psi)^S = \varphi^S \wedge \psi^S \tag{1}$$

(where $(A \otimes B)^S$ is regarded as a tensor product of A^S and B^S). For we have

$$\varphi^S \wedge \psi^S = (\varphi^S \otimes \psi^S) \circ U^S, \qquad \varphi^S \otimes \psi^S = (\varphi \otimes \psi)^S,$$

whence

$$\varphi^S \wedge \psi^S = ((\varphi \otimes \psi) \circ U)^S = (\varphi \wedge \psi)^S.$$

Let M and N be modules over R, and γ a bilinear form on $M \times N$. Let E and F be exterior algebras on M and N. Then there is associated with γ a homomorphism Λ of E into the dual algebra F^* of F, which maps any element $x \in M$ upon the linear form on F which maps any $y \in N$ upon $\gamma(x, y)$ and every homogeneous element of degree $\neq 1$ of F upon 0. Let γ^S be the bilinear form on $M^S \times N^S$ which is deduced from γ by transfer of the basic ring to S. Then there is associated with γ^S a homomorphism Λ' of E^S into the dual algebra $(F^S)^*$ of F^S. If t is any element of E, then $\Lambda(t)$ is a linear form on F and $(\Lambda(t))^S$ a linear form on F^S. We shall see that

$$\Lambda'(1_S \otimes t) = (\Lambda(t))^S. \tag{2}$$

Consider first the case where t is an element x of M. Then $(\Lambda(t))^S$ maps $1_S \otimes y$ (where $y \in N$) upon

$$1_S \otimes ((\Lambda(t)(y)) = \rho((\Lambda(t))(y)) = \rho(\gamma(x, y)) = \gamma^S(1_S \otimes x, 1_S \otimes y),$$

which is $(\Lambda'(1_S \otimes x))(1_S \otimes y)$; on the other hand, $(\Lambda(t))^S$ clearly maps every homogeneous element of degree > 1 of F^S upon 0; this proves (2) in the case where $t = x$. In order to prove it in the general case, it is obviously sufficient to consider the case where $t = x_1 \cdots x_n$ is a product of n elements of M. We then have $1_S \otimes t = \prod_{i=1}^n (1_S \otimes x_i)$, and the image of this element under Λ' is $\Lambda'(1_S \otimes x_i) \wedge \cdots \wedge \Lambda'(1_S \otimes x_n) = (\Lambda(x_1))^S \wedge \cdots \wedge (\Lambda(x_n))^S$. This is equal to $(\Lambda(x_1) \wedge \cdots \wedge \Lambda(x_n))^S$ by virtue of formula (1), and therefore to $(\Lambda(t))^S$.

Theorem 54. *Let M and N be modules over the ring R, E and F exterior algebras on M and N, γ a bilinear form on $M \times N$ and Γ the prolongation of γ to $E \times F$. Let γ^S and Γ^S be the bilinear forms on $M^S \times N^S$ and on $E^S \times F^S$ deduced from γ and Γ by transfer of the basic ring to S. Then Γ^S is the prolongation of γ^S to $E^S \times F^S$.*

Let the notation be as above. Let t and u be elements of E and F respectively; denote by Γ' the prolongation of γ^S to $E^S \times F^S$. We have

$$\begin{aligned}\Gamma'(1 \otimes t, 1 \otimes u) &= (\Lambda'(1 \otimes t))(1 \otimes u) = (\Lambda(t))^S(1 \otimes u)\\ &= \rho((\Lambda(t))(u)) = \rho(\Gamma(t, u)),\end{aligned}$$

and this is equal to $\Gamma^S(1 \otimes t, 1 \otimes u)$, which proves theorem 54.

Corollary. Let $A = (a_{ij})$ be a square matrix of degree n with elements in R; denote by A' the matrix $(\rho(a_{ij}))$ with elements in S. Then we have $\det A' = \rho(\det A)$.

Let M be a free module over R with a base $(x_1, \cdots, x_n)$ of n elements. Let γ be the bilinear form on $M \times M$ defined by $\gamma(x_i, x_j) = a_{ij}$ $(1 \leqslant i, j \leqslant n)$. Define Γ, γ^S, Γ^S as in theorem 54 (N being here identical to M). The elements $1 \otimes x_i$ form a base of M^S, and we have $\gamma^S(1 \otimes x_i, 1 \otimes x_j) = \rho(a_{ij})$. Set $t = x_1 \cdots x_n$; then we have $\det A = \Gamma(t, t)$, whence $\rho(\det A) = \Gamma^S(1 \otimes t, 1 \otimes t)$. Since $1 \otimes t = \prod_{i=1}^n (1 \otimes x_i)$, $\Gamma^S(1 \otimes t, 1 \otimes t)$ is equal to $\det A'$, which proves the corollary.

The corollary could also be deduced immediately from the expansion formula

$$\det A = \Sigma_p \chi(p) a_{p(1),1} \cdots a_{p(n),n}$$

where the sum is extended to all permutations p of $\{1, \cdots, n\}$ and where $\chi(p)$ is the signature of p.

Using the formula $\operatorname{Tr} A = \Sigma_{i=1}^n e_{ii}$, we obtain the formula

$$\operatorname{Tr} A' = \rho(\operatorname{Tr} A).$$

This could also be deduced from the result contained in the next theorem.

Theorem 55. *Let A be a graded algebra over R, with $\underline{Z}$ as its group of degrees. If d is a derivation of degree i of A, then d^S is a derivation of degree i of A^S.*

It is clear that d^S is a homogeneous linear mapping of degree 0 of A^S into itself. To prove that it is a derivation, we first observe that, if J is the main involution of E, then J^S is the main involution of A^S, as follows immediately from the definitions; we therefore have $(J^S)^i = (J^i)^S$. Let x and y be elements of A. Then we have

$$\begin{aligned} d^S((1 \otimes x)(1 \otimes y)) &= d^S(1 \otimes xy) = 1 \otimes d(xy) \\ &= 1 \otimes d(x)y + 1 \otimes J^i(x)d(y) = (d^S(1 \otimes x))(1 \otimes y) + ((J^S)^i(1 \otimes x))d^S(1 \otimes y). \end{aligned}$$

The mapping $(u, v) \to d^S(uv) - d^S(u)v - (J^S)^i(u)d^S(v)$ of $A^S \times A^S$ into A^S is bilinear. Since it maps every element of the form $(1 \otimes x, 1 \otimes y)$ (x, y in A) upon 0, it is the zero mapping which proves the theorem.

Now, let M be a module over R, γ an alternating bilinear form on $M \times M$ and E an exterior algebra on M. Then the bilinear form γ^S on $M^S \times M^S$ is alternating. For there is a homogeneous linear form of degree 2 on E, say φ, such that $\varphi(xy) = \gamma(x, y)$ for any x, y in M. Then φ^S is a homogeneous linear form of degree 2 on E^S, and we have

$$\varphi^S((1 \otimes x)(1 \otimes y)) = \gamma^S(1 \otimes x, 1 \otimes y)$$

whenever x, y are in M. It follows immediately that $\varphi^S(x'y') = \gamma^S(x', y')$ for all x', y' in M^S, whence $\gamma^S(x', x') = 0$. We have associated with γ and with γ^S algebras $\bar{E}$ and $\bar{E}'$ whose underlying modules are the same as those of E, E^S (cf. Sect. 14). These algebras were defined as follows. If $x \in M$ (resp.: $x' \in M^S$), denote by L_x (resp. : $L'_{x'}$) the operator of left multiplication by x (resp.: x') in E (resp.: E^S) and by d_x(resp.: $d'_{x'}$) the derivation of E (resp.: E') which maps any $y \in M$ (resp.: $y' \in M^S$) upon $\gamma(x, y)$ (resp.: $\gamma^S(x', y')$); then the operator of left multiplication by x in $\bar{E}$ (resp.: by x' in $\bar{E}'$) is $L_x + d_x$ (resp.: $L'_{x'} + d'_{x'}$). It follows immediately from the definitions that $L'_{1\otimes x} = L^S_x$. On the other hand, d^S_x is a derivation of E^S (theorem 55) and maps $1 \otimes y$ upon $\rho(\gamma(x, y))$ which is also $\gamma^S(1 \otimes x, 1 \otimes y)$ (y being any element of M). Since M^S is a set of generators of E^S, the same is true of the set of elements $1 \otimes x$, $x \in M$; since $d'_{1\otimes x}$ and d^S_x coincide with each other on this set, these two operations are identical. It follows that

$$L'_{1\otimes x} + d'_{1\otimes x} = (L_x + d_x)^S.$$

There is an isomorphism Ω of E with $\bar{E}$ (resp.: Ω' of E^S with $\bar{E}'$) which maps any element of the form $x_1 \cdots x_n$ (resp.: $x'_1 \cdots x'_n$) with $x_i \in M$ (resp.: $x'_i \in M^S$) upon the image of the unit element under the mapping

$$(L_{x_1} + d_{x_1}) \circ \cdots \circ (L_{x_n} + d_{x_n}) \text{ (resp.: } (L'_{x'_1} + d'_{x'_1}) \circ \cdots \circ (L'_{x'_n} + d'_{x'_n})).$$

We shall see that $\Omega' = \Omega^S$. The elements of the form

$$\Pi^n_{i=1}(1 \otimes x_i) = 1 \otimes \Pi^n_{i=1} x_i$$

(for all n and for all choices of $x_1, \cdots, x_n$ in M) form a set of module generators of E^S; it will therefore be sufficent to prove that any element t' of this form has the same image under Ω' and Ω^S. Set $x'_i = 1 \otimes x_i$ and

$$\theta = (L_{x_1} + d_{x_1}) \circ \cdots \circ (L_{x_n} + d_{x_n}),\ \theta' = (L'_{x'_1} + d'_{x'_1}) \circ \cdots \circ (L'_{x'_n} + d'_{x'_n});$$

then it follows from what we have proved above that $\theta' = \theta^S$. The element $\Omega'(t')$ is $\theta'(1_{E^S}) = \theta^S(1 \otimes 1_E) = \Omega^S(t')$ (since $\Omega^S(x_1 \cdots x_n) = \theta(1_E)$; 1_{E^S} and 1_E are the unit elements of E^S and E). This proves our assertion.

Theorem 56. *Let $A = (a_{ij})$ be an alternating matrix of degree n with elements in R; let A' be the matrix $(\rho(a_{ij}))$. Then we have* $\mathrm{Pf}\, A' = \rho(\mathrm{Pf}\, A)$.

Let M be a free module over R with a base $(x_1, \cdots, x_n)$ of n elements. Let γ be the alternating bilinear form on $M \times M$ defined by $\gamma(x_i, y_j) = a_{ij}$. Define γ^S, Ω, $\Omega' = \Omega^S$ as above. The elements $1 \otimes x_i$ form a base of M^S, and we have $\gamma^S(1 \otimes x_i, 1 \otimes x_j) = \rho(a_{ij})$. Set $t = x_1 \cdots x_n$; then $(\mathrm{Pf}\, A)1_E$ is the homogeneous component of degree 0 of $\Omega(t)$. We have

$$\Omega'(1 \otimes t) = \Omega^S(1 \otimes t) = 1_S \otimes \Omega(t);$$

the homogeneous component of degree 0 of this element is

$$1_S \otimes ((\mathrm{Pf}\, A)1_E) = \rho(\mathrm{Pf}\, A)1_{E^S}.$$

Since $1 \otimes t = (1 \otimes x_1) \cdots (1 \otimes x_n)$, this homogeneous component of degree 0 is also $(\mathrm{Pf}\, A')1_{E^S}$, which proves theorem 56.

17. Commutative tensor products

Let A and B be graded algebras over a commutative ring R, having $\underline{Z}$ as their group of degrees. Let A_n and B_n be the modules of homogeneous elements of degree n of A and B. Set $A'_n = \{0\}$ when n is odd, $A'_n = A_{n/2}$ when n is even; then A is the direct sum of the modules A'_n, for all $n \in \underline{Z}$, and, if m and n are any integers, the product of an element of A'_m by an element of A'_n is in A'_{m+n}. Thus the formula $A = \Sigma_{n \in Z} A'_n$ defines on A a new structure of graded algebra A'; we say that A' is obtained from A by *duplicating the degrees*. Every homogeneous element of A' of odd degree is 0. Conversely let C be a graded algebra, having $\underline{Z}$ as its group of degrees, in which every homogeneous element of odd degree is 0. Then C may be obtained from some graded algebra $\overline{C}$ by the operation of duplicating the degrees, and $\overline{C}$ is uniquely determined. For, denote by C_n the module of homogeneous elements of degree n of C. Set $\overline{C}_n = C_{2n}$; then it follows from our assumption that C is the direct sum of the modules $\overline{C}_n$, and the product of an element of $\overline{C}_m$ by an element of $\overline{C}_n$ is in $\overline{C}_{m+n}$. Thus, the decomposition $C = \Sigma_{n \in \underline{Z}} \overline{C}_n$ defines on C a new structure of a graded algebra $\overline{C}$. It is clear that C is obtained from $\overline{C}$ by duplication of the degrees, and that $\overline{C}$ is uniquely determined by this condition.

Now, let A' and B' be the algebras deduced from A and B by duplicating the degrees; let $C' = A' \otimes B'$ be a tensor product of these algebras. We consider C' as graded by means of the total degree; every homogeneous element of odd degree of C' is then 0. For, we know that, for any p, the module C'_p of homogeneous elements of degree p of C' is $\Sigma_{m+n=p} A'_m \otimes B'_n$, where A'_m, B'_n are the modules of homogeneous elements of respective degrees m, n of A', B'. If p is odd and $m + n = p$, then one of m, n has to be odd; thus, one of A'_m, B'_n is reduced to $\{0\}$ and $A'_m \otimes B'_n = \{0\}$. It follows that there is a graded algebra C such that C' is obtained from C by duplicating the degrees. The algebra C is called a *commutative tensor product of A and B*, and is denoted by $A \otimes_c B$. The module C is a tensor product of the modules A and B. Moreover, the module C_p of homogeneous elements of degree p of C is the same as the module $(A \otimes B)_p$ of homogeneous elements of degree p in $A \otimes B$, graded by the total degree. For, we have $C_p = C'_{2p} = \Sigma_{m+n=2p} A'_m \otimes B'_n$; since $A'_m = \{0\}$ if m is odd and $B'_n = \{0\}$ if n is odd, while $A'_m = A_{m/2}$, $B'_n = B_{n/2}$ if m, n are even, we have $C_p = \Sigma_{m+n=p} A_m \otimes B_n$, which proves our assertion. Thus, the graded algebras $A \otimes B$ and $A \otimes_c B$ differ from each other only by their multiplication operations.

If a, a' are in A and b, b' in B, then the product $(a \otimes b)(a' \otimes b')$ in $A \otimes_c B$

is equal to $aa' \otimes bb'$. For, let $b = \sum_{n \in \underline{Z}} b_n$, $a' = \sum_{m \in \underline{Z}} a'_m$ be the decompositions of b and a' into their homogeneous components. Using the same notation as above, b_n is homogeneous of degree $2n$ in B' and a'_m homogeneous of degree $2m$ in A'; it follows that

$$(a \otimes b_n)(a'_m \otimes b) = (-1)^{4mn} aa'_m \otimes b_n b' = aa'_m \otimes b_n b';$$

our assertion follows immediately from this.

If every homogeneous element of odd degree of A is 0, then $A \otimes B$ and $A \otimes_c B$ are identical. To prove this, it is sufficient to show that the identity mapping of the *module* $A \otimes B$ onto itself is a homomorphism of the algebra $A \otimes B$ into $A \otimes_c B$. Let Z be the set of elements $a \otimes b$, where a is homogeneous in A and b in B; then Z is a set of module generators of $A \otimes B$, and the product of two elements of Z lies in Z. It will therefore be sufficient to prove that the product of two elements $a \otimes b$ (a homogeneous of degree d and b homogeneous of degree e) and $a' \otimes b'$ (a' homogeneous of degree d' and b' homogeneous of degree e') in $A \otimes_c B$ is the same as their product in $A \otimes B$. Their product is $(-1)^{ed'} aa' \otimes bb'$; this is equal to $aa' \otimes bb'$ because either d' is even or a' is 0.

The multiplication in the algebra $A \otimes_c B$ is obviously uniquely determined by the condition that $(a \otimes b)(a' \otimes b') = aa' \otimes bb'$ whenever a, a' are in A and b, b' in B; i. e., this multiplication is completely independent of the gradations of A and B. Let ρ be a homomorphism of R into a commutative ring R', and let A be any graded algebra over R; in defining the algebra A^R deduced from A by transfer of the basic ring to R' by ρ, we have made use of the tensor product $R' \otimes A$, where R' is given the structure of an algebra over R by means of ρ and R' is regarded as a graded algebra in which every homogeneous element is of degree 0. Thus we see that the multiplication of $A^{R'}$ is the same as that of $R' \otimes_c A$.

Theorem 57. *Let A and B be graded algebras over a commutative ring R and C an algebra over R. Let f (resp.: g) be a homomorphism of the algebra A (resp.: B) into C; assume that every element of $f(A)$ commutes with every element of $g(B)$. Then the linear mapping h of the module $A \otimes B$ into C defined by the condition that $h(a \otimes b) = f(a)g(b)$ for any $a \in A$, $b \in B$, is a homomorphism of the algebra $A \otimes_c B$ into C. If C is graded and if f, g are both homogeneous of degree 0, then h is homogeneous of degree 0.*

Let Z be the set of elements of the form $a \otimes b$, with a in A and b in B; then Z is a set of module generators of $A \otimes B$ and the product of two elements of Z is in Z. Since h maps the unit element of $A \otimes_c B$ upon that of C, it will be sufficient, in order to prove that h is a homomorphism of $A \otimes_c B$, to show that $h((a \otimes b)(a' \otimes b')) = h(a \otimes b)h(a' \otimes b')$ if a, a' are in A and b, b' in B. The left side is $h(aa' \otimes bb') = f(aa')g(bb')$, which is equal to $f(a)f(a')g(b)g(b')$. The right side is $f(a)g(b)f(a')g(b')$, and our assertion follows from the fact that $g(b)$ commutes with $f(a')$. Assuming that C is graded, and that f, g are homogeneous of degree 0, denote by A_n, B_n and C_n the modules of homogeneous elements of degree n of A, B and C. The module of homogeneous elements of degree p of $A \otimes_c B$ is $\sum_{m+n=p} A_m \otimes B_n$. If $a \in A_m$, $b \in B_n$, then $h(a \otimes b) = f(a)g(b)$ belongs to C_{m+n}; it follows immediately that h maps $A_m \otimes B_n$ into C_{m+n}, which proves the last assertion.

Theorem 58. *Let A and B be commutative graded algebras, having $\underline{Z}$ as their group of degrees. Then $A \otimes_c B$ is a commutative algebra.*

Let the set Z be defined as in the proof of theorem 57. In order to prove that the bilinear mapping $(x, y) \rightarrow xy - yx$ of $(A \otimes_c B)(A \otimes_c B)$ into $A \otimes_c B$ is the zero mapping, it will be sufficient to prove that the image of every element of $Z \times Z$ is 0. If a, a' are in A and b, b' in B, we have

$$(a \otimes b)(a' \otimes b') = aa' \otimes bb' = a'a \otimes b'b = (a' \otimes b')(a \otimes b),$$

which proves theorem 58.

18. Symmetric algebras

Let R be a commutative ring and M a module over R. By a *symmetric algebra on M*, we mean an object formed by an algebra S over R and a linear mapping ψ of M into S which satisfy the following conditions: the elements of $\psi(M)$ commute with each other in S; if φ is any linear mapping of M into an algebra A over R such that the elements of $\varphi(M)$ commute with each other, then there exists a unique homomorphism f of S into A such that $f \circ \psi = \varphi$.

If (S, ψ) and (S', ψ') are symmetric algebras on the same module M, then there exists a unique isomorphism J of S with S' such that $J \circ \psi = \psi'$. On the other hand, if (S, ψ) is any symmetric algebra on M, then $\psi(M)$ is a set of generators of the algebra S. These statements are established exactly in the same way as the corresponding statements for free monoids, free modules, etc.

We shall now prove that, given any module M over R, there exists a symmetric algebra on M. Let (T, θ) be a tensor algebra on M. Denote by K the ideal generated in T by the elements

$$\theta(x)\theta(y) - \theta(y)\theta(x) \tag{1}$$

for all x, y in M. Let S be the algebra T/K, and π the natural homomorphism of T on S; set $\psi = \pi \circ \theta$. If x, y are in M, we have

$$\psi(x)\psi(y) - \psi(y)\psi(x) = \pi(\theta(x)\theta(y) - \theta(y)\theta(x)) = 0,$$

since $\theta(x)\theta(y) - \theta(y)\theta(x)$ is in K; this shows that the elements of $\psi(M)$ commute with each other. Let φ be a linear mapping of M into an algebra A over R such that the elements of $\varphi(M)$ commute with each other. Then, since (T, θ) is a tensor algebra on M, there exists a homomorphism g of T into A such that $g \circ \theta = \varphi$. If x and y are in M, then we have

$$g(\theta(x)\theta(y) - \theta(y)\theta(x)) = \varphi(x)\varphi(y) - \varphi(y)\varphi(x) = 0;$$

thus, the kernel of g, which contains a set of generators of the ideal K, contains K. It follows that g may be factored in the form $g = f \circ \pi$, where f is a homomorphism of the algebra S into A. We have

$$f \circ \psi = f \circ \pi \circ \theta = g \circ \theta = \varphi.$$

Since $\theta(M)$ is a set of generators of T, $\psi(M) = \pi(\theta(M))$ is a set of generators of S; therefore, there cannot exist more than one homomorphism f of S into A such that $f \circ \psi = \varphi$. We have proved that (S, ψ) is a symmetric algebra on M.

The elements (1) are homogeneous of degree 2; it follows that the ideal K is homogeneous (theorem 4, Sect. 2) and therefore that S has the structure of a graded algebra, in which the module S_n of homogeneous elements of degree n is the image under π of the module T_n of homogeneous elements of degree n of T. It follows that $S_n = \{0\}$ if $n < 0$, and that, for $n \geqslant 0$, every element of S_n is a linear combination of products of n elements of $S_1 = \psi(M)$. Making use of theorem 5, Sect. 2, we see that S is regularly graded and that π induces an isomorphism of T_1 with S_1. Since θ is an isomorphism of M with T_1, we conclude that ψ is an isomorphism of M with S_1.

Taking into account the isomorphism theorem for symmetric algebras on a given module M, we obtain the following results:

Theorem 59. *Let M be a module over a commutative ring R and (S, ψ) a symmetric algebra on M. Then S has the structure of a regularly graded algebra over R; ψ is an isomorphism of M with the module of homogeneous elements of degree 1 of S; every homogeneous element of degree $n \geqslant 0$ of S is a linear combination of products of n homogeneous elements of degree 1.*

Theorem 60. *Let (S, ψ) be a symmetric algebra on a module M. Then S is a commutative algebra.*

This will follow from the more general result :

Lemma 1. *Let S be an algebra over a commutative ring R. Assume that S has a set of generators T whose elements commute with each other. Then S is a commutative algebra.*

Let T' be the submonoid of the multiplicative monoid of elements of S which is generated by T; then T' is commutative (corollary 2 to theorem 5,

Chapter I, Sect. 2). On the other hand, T' is a set of module generators of S (cf. theorem 1, Chapter IV, Sect. 2 and Sect. 1). The bilinear mapping $(x,y) \to xy - yx$ of $S \times S$ into S, which maps $T' \times T'$ upon $\{0\}$, is the zero mapping, which proves the lemma.

Let M and N be modules over a commutative ring R and φ a linear mapping of M into N; let (S_M, ψ_M) and (S_N, ψ_N) be symmetric algebras on M and N. Then $\psi_N \circ \varphi$ is a linear mapping of M into the commutative algebra S_N. Therefore, there exists a unique homomorphism f of S_M into S_N such that

$$f \circ \psi_M = \psi_N \circ \varphi;$$

f is called the *prolongation of* φ *to* S_M. Since $\varphi(\psi_M(M)) \subset \psi_N(N)$, f maps the product of n elements of $\psi_M(M)$ into an element which is the product of n elements of $\psi_N(N)$ (where n is any integer $\geqslant 0$). It follows immediately that f is homogeneous of degree 0.

Let P be a third module over R and (S_P, ψ_P) a symmetric algebra on P. Let φ' be a linear mapping of N into P, and f' its prolongation to a homomorphism of S_N into S_P. Then $f' \circ f$ is the prolongation of $\varphi' \circ \varphi$ to S_M; for, $f' \circ f$ is a homomorphism, and we have $f' \circ f \circ \psi_M = f' \circ \psi_N \circ \varphi = \psi_P \circ \varphi' \circ \varphi$.

Theorem 61. *Let M be a module over a commutative ring R which is represented as the direct sum of two submodules N and P; let (S_M, ψ_M), (S_N, ψ_N) and (S_P, ψ_P) be symmetric algebras on M, N and P. Then there is a unique isomorphism f of S_M with $S_N \otimes_c S_P$ such that*

$$f(\psi_M(y + z)) = \psi_N(y) \otimes 1 + 1 \otimes \psi_P(z)$$

whenever $y \in N$, $z \in P$.

There are linear mappings π_N, π_P of M onto N and P such that $x = \pi_N(x) + \pi_P(x)$ for any $x \in M$. The mapping

$$\rho : x \to \psi_N(\pi_N(x)) \otimes 1 + 1 \otimes \psi_P(\pi_P(y))$$

of M into $S_N \otimes_c S_P$ is linear. Since $S_N \otimes_c S_P$ is a commutative algebra (theorem 58, Sect. 17), there is a unique homomorphism f of S_M into $S_N \otimes_c S_P$ such that $f \circ \psi_M = \rho$, whence $(f \circ \psi_M)(y + z) = \pi_N(y) \otimes 1 + 1 \otimes \pi_P(z)$ if $y \in N$, $z \in P$.

The identity mappings j_N and j_P of N and P into M have prolongations J_N and J_P which are homomorphisms of S_N and S_P into S_M. Since S_M is commutative, there exists a homomorphism g of $S_N \otimes_c S_P$ into S_M such that $g(t \otimes u) = J_N(t) J_P(u)$ if $t \in S_N$, $u \in S_P$ (theorem 57, Sect. 17).

We have, for $y \in N$, $z \in P$,

$$\begin{aligned}(g \circ f)(\psi_M(y + z)) &= g(\psi_N(y) \otimes 1) + g(1 \otimes \psi_P(z)) \\ &= J_N(\psi_N(y)) + J_P(\psi_P(z)) = \psi_M(y + z).\end{aligned}$$

Since $\psi_M(M)$ is a set of generators of S_M, $g \circ f$ is the identity automorphism of S_M; it follows immediately that f is a monomorphism. The subalgebra $f(S_M)$ of $S_N \otimes_c S_P$ contains $(\psi_N(N)) \otimes \{1\}$ and $\{1\} \otimes (\psi_P(P))$. Since $\psi_N(N)$ generates S_N and $u \to u \otimes 1$ is a homomorphism of S_N into $S_N \otimes_c S_P$, $f(S_M)$ contains $S_N \otimes \{1\}$. Similarly, $f(S_M)$ contains $\{1\} \otimes S_P$. Since $(S_N \otimes \{1\}) \cup (\{1\} \otimes S_P)$ is a set of generators of $S_N \otimes_c S_P$, $f(S_M) = S_N \otimes_c S_P$, which proves that f is an isomorphism.

We observe further that the mapping $v \to v \otimes 1$ of S_N into $S_N \otimes_c S_P$ is a monomorphism. For S_P, being graded, is the direct sum of $R \cdot 1$, which is the module of homogeneous elements of degree 0 of S_P, and of a module S_P^+ which is spanned by the homogeneous elements of degrees > 0 of S_P. Thus we may write $S_N \otimes S_P = S_N \otimes (R \cdot 1) + S_N \otimes S_P^+$ (direct); since $\alpha \to \alpha \cdot 1$ is an isomorphism of R with $R \cdot 1$, there is an isomorphism of $S_N \otimes (R \cdot 1)$ with $S_N = S_N \otimes R$ which maps $v \otimes 1$ upon v ($v \in S_N$); this proves our assertion. Thus, we have the following result:

Theorem 61 *a. Let M be a module over a commutative ring and N a submodule of M which is a direct summand of M. Let (S_N, ψ_N) and (S_M, ψ_M) be symmetric algebras on N and M; then the prolongation to S_N of the identity mapping of N into M is an isomorphism of S_N with the subalgebra of S_M generated by $\psi(N)$.*

Theorem 62. *Let M be a free module over a commutative ring R, and let $(x_i)_{i \in I}$ be a base of M. Let (S, ψ) be a symmetric algebra on M; set $X_i = \psi(x_i)$. Then, for every $n \geqslant 0$, the module S_n of homogeneous elements of degree n of S has a base composed of all elements $\prod_{i \in I} X_i^{e(i)}$, where $(e(i))_{i \in I}$ runs over all families of integers $\geqslant 0$ such that $\sum_{i \in I} e(i)$ is defined and equal to n.*

We first consider the case where I is a set with a single element i; we set $x_i = x$, $X_i = X$; S_n is then spanned by the unique element X^n, and it will therefore be sufficient to prove that $\alpha X^n \neq 0$ if α is an element $\neq 0$ in R. There is a linear mapping of M into R which maps x upon 1; it follows that there is a homomorphism f of S into R such that $f(X) = 1$, whence $f(X^n) = 1$, $f(\alpha X^n) = \alpha$, which proves our assertion in that case. Next we consider the case where I is finite, and we then proceed by induction on the number ν of elements of I; we may assume without loss of generality that I consists of the integers $1, \cdots, \nu$. The theorem is trivial if $I = \emptyset$ (we then have $S_n = \{0\}$ for every $n > 0$). Assume that $\nu > 0$ and that the theorem is true for the sets I with $\nu - 1$ elements. Let N be the submodule of M spanned by $x_1, \cdots, x_{\nu-1}$ and P the submodule spanned by x_ν; let T and U be the subalgebras of S generated by $\psi(N)$ and $\psi(P)$ respectively. Let ψ_N and ψ_P be the restrictions of ψ to N and P respectively; then (T, ψ_N) and (U, ψ_P) are symmetric algebras on N and P, by theorem

61 *a*. It follows that the elements $X_1^{e(1)} \cdots X_{\nu-1}^{e(\nu-1)}$ (for all systems of integers $e(1) \geqslant 0, \cdots, e(\nu-1) \geqslant 0$) form a base of T and that the elements $X_\nu^{e(\nu)} (e(\nu) \geqslant 0)$ form a base of U; thus, the elements $X_1^{e(1)} \cdots X_{\nu-1}^{e(\nu-1)} \otimes X_\nu^{e(\nu)}$ form a base of $T \otimes U$. Making use of theorem 61, we conclude that the elements $X_1^{e(1)} \cdots X_\nu^{e(\nu)}$, for all systems of integers $e(1) \geqslant 0, \cdots, e(\nu) \geqslant 0$, form a base of S. Since $X_1^{e(1)} \cdots X_\nu^{e(\nu)}$ is homogeneous of degree $e(1) + \cdots + e(\nu)$, those elements $X_1^{e(1)} \cdots X_\nu^{e(\nu)}$ for which $e(1) + \cdots + e(\nu) = n$ form a base of S_n.

We consider now the general case. The elements $\prod_{i \in I} X_i^{e(i)}$ for all families $(e(i))_{i \in I}$ such that $e(i) \geqslant 0$ for all i, $e(i) = 0$ for almost all i, clearly form a submonoid of the multiplicative monoid of elements of S and this submonoid contains 1; the submodule S' generated by these elements is therefore a subalgebra. Since $\psi(x_i) = X_i \in S'$ for all $i \in I$, S' contains $\psi(M)$ whence $S' = S$. It will therefore be sufficient to prove that the elements $Q_e = \prod_{i \in I} X_i^{e(i)}$ (for all mappings e of I into the set of integers $\geqslant 0$ such that $e(i) = 0$ for almost all i) are linearly independent in S. Let $Q_{e_1}, \cdots, Q_{e_h}$ be a finite number of these elements. The set I^* of those $i^* \in I$ for which $e_k(i^*) \neq 0$ for at least one k $(1 \leqslant k \leqslant h)$ is finite; let M^* be the module generated by the elements x_{i^*}, $i^* \in I^*$, ψ^* the restriction of ψ to M^* and S^* the subalgebra of S generated by $\psi^*(M^*)$. Then (S^*, ψ^*) is a symmetric algebra over M^* (theorem 61 *a*), and $Q_{e_1}, \cdots, Q_{e_h}$ belong to S^*. The theorem being true for modules with finite bases, $Q_{e_1}, \cdots, Q_{e_h}$ are linearly independent, and theorem 62 is proved.

It follows in particular from theorem 62 that, if I is a finite set with ν elements, S_n is of finite dimension. We propose to compute this dimension, which we shall denote by $d(\nu, n)$; $d(\nu, n)$ is equal to the number of elements of the set $\Sigma_{\nu,n}$ of systems of ν positive integers $(e(1), \cdots, e(\nu))$ for which $e(1) + \cdots + e(\nu) = n$. We have $d(1, n) = 1$, $d(\nu, 1) = \nu$. Assume now that n and ν are > 1; let Σ' be the set of all sytems $(e(1), \cdots, e(\nu)) \in \Sigma_{\nu,n}$ for which $e(\nu) = 0$ and Σ'' the complementary set of Σ' with respect to $\Sigma_{\nu,n}$. It is clear that Σ' is equipotent to $\Sigma_{\nu-1,n}$. On the other hand, the mapping

$$(e(1), \cdots, e(\nu)) \to (e(1), \cdots, e(\nu-1), e(\nu) - 1)$$

is a bijection of Σ'' on $\Sigma_{\nu,n-1}$: this gives the relation

$$d(\nu, n) = d(\nu-1, n) + d(\nu, n-1).$$

In order to solve this recurrence relation, we first prove the formula

$$\binom{p}{q} = \binom{p-1}{q} + \binom{p-1}{q-1} \tag{2}$$

where p, q are integers such that $p > q > 0$ and the number $\binom{p}{q}$ is the number of subsets with q elements of a set A with p elements $a_1, \cdots, a_p$. The number of those among these subsets which do not contain a_p is $\binom{p-1}{q}$; on the other hand, if we map any subset containing a_p upon the set obtained by removing a_p from it, we obtain a bijection of the set of all sets with q elements containing a_p on the set of all subsets with $q-1$ elements of the set $\{a_1, \cdots, a_{p-1}\}$. This proves formula (2).

This being said, we shall now prove that

$$d(\nu, n) = \binom{\nu + n - 1}{\nu - 1} \qquad (\nu > 0, n > 0)$$

This is true if $n = 1$ since $d(\nu, 1) = \nu$. Assume that $n > 1$ and that the formula is true for $n - 1$. Then

$$d(1, n) = 1 = \binom{n}{0}$$

and, if $\nu > 1$,

$$d(\nu, n) - d(\nu - 1, n) = \binom{\nu + n - 2}{\nu - 1} = \binom{\nu + n - 1}{\nu - 1} - \binom{\nu + n - 2}{\nu - 2}$$

It follows that, if $\delta(\nu, n) = d(\nu, n) - \binom{\nu + n - 1}{\nu - 1}$, we have $\delta(\nu, n) = \delta(\nu - 1, n)$ if $\nu > 1$, $\delta(1, n) = 0$; this proves that $\delta(\nu, n) = 0$ for every $\nu \geqslant 1$, and our formula is proved for n.

Let A be a graded algebra over a commutative ring, having $\underline{Z}$ as its group of degrees. Let A' be the graded algebra which is deduced from A by the operation of duplicating the degrees (cf. Sect. 17). A homogeneous linear mapping d of degree i of A into itself is homogeneous of degree $2i$ when considered as a linear mapping of A' into itself. If d is a derivation of degree $2i$ of A', then we say that d is a *commutative derivation* of degree i of A. Thus, a commutative derivation of degree i of A is a linear mapping d of A into itself which is homogeneous of degree i and which is such that

$$d(xy) = d(x)y + xd(y)$$

for any x, y in A. This notion may also be defined as follows. Let A_0 be the graded algebra which has the same elements, the same addition, the same multiplication and the same scalar multiplication as A and in which every element is homogeneous of degree 0. Then a linear mapping d of A into itself is a commutative derivation of degree i if and only if it satisfies the following conditions: d is homogeneous of degree i and d is a derivation (of degree 0) of A_0.

The properties of commutative derivations follow easily from the corresponding properties of derivations. Thus, if two commutative derivations d, d' of A coincide with each other on a set of generators of A, they are identical (this follows immediately from the corollary to theorem 17, Sect. 6); if d, d' are commutative derivations of respective degrees i and i' of A, then $d \circ d' - d' \circ d$ is a commutative derivation of degree $i + i'$ of A (this follows immediately from theorem 18, Sect. 6); finally, the set of all commutative derivations of a given degree i of A is a submodule of the module of linear mappings of A into itself.

Theorem 63. *Let M be a module over a commutative ring R and λ a linear form on M. Let (S, ψ) be a symmetric algebra on M. Then there exists a unique commutative derivation d_λ of degree -1 of S such that $d_\lambda(\psi(x)) = \lambda(x) \cdot 1$ for all $x \in M$. The mapping $\lambda \to d_\lambda$ is a linear mapping of the dual module M^* of M into the module of commutative derivations of S, and we have $d_\lambda \circ d_{\lambda'} = d_{\lambda'} \circ d_\lambda$ for any λ, λ' in M^*.*

Let N be the module $M \times R$ (R being regarded as a module over itself). The mapping $x \to (x, 0)$ is an isomorphism ρ of M with a submodule M_1 of N, and N is the direct sum of M_1 and of the module composed of all elements $(0, a)$, $a \in R$. Let (U, ψ_R) be a symmetric algebra on the module R. Then it follows immediately from theorem 61 that there exists a linear mapping ψ_N of N into $S \otimes_c U$ which maps any element (x, a) of N upon $\psi(x) \otimes 1 + 1 \otimes \psi_R(a)$, such that $(S \otimes_c U, \psi_N)$ is a symmetric algebra on N. Let λ be a linear form on M; then $x \to (x, \lambda(x))$ is a linear mapping of M into N, whose prolongation is a homomorphism f_λ of S into $S \otimes_c U$. Set $u = \psi_R(1)$; since $\{1\}$ is a base of R, the elements u^n $(0 \leqslant n < \infty)$ form a base of U (theorem 62). Let U_n be the submodule of U with base $\{u^n\}$; then $S \otimes_c U$ is the direct sum of the modules $S \otimes U_n$ (because U is the direct sum of the modules U_n). Since U_n has a base of one element, it is isomorphic to R; it follows that $S \otimes U_n$ is isomorphic to $S = S \otimes R$ under an isomorphism which maps $s \otimes u^n$ upon s whenever $s \in S$. Thus, every element of $S \otimes_c U$ may be written in one and only one way in the form $\sum_{n \geqslant 0} s_n \otimes u^n$, where the s_n are elements of S of which only a finite number are $\neq 0$. Denote by L the sum of the modules $S \otimes U_n$ for $n \geqslant 2$; then $S \otimes U$ is the direct sum of the modules $S \otimes U_0$, $S \otimes U_1$ and L. If s, s' are elements of S and m, m' integers $\geqslant 0$, then we have

$$(s \otimes u^m)(s' \otimes u^{m'}) = ss' \otimes u^{m+m'};$$

it follows immediately that the product of any element of $S \otimes_c U$ by an element of L is in L (i. e., L is an ideal in $S \otimes_c U$). If $s \in S$, we write

$$f_\lambda(s) \equiv f'_\lambda(s) \otimes 1 + d_\lambda(s) \otimes u \pmod{L},$$

where $f'_\lambda(s)$ and $d_\lambda(s)$ are elements of S. It is clear that the mappings f'_λ and d_λ are linear. Let s, s' be elements of S; then we have $f_\lambda(ss') = f_\lambda(s) f_\lambda(s')$

and

$$(f'_\lambda(s) \otimes 1 + d_\lambda(s) \otimes u)(f'_\lambda(s') \otimes 1 + d_\lambda(s') \otimes u)$$
$$\equiv f'_\lambda(s)f'_\lambda(s') \otimes 1 + (f'_\lambda(s)d_\lambda(s') + d_\lambda(s)f'_\lambda(s')) \otimes u \pmod{L},$$

whence

$$f'_\lambda(ss') = f'_\lambda(s)f'_\lambda(s') \tag{3}$$

$$d_\lambda(ss') = d_\lambda(s)f'_\lambda(s') + f'_\lambda(s)d_\lambda(s'). \tag{4}$$

Formula (3) means that f' is a homomorphism of S into itself.

Let x be an element of M. Then we have

$$f(\psi(x)) = \psi_N(x, \lambda(x)) = \psi_M(x) \otimes 1 + 1 \otimes \psi_R(\lambda(x))$$
$$= \psi_M(x) \otimes 1 + 1 \otimes \lambda(x)u = \psi_M(x) \otimes 1 + \lambda(x)\cdot 1 \otimes u,$$

whence $f'_\lambda(\psi_M(x)) = \psi_M(x)$ and $d_\lambda(x) = \lambda(x)\cdot 1$. Since the homomorphism f'_λ coincides with the identity on the set of generators $\psi(M)$ of S, it is the identity mapping, and formula (4) above gives

$$d_\lambda(ss') = d_\lambda(s)s' + sd_\lambda(s'). \tag{5}$$

In particular, we have $d_\lambda(1) = d_\lambda(1\cdot 1) = 2d_\lambda(1)$, whence $d_\lambda(1) = 0$. We shall now prove that d_λ is homogeneous of degree -1. Let S_n be the module of homogeneous elements of degree n of S; we prove by induction on n that d_λ maps S_n into S_{n-1}. This is true for $n = 0$, since $d_\lambda(1) = 0$. Assume that $n > 0$, and that our statement is true for $n - 1$. Every element of S_n may be written as a linear combination of elements of the form $\psi(x)s$, with $x \in M$, $s \in S_{n-1}$. Making use of formula (5), we have

$$d_\lambda(\psi(x)s) = \lambda(x)s + \psi(x)d_\lambda(s);$$

since $d_\lambda(s) \in S_{n-2}$, $d_\lambda(\psi(x)s)$ is in S_{n-1}, and this proves that $d_\lambda(S_n) \subset S_{n-1}$. Thus, d_λ is a commutative derivation of degree -1 with the required property. It is the only commutative derivation of degree -1 which maps $\psi(x)$ upon $\lambda(x)\cdot 1$ for any $x \in M$ because $\psi(M)$ is a set of generators of M. Let λ and λ' be in M^*; then $d_\lambda + d_{\lambda'}$ is a commutative derivation which maps $\psi_M(x)$ upon $((\lambda + \lambda')(x))\cdot 1$ if $x \in M$, whence $d_\lambda + d_{\lambda'} = d_{\lambda+\lambda'}$. If $a \in R$, ad_λ is a commutative derivation of degree -1 which maps $\psi_M(x)$ upon $((a\lambda)(x))\cdot 1$ if $x \in M$, whence $ad_\lambda = d_{a\lambda}$. Moreover, $d_\lambda \circ d_{\lambda'} - d_{\lambda'} \circ d_\lambda$ is a commutative derivation of degree -2; it maps $\psi_M(M)$ into $S_{-1} = \{0\}$; since $\psi_M(M)$ is a set of generators of S, $d_\lambda \circ d_{\lambda'} - d_{\lambda'} \circ d_\lambda = 0$. Theorem 63 is thereby proved.

Theorem 64. *Let M be a module over a commutative ring R, and (S, ψ) a symmetric algebra on M. Let ρ be a homomorphism of R into a commutative ring R'. Let $S^{R'}$ be an algebra over R' deduced from S by transfer of the basic* *ring to R' by ρ, and let $\psi^{R'}$ be the linear mapping of $M^{R'}$ into $S^{R'}$ deduced from ψ by transfer of the basic ring to R'. Then $(S^{R'}, \psi^{R'})$ is a symmetric algebra on $M^{R'}$.*

Let (T, θ) be a tensor algebra on M. Then we know that there exists an epimorphism f of the algebra T on the algebra S such that $f \circ \theta = \psi$, and that the kernel K of f is the ideal generated by the elements $\theta(x)\theta(y) - \theta(y)\theta(x)$ for x, y in M. On the other hand, we know that $(T^{R'}, \theta^{R'})$ is a tensor algebra on $M^{R'}$ (theorem 52, Sect. 16) and that the mapping $f^{R'}$, which is an epimorphism of $T^{R'}$ on $S^{R'}$, is an algebra homomorphism (theorem 51, Sect. 16). Since $f^{R'} = I \otimes f$, where I is the identity mapping of R', the kernel of $f^{R'}$ is the module K' generated in T by the elements $1 \otimes t$, where $t \in K$ (theorem 29, Chapter III, Sect. 8). If x, y are in M, set

$$Z(x, y) = \theta(x)\theta(y) - \theta(y)\theta(x);$$

then every element of K is a sum of elements of the form $aZ(x, y)b$, with a, b in T. We have

$$1 \otimes aZ(x, y)b = (1 \otimes a)(1 \otimes Z(x, y))(1 \otimes b).$$

If x', y' are elements of $M^{R'}$, set $Z'(x', y') = \theta^{R'}(x')\theta^{R'}(y') - \theta^{R'}(y')\theta^{R}(x')$. Since $1 \otimes \theta(x)\theta(y) = (1 \otimes \theta(x))(1 \otimes \theta(y))$, we have

$$1 \otimes Z(x, y) = Z'(1 \otimes x, 1 \otimes y)$$

if x and y are in M. This shows that K' is contained in the ideal K'' generated in $T^{R'}$ by the elements $Z'(x', y')$, for x', y' in $M^{R'}$. On the other hand, the elements of the form $1 \otimes x$, $x \in M$, form a set Q of module generators of $M^{R'}$; since the bilinear mapping Z' of $M^{R'} \times M^{R'}$ into $T^{R'}$ maps $Q \times Q$ into K', it maps the whole of $M^{R'} \times M^{R'}$ into K', and we have $Z'(x', y') \in K'$ for any x', y' in $M^{R'}$. Since K' is an ideal, we have $K'' \subset K'$, whence $K' = K''$. Let π' be the natural mapping of $T^{R'}$ into $T^{R'}/K''$; then $f^{R'}$ may be factored in the form $g \circ \pi'$, where g is an isomorphism of $T^{R'}/K''$ with $S^{R'}$. Since $f \circ \theta = \psi$, we have $f^{R'} \circ \theta^{R'} = \psi^{R'}$, whence $g \circ (\pi' \circ \theta^{R'}) = \psi^{R'}$. By our contruction of a symmetric algebra on a module, we know that $(T^{R'}, \pi \circ \theta^{R'})$ is a symmetric algebra on $M^{R'}$; it follows immediately that $(S^{R'}, \psi^{R'})$ is a symmetric algebra on $M^{R'}$.

19. Polynomial algebras

Let R be a commutative ring and U be a set. By a *polynomial algebra* on the set U over the ring R is meant an algebra S over R which satisfies the following conditions: S contains U; the submodule M of S generated by U is a free module with U as a base; if ψ is the identity mapping of M into S, then (S, ψ) is a symmetric algebra on M.

If M_1 is any free module over R, U_1 a base of M_1, and (S_1, ψ_1) a symmetric algebra on M_1, then S_1 is a polynomial algebra on the set $\psi_1(U_1)$. It follows that, for any cardinal number a, there exists at least one polynomial algebra on a set whose cardinal number is a.

When S is a polynomial algebra on a set U, the elements of U are often called "indeterminates", or "variables". When we use an expression like "let $X_1, \cdots, X_n$ be n indeterminates", we mean that we have introduced a polynomial algebra on a set U with n elements which are denoted by $X_1, \cdots, X_n$. When the indeterminates of a polynomial algebra are indexed by means of a set of indices I, it is always tacitly understood that two indeterminates with distinct indices are distinct.

Let S be a polynomial algebra on the indeterminates X_i $(i \in I)$. Then S has a base composed of the elements $\prod_{i \in I} X_i^{e(i)}$, where $(e(i))_{i \in I}$ runs over the families of integers $\geqslant 0$ indexed by I which are such that $e(i) = 0$ for almost all i (theorem 62, Sect. 18). The elements $\prod_{i \in I} X_i^{e(i)}$ are called the *monomials*. The elements of S are called the *polynomials* in the indeterminates X_i; if

$$P = \sum_{(e(i))} c((e(i))_{i \in I}) \prod_{i \in I} X_i^{e(i)} \tag{1}$$

is a polynomial, then the element $c((e(i))_{i \in I})$ is called the *coefficient of the monomial* $\prod_{i \in I} X_i^{e(i)}$ *in the polynomial* P.

Theorem 65. *Let S be a polynomial algebra on the indeterminates X_i $(i \in I)$; denote by J a subset of I and by J' the complementary set of J with respect to I. Let T be the subalgebra of S generated by the elements X_j $(j \in J)$; then T is a polynomial algebra on the indeterminates X_j $(j \in J)$. There is an algebra S' over T whose elements, addition and multiplication are the same as those of S and whose scalar multiplication is the restriction to $T \times S$ of the multiplication of S. The algebra S' is a polynomial algebra on the indeterminates $X_{j'}$ $(j' \in J')$ over T.*

The module generated by the elements X_i $(i \in I)$ in S is the direct sum of the module N generated by the elements X_j $(j \in J)$ and of the module N' generated by the elements $X_{j'}$ $(j' \in J')$. Therefore, the first assertion of theorem 65 follows from theorem 61 *a*, Sect. 18. The second assertion follows from the fact that S is commutative (cf. Sect. 1). Let T' be the subalgebra of S generated by the elements $X_{j'}$ $(j' \in J')$. Then there exists an isomorphism φ of S with $T \otimes_c T'$ which maps X_j upon $X_j \otimes 1$ if $j \in J$ and $X_{j'}$ upon $1 \otimes X_{j'}$ if $j' \in J'$ (theorem 61, Sect. 18). Let ρ be the homomorphism $\alpha \to \alpha \cdot 1$ of R into the ring T; this homomorphism defines on T a structure of an algebra over R (cf. Sect. 16, beginning) which is obviously identical to the one we have already. Let T'^T be the algebra over T deduced from T' by transfer of the basic ring to T by means of ρ; then the elements, addition and multiplication of T'^T are the same as those of $T \otimes_c T'$ (cf. Sect. 17). We may consider φ as a mapping of the algebra S' into T'^T (S' and T'^T both are algebras over T). If $x, y \in S'$, we have $\varphi(x+y) = \varphi(x) + \varphi(y)$, $\varphi(xy) = \varphi(x)\varphi(y)$, and φ maps the unit element of S' upon that of T'^T. We shall see that $\varphi(t \cdot x) = t \cdot \varphi(x)$ if $t \in T$, $x \in S$. The left side is $\varphi(tx) = \varphi(t)\varphi(x)$. The mapping $t \to t \otimes 1$ is a homomorphism of T into $T \otimes_c T'$; if $j \in J$, then this homomorphism maps X_j upon the same element $X_j \otimes 1$ as φ; since the set of the elements X_j, $j \in J$, generates T, we have $\varphi(t) = t \otimes 1$ for every $t \in T$, whence $\varphi(t \cdot x) = (t \otimes 1)\varphi(x)$; this is equal to $t \cdot \varphi(x)$ by virtue of the definition of the scalar multiplication of T'^T. Thus, φ is a homomorphism of the algebra S' into T'^T; since it is a bijection, it is an isomorphism of S' with T'^T. Let I be the identity mapping of N' into T' and I^T the mapping of N'^T into T'^T which is deduced from I by transfer to T of the basic ring. Since (T', I) is a symmetric algebra on N', (T'^T, I^T) is a symmetric algebra on N'^T (theorem 64, Sect. 18). Let N'' be the submodule of S' generated by the elements $X_{j'}$ ($j' \in J'$), and I'' the identity mapping of N'' into S'. Then $\varphi(N'')$ is the submodule of T'^T generated by the elements $\varphi(X_{j'}) = 1 \otimes X_{j'}$ ($j' \in J'$). Since $1 \otimes X_{j'} = I^T(X_{j'})$, we have $\varphi(N'') = N'^T$, and, since (T'^T, I^T) is a symmetric algebra on N'^T, (S', I'') is a symmetric algebra on N''. Moreover, the elements $1 \otimes X_{j'}$ ($j' \in J'$) form a base of N'^T, from which it follows that the elements $X_{j'}$ ($j' \in J'$) form a base of N''; S' is therefore a polynomial algebra on the indeterminates $X_{j'}$($j' \in J'$).

Theorem 65 says that a polynomial in the indeterminates X_i ($i \in I$) may be considered as a polynomial in the indeterminates $X_{j'}$ ($j' \in J'$) whose coefficients are in the ring of polynomials in the indeterminates X_j ($j \in J$).

If $\prod_{i \in I} X_i^{e(i)}$ is a monomial, the number $\sum_{i \in I} e(i)$ is called the *degree* of this monomial. The *homogeneous polynomials of degree n* (where n is any integer $\geqslant 0$) are linear combinations of the monomials of degree n. If a polynomial P is written in the form (1) and is $\neq 0$, then the largest n such that there exists a monomial of degree n whose coefficient in P is $\neq 0$ is called the *degree* of the polynomial P; if P and Q are polynomials $\neq 0$ such that $P + Q$ is $\neq 0$, the degree of $P + Q$ is obviously at most equal to the largest of the degrees of P and Q.

Theorem 66. *Let R be a domain of integrity. If P and Q are polynomials $\neq 0$ in the indeterminates X_i, $i \in I$, with coefficients in R, then PQ is $\neq 0$ and the degree of PQ is the sum of the degrees of P and Q.*

In order to prove that $PQ \neq 0$, we first consider the case where I is finite. We then proceed by induction on the number ν of elements of I. The theorem is true if $\nu = 0$, for the polynomial algebra is then isomorphic to R

and every polynomial $\neq 0$ is of degree 0. Assume that $\nu > 0$ and that the theorem is true for polynomials in $\nu - 1$ indeterminates. We may assume without loss of generality that $I = \{1, \cdots, \nu\}$. We write

$$P = \Sigma_{i=0}^{p} P_i X_\nu^i, \qquad Q = \Sigma_{j=0}^{q} Q_j X_\nu^j$$

where $P_0, \cdots, P_p, Q_0, \cdots, Q_q$ are polynomials in $X_1, \ldots, X_{\nu-1}$, and, since $P \neq 0$, $Q \neq 0$, we may assume that $P_p \neq 0$, $Q_q \neq 0$. We have

$$PQ = P_p Q_q X_\nu^{p+q} + \Sigma_{k=0}^{p+q-1} (\Sigma_{i+j=k} P_i Q_j) X_\nu^k;$$

it follows from the inductive assumption that $P_p Q_q \neq 0$; we conclude that $PQ \neq 0$. Suppose now that I is infinite; then there is a finite subset J of I such that P and Q belong to the algebra generated by the elements X_j, for $j \in J$, which proves that $PQ \neq 0$.

Now, let d and e be the degrees of P and Q. Let

$$P = \Sigma_{i=0}^{d} P'_i, \qquad Q = \Sigma_{j=0}^{e} Q'_j$$

be the decompositions of P and Q into their homogeneous components; then

$$PQ = P'_d Q'_e + \Sigma_{k=0}^{d+e-1} (\Sigma_{i+j=k} P'_i Q'_j);$$

for each k, $\Sigma_{i+j=k} P'_i Q'_j$ is homogeneous of degree k, and $P'_d Q'_e$ is homogeneous of degree $d + e$. Since d and e are the degrees of P and Q respectively, we have $P'_d \neq 0$, $Q'_e \neq 0$, whence $P'_d Q'_e \neq 0$. It follows that PQ is of degree $d + e$.

Let J and J' be complementary subsets of I, and let P be a polynomial $\neq 0$ in the indeterminates X_i, $i \in I$. If we consider P as a polynomial in the indeterminates $X_{j'}$ $(j' \in J')$ whose coefficients are polynomials in the X_j $(j \in J)$, then the degree of this polynomial is called the *partial degree of P with respect to the indeterminates $X_{j'}$*. If the basic ring R is a domain of integrity, then the partial degree of the product of two polynomials $\neq 0$ is the sum of the partial degrees of these polynomials.

Let S be a polynomial algebra on the set U over a ring R and let A be an algebra over R. Let φ be any mapping of U into A such that the elements of $\varphi(U)$ commute with each other. Then there exists a unique homomorphism f of S into A which extends φ. For, let M be the submodule of S generated by U; since U is a base of M, there is a unique extension φ_1 of φ to a linear mapping of M into A; the elements of $\varphi_1(M)$ belong to the subalgebra of A generated by $\varphi(U)$, and this subalgebra is commutative, which shows that the elements of $\varphi_1(M)$ commute with each other. If ψ is the identity map of M into S, then (S, ψ) is a symmetric algebra on M; therefore, there is a uniquely determined homomorphism f of S into A which extends φ_1, which proves our assertion. Assume that the elements X_i of U have been indexed by a set I, and let $(a_i)_{i \in I}$ be any family of elements of A indexed by I whose elements commute with each other. Then there is a mapping φ of U into A which maps X_i upon a_i for every i. If f is the corresponding homomorphism of S into A, and $P \in S$ is any polynomial, then the element $f(P)$ is often denoted by $P(\cdots, a_i, \cdots)$; this element of A is called the *result of the substitution of the values a_i for the arguments X_i in P*. If $I = \{1, \cdots, n\}$, then one writes $P(a_1, \cdots, a_n)$ instead of $P(\cdots, a_i, \cdots)$. If we take $A = S$, $a_i = X_i$, f is obviously the identity mapping; we may therefore write

$$P = P(\cdots, X_i, \cdots)$$

or, if $I = \{1, \cdots, n\}$,

$$P = P(X_1, \cdots, X_n).$$

The notation being as above, let i be any index in I. Then there is a linear mapping of M into the basic ring R which maps X_i upon 1 and X_j upon 0 if $j \neq i$. This linear mapping may be uniquely extended to a commutative derivation ∂_i of S (theorem 63, Sect. 18); ∂_i is called the *partial derivation with respect to X_i*; if $P \in S$, the polynomial $\partial_i P$ is also denoted by $\partial P/\partial X_i$ and is called the *partial derivative of P with respect to X_i*. If U consists of a single element X, $\partial P/\partial X$ is called the *derivative* of P and is denoted by dP/dX.

Theorem 67. *Let S be a polynomial algebra on the indeterminates X_i ($i \in I$). Then the partial derivations ∂_i with respect to the various indeterminates X_i commute with each other.*

This follows immediately from theorem 63, Sect. 18.

The partial derivations ∂_i are elements of the algebra $\mathfrak{E}$ of endomorphisms of the module S; they generate a commutative subalgebra $\mathfrak{D}$ of $\mathfrak{E}$. The elements of $\mathfrak{D}$ are called the *differential operators on S*. If $I = \{1, \cdots, n\}$, the algebra is spanned by the elements $\partial_1^{e(1)} \cdots \partial_n^{e(n)}$, for all systems of integers $e(1) \geqslant 0, \cdots, e(n) \geqslant 0$. If $P \in S$, then $\partial_1^{e(1)} \cdots \partial_n^{e(n)} P$ is denoted by

$$\frac{\partial^{e(1)+\cdots+e(n)}}{\partial X_1^{e(1)} \cdots \partial X_n^{e(n)}} P.$$

Theorem 68. *Let P be a polynomial $\neq 0$ of degree d in the indeterminates X_i ($i \in I$), and of partial degree e_i with respect to X_i. Then $\partial P/\partial X_i$ is either 0 or a polynomial of degree $\leqslant d-1$ and of partial degree $\leqslant e_i - 1$ with respect to X_i. If the basic ring R is a domain of integrity of characteristic 0 and $e_i > 0$. then $\partial P/\partial X_i$ is $\neq 0$ and of partial degree $e_i - 1$ with respect to X_i.*

We have

$$\frac{\partial}{\partial X_i}(\Pi_{j\in I} X_j^{e(j)}) = e(i)\Pi_{j\in I} X_j^{e'(j)}$$

where $e'(j) = e(j)$ if $j \neq i$, $e'(i) = e(i) - 1$ if $e(i) > 0$, $e'(i) = 0$ if $e(i) = 0$, In order to prove this, we write

$$\Pi_{j\in I} X_j^{e(j)} = X_i^{e(i)} N$$

where $N = \Pi_{j\neq i} X_j^{e(j)}$ belongs to the algebra T generated by the elements X_j, $j \neq i$. Let ∂_i be the partial derivation with respect to X_i; since $\partial_i X_j = 0$ for $j \neq i$, ∂_i maps every element of T upon 0, whence $\partial_i N = 0$, and $\partial_i(X_i^{e(i)} N) = (\partial_i X_i^{e(i)})N$. It will therefore be sufficient to prove that $\partial_i X_i^e = eX_i^{e-1}$ if $e > 0$, $\partial_i 1 = 0$. The second formula is true because ∂_i is a commutative derivation. The first one is true if $e = 1$, since $\partial_i X_i = 1$. Assume that $e > 1$ and that the first formula is true for $e - 1$. Then

$$\partial_i X_i^e = \partial_i(X_i X_i^{e-1}) = (\partial_i X_i)X_i^{e-1} + X_i \partial_i(X_i^{e-1}) = X_i^{e-1} + (e-1)X_i^{e-1} = eX_i^{e-1}$$

which proves that the formula is true for e.

Now, write $P = \Sigma_{k=1}^h c_k M_k$ where $M_1, \cdots, M_h$ are distinct monomials and $c_1 \neq 0, \cdots, c_h \neq 0$; assume that $\partial M_k/\partial X_i \neq 0$ if $1 \leqslant k \leqslant h'$, $\partial M_k/\partial X_i = 0$ if $h' < k \leqslant h$. Then

$$\frac{\partial P}{\partial X_i} = \Sigma_{k=1}^{h'} c_k \partial M_k/\partial X_i.$$

It follows immediately from the formula written above that, if $k \leqslant h'$, then $\partial M_k/\partial X_i = f_k M_k'$, where f_k is the partial degree of M_k with respect to X_i, $M_1', \cdots, M_h'$ are *distinct* monomials, and M_k' is of partial degree $f_k - 1$ with respect to X_i. Moreover, if M_k is of degree d_k, then M_k' is of degree $d_k - 1$. From this it follows that $\partial P/\partial X_i$ is of degree $\leqslant d - 1$ and of partial degree $\leqslant e - 1$ with respect to X_i. Assume now that the basic ring R is a domain of integrity of characteristic 0 and that $e > 0$. Let k_0 be an index such that M_{k_0} is of partial degree e with respect to X_i. Then $f_{k_0} = e$, whence $k \leqslant h'$ and $c_{k_0} f_{k_0} \neq 0$, which proves that $\partial P/\partial X_i$ is $\neq 0$ and of partial degree $e - 1$ with respect to X_i.

Theroem 69. *Let S be the algebra of polynomials in n indeterminates $X_1, \cdots, X_n$ and T the algebra of polynomials in p indeterminates $Y_1, \cdots, Y_p$. Let P be an element of S and $Q_1, \cdots, Q_n$ elements of T. Then we have*

$$\frac{\partial}{\partial Y_j}(P(Q_1, \cdots, Q_n)) = \Sigma_{i=1}^n \frac{\partial P}{\partial X_i}(Q_1, \cdots, Q_n)\frac{\partial Q_i}{\partial Y_j} \quad (1 \leqslant j \leqslant P).$$

Let f be the homomorphism of S into T which maps X_i upon Q_i $(1 \leqslant i \leqslant n)$. Then $(\partial/\partial Y_j) \circ f$ is an f-derivation of S into T, and so is $f \circ (\partial/\partial X_i)$ for every i $(1 \leqslant i \leqslant n)$ (cf. theorem 16, Sect. 6; here, we consider S and T as graded algebras in which every element is homogeneous of degree 0). If R is any element of T, denote by L the operator of multiplication by R in T. Then if δ is any f-derivation of S into T, so is $L \circ \delta$; for we have, if $P, P' \in S$,

$$\begin{aligned}(L \circ \delta)(PP') &= L((\delta P)f(P') + f(P)\delta(P')) = R(\delta P)f(P') + Rf(P)\delta(P') \\ &= (L \circ \delta)(P)f(P') + f(P)(L \circ \delta)(P'),\end{aligned}$$

which proves our assertion. Let L_i be the operator of left multiplication by $\partial Q_i/\partial Y_j$; then $(\partial/\partial Y_j) \circ f$ and $\sum_{i=1}^n L_i \circ f \circ \frac{\partial}{\partial X_i}$ are f-derivations of S into T. They both map X_i upon $\partial Q_i/\partial Y_j$ $(1 \leqslant i \leqslant n)$; since $X_1, \cdots, X_n$ generate S, we have

$$\frac{\partial}{\partial Y_j} \circ f = \sum_{i=1}^n L_i \circ f \circ \frac{\partial}{\partial X_i}$$

which proves the theorem.

Consider now a polynomial algebra in $2n$ indeterminates $X_1, \cdots, X_n$, $Y_1, \cdots, Y_n$. Let P be a polynomial in $X_1, \cdots, X_n$ only. Then we may write

$$P(X_1 + Y_1, \cdots, X_n + Y_n) = \sum P_{e_1, \cdots, e_n} Y_1^{e_1} \cdots Y_n^{e_n}$$

where the summation is extended to all systems of n integers $e_1 \geqslant 0, \cdots, e_n \geqslant 0$ and where each $P_{e_1, \cdots, e_n}$ is a polynomial in $X_1, \cdots, X_n$. Denote by $\partial_1, \cdots, \partial_n$ the operations of partial derivation with respect to $X_1, \cdots, X_n$ and by $\delta_1, \cdots, \delta_n$ the operations of partial derivation with respect to $Y_1, \cdots, Y_n$. Then δ_i maps upon 0 every polynomial in $X_1, \cdots, X_n$, since $\delta_i X_j = 0$ $(1 \leqslant i, j \leqslant n)$. Let $f_1, \cdots, f_n$ be integers $\geqslant 0$; then it follows easily from the formula written above for the partial derivatives of a monomial that

$$\delta_1^{f_1} \cdots \delta_n^{f_n}(Y_1^{e_1} \cdots Y_n^{e_n}) = \begin{cases} 0 & \text{if } e_i < f_i \text{ for some } i \\ c_{e,f} Y_1^{e_1 - f_1} \cdots Y_n^{e_n - f_n} & \text{if } e_i \geqslant f_i \text{ for all } i \end{cases}$$

where $c_{e,f} = \prod_{i=1}^n \left(\prod_{k=0}^{f_i - 1}(e_i - k)\right)$. Thus we have

$$\begin{aligned}&\delta_1^{f_1} \cdots \delta_n^{f_n} \cdot P(X_1 + Y_1, \cdots, X_n + Y_n) \\ &= \sum_{e_1 \geqslant f_1, \cdots, e_n \geqslant f_n} P_{e_1, \cdots, e_n} c_{e,f} Y_1^{e_1 - f_1} \cdots Y_n^{e_n - f_n}.\end{aligned}$$

Now, it follows immediately from theorem 69 that

$$\delta_i(P(X_1 + Y_1, \cdots, X_n + Y_n)) = (\partial_i P)(X_1 + Y_1, \cdots, X_n + Y_n)$$

for any polynomial P in $X_1, \cdots, X_n$. We conclude easily from this that

$$\begin{aligned}&\delta_1^{f_1} \cdots \delta_n^{f_n}(P(X_1 + Y_1, \cdots, X_n + Y_n)) \\ &= ((\partial_1^{f_1} \cdots \partial_n^{f_n})(P))(X_1 + Y_1, \cdots, X_n + Y_n)\end{aligned}$$

whence

$$\begin{aligned}&(\partial_1^{f_1} \cdots \partial_n^{f_n} \cdot P)(X_1 + Y_1, \cdots, X_n + Y_n) \\ &= \sum_{e_1 \geqslant f_1, \cdots, e_n \geqslant f_n} P_{e_1, \cdots, e_n} c_{e,f} Y_1^{e_1 - f_1} \cdots Y_n^{e_n - f_n}.\end{aligned}$$

Now, we take the images of both sides under the homomorphism of S into itself which maps X_i upon X_i and Y_i upon 0 $(1 \leqslant i \leqslant n)$. If P' is any polynomial in $X_1, \cdots, X_n$, the image of $P'(X_1 + Y_1, \cdots, X_n + Y_n)$ under this homomorphism is P'. On the other hand, the image of $Y_1^{e_1-f_1} \cdots Y_n^{e_n-f_n}$ is 0 if $e_i > f_i$ for at least one i, and 1 if $e_i = f_i$ $(1 \leqslant i \leqslant n)$. Since $c_{e,e} = (e_1!) \cdots (e_n!)$, we obtain the formula

$$\partial_1^{e_1} \cdots \partial_n^{e_n} \cdot P = (e_1!) \cdots (e_n!) P_{e_1, \cdots, e_n}.$$

If we assume that the basic ring R is a field of characteristic 0, we obtain the formula

$$P(X_1 + Y_1, \cdots, X_n + Y_n) = \Sigma (e_1!)^{-1} \cdots (e_n!)^{-1} \left(\frac{\partial^{e_1 + \cdots + e_n}}{\partial X_1^{e_1} \cdots \partial X_n^{e_n}} P \right) Y_1^{e_1} \cdots Y_n^{e_n}$$

which is called the *Taylor formula.*

Exercises on Chapter V

1. Let G be a group, R a commutative ring and A an algebra of G over R. Show that A is isomorphic to its opposite algebra.
2. Let C be the center of an algebra A, i. e., the set of elements x of A such that $xy = yx$ for every $y \in A$. Show that C is a subalgebra of A and that there exists an algebra over C which has the same elements, the same addition and the same multiplication as A.
3. Let A be an algebra over a field which has a finite set of generators, and let K be an ideal of A. Assume that the vector space A/K is finite dimensional. Show that K then has a finite set of ideal generators. Define inductively a sequence (K_n) of ideals of A as follows: K_1 is K, and, for any $n > 0$, K_{n+1} is the ideal generated by the products xy, with $x \in K$, $y \in K_n$. Show that, for every $n > 0$, the space A/K_n is finite dimensional.
4. Let A be an algebra and $(K_n)_{0 \leqslant n < \infty}$ a sequence of ideals of A with the following properties: *a*) K_0 is A; *b*) for any $n \geqslant 0$, K_{n+1} is contained in K_n; *c*) if m, n are integers $\geqslant 0$, the product of an element of K_m by an element of K_n is in K_{m+n}. Let M_n be the module K_n/K_{n+1} and π_n the natural mapping of K_n onto M_n. Let $P = \prod_{n \geqslant 0}^{w} M_n$; denote by ψ_n the natural injection of M_n into P and set $\theta_n = \psi_n \circ \pi_n$. Define on the module P a multiplication relative to which P becomes an algebra in such a way that $\theta_{m+n}(xy) = \theta_m(x)\theta_n(y)$ whenever $x \in K_m$, $y \in K_n$; show that the decomposition $P = \Sigma_{n \geqslant 0} \psi_n(M_n)$ defines on P the structure of a graded algebra.

5. Let M be a module over the ring $\underline{Z}$, (T, θ) a tensor algebra on M and T_n the module of homogeneous elements of degree n of T. Determine the modules T_n in the following cases: *a*) $M = \underline{Z}_m$, where m is some integer > 0; *b*) $M = \underline{Q}/\underline{Z}$. Let M' be a submodule of M, (T', θ') a tensor algebra on M' and f the homomorphism of T' into T such that $f \circ \theta' = \theta$; show by an example that f is not always a monomorphism.

6. Let R be a domain of integrity, M a free module over R and T a tensor algebra on M; show that T has no zero divisor $\neq 0$. Show by an example that the conclusion would not be valid without the assumption that M is a free module [use ex. 5].

7. Generalize the definitions and theorems relative to the notions of tensor products of graded algebras and of derivations of a graded algebra to the case of graded algebras having $\underline{Z}_2$ as their group of degrees.

8. Let M be a module over a commutative ring R. A mapping q of M into R is called a quadratic form on M if the following conditions are satisfied: *a*) $q(\alpha x) = \alpha^2 q(x)$ for all $\alpha \in R$, $x \in M$; *b*) the mapping

$$(x, y) \to q(x + y) - q(x) - q(y)$$

is a bilinear form on $M \times M$. Let q be a quadratic form on M. An object formed by an algebra C over R and a linear mapping ψ of M into C is called a Clifford algebra for q if the following conditions are satisfied: *a*) $(\psi(x))^2 = q(x)\cdot 1$ for all $x \in M$; *b*) if φ is any linear mapping of M into an algebra A such that $(\varphi(x))^2 = q(x)\cdot 1$ for every $x \in M$, then there exists a unique homomorphism f of C into A such that $f \circ \psi = \varphi$. Formulate and prove an isomorphism theorem for Clifford algebras. Show that, given any quadratic form q on M, there exists a Clifford algebra (C, ψ) for q. Show that there exists a uniquely determined gradation of C having $\underline{Z}_2$ as its group of degrees such that the elements of $\psi(M)$ are homogeneous of degree 1^* (1^* being the image of 1 under the natural mapping of $\underline{Z}$ on $\underline{Z}_2$). Show that there exist an automorphism J of C such that $J(\psi(x)) = -\psi(x)$ for every $x \in M$, and an anti-automorphism ρ of C (i. e., an isomorphism of C with its opposite algebra) such that $\rho(\psi(x)) = \psi(x)$ for every $x \in M$. Show that we have

$$\psi(x)\psi(y) + \psi(y)\psi(x) = (q(x + y) - q(x) - q(y))\cdot 1$$

for any x, y in M.

If $\beta: M\times M \to R$ is this form then: $q(x) = \frac{1}{2}\beta(x,x)$.

9. The notation being as in ex. 8, assume further that $M = R$ (R being regarded as a module over itself). Show that C is a free module with a base of 2 elements. Show that, in order for C to be a field, it is necessary and sufficient that the following conditions be satisfied: *a*) R is a field; *b*) $q(1)$ is not the square of any element of R.

10. The notation being as in ex. 8, assume that M is a free module with a base of two elements x and y. Set $q(x) = a$, $q(y) = b$ and assume that $q(x + y) = a + b$. Show that 1, $u = \psi(x)$, $v = \psi(y)$ and uv form a base

of C, and that $u^2 = a \cdot 1$, $v^2 = b \cdot 1$, $(uv)^2 = -ab \cdot 1$. Show that there exists an anti-automorphism χ of C such that $\chi(u) = -u$, $\chi(v) = -v$, $\chi(uv) = -uv$, and that $z\chi(z) = Q(z) \cdot 1$, Q being a quadratic form on the module C. Show that the elements of R which are of the form $Q(z)$, for $z \in C$, form a set stable under multiplication. Show that, in order for C to be a sfield, it is necessary and sufficient that the following conditions be satisfied: R is a field and the only solution of the equation $\alpha^2 - a\beta^2 - b\gamma^2 + ab\delta^2 = 0$ in elements $\alpha, \beta, \gamma, \delta$ of R is $(0, 0, 0, 0)$. Construct an algebra over the field $\underline{Q}$ which is a vector space of dimension 4 and a sfield.

11. The notation being as in ex. 10, assume further that $a = b = -1$. Define a multiplication on the module $C \times C$ by the formula

$$(X, Y)(Z, T) = (XZ - \chi(T)Y,\ Y\chi(Z) + TX).$$

Show that, with this multiplication, $\Gamma = C \times C$ becomes an alternative algebra; this algebra is called the algebra of octonions over R. Show that the multiplication in Γ has a unit element E. If $(X, Y) \in \Gamma$, set $\bar{\chi}(X, Y) = (\chi(X), -Y)$; show that $\bar{\chi}(UV) = \bar{\chi}(V)\bar{\chi}(U)$ for any U and V in Γ, and that $U\bar{\chi}(U) = M(U) \cdot E$, with some $M(U) \in R$. Compute $M(U)$ in terms of the coefficients of the expression of U as a linear combination of the elements of a suitable base in Γ, and deduce from the result that the set of elements of R which are representable as sums of 8 squares of elements of R is stable under multiplication.

12. Let R be the ring $\underline{Z}_4$ and M the module $2\underline{Z}_4$ over R. Show that M has 2 elements 0 and x, and that there exists a quadratic form q on M such that $q(x) = 1_R$ (the unit element of R). Let (C, ψ) be a Clifford algebra for q (cf. ex. 8). Show that $2 \cdot 1_C = 0$, if 1_C is the unit element of C. Let M_1 be a free module over R with a base of one element y; show that there is a quadratic form $\bar{q}$ on $M_1 \times M$ such that $\bar{q}((ax, by)) = a^2$ (if $a, b \in R$). Let $(\bar{C}, \psi)$ be a Clifford algebra for $\bar{q}$; show that $\psi(2y) = 0$, although $2y \neq 0$.

13. Let M be a module over a commutative ring R and (T, θ) a tensor algebra on M. Let λ be any linear form on M; show that there exists a unique derivation d_λ of T of degree -1 such that $d_\lambda(\theta(x)) = \lambda(x) \cdot 1$ for every $x \in M$ [define d_λ in such a way that

$$d_\lambda(\theta(x_1) \cdots \theta(x_n)) = \textstyle\sum_{i=1}^n (-1)^{i-1} \lambda(x_i) \left(\prod_{j<i} \theta(x_j)\right)\left(\prod_{j>i} \theta(x_j)\right)$$

whenever $x_1, \cdots, x_n$ are in M]. Show that $\lambda \to d_\lambda$ is a linear mapping of the dual module of M into the module of derivations of degree -1 of T and that $d_\lambda \circ d_\lambda = 0$.

14. Let M be a module and q a quadratic form on M (cf, ex. 8). Assume that there exists a bilinear form β on $M \times M$ such that $q(x) = \beta(x, x)$ for all $x \in M$. Let (T, θ) be a tensor algebra on M. If $x \in M$, let L_x be the operator of left multiplication by x in T and d_x the derivation of degree -1 of T which maps $\theta(y)$ upon $\beta(x, y) \cdot 1$ for every $y \in M$ (cf. ex. 12). Let A

be the algebra of endomorphisms of the module T, with the law of composition $(f, g) \to f \circ g$. Denote by Λ_t the image of an element t of T under the homomorphism of the algebra T into A which maps $\theta(x)$ upon $L_x - d_x$ if $x \in M$; set $\Omega(t) = \Lambda_t(1)$. Denote by T_p the module of homogeneous elements of degree p of T. Show that, if $t \in T_m$, $u \in T_n$ then $\Lambda_t(u) - tu$ belongs to $\sum_{p<m+n} T_p$. Deduce from this that Ω is an automorphism of the *module* T [prove by induction on n that Ω induces an automorphism of the module $\sum_{p \leqslant n} T_p$]. Show that, if $t = (\theta(x))^2$ (where $x \in M$), then $\Lambda_t = L_t - q(x)I$, where L_t is the operator of left multiplication by t and I the unit element of E. Denote by K the ideal generated in T by the elements $(\theta(x))^2$ $(x \in M)$ and by K' the ideal generated by the elements $(\theta(x))^2 - q(x)\cdot 1$. Show that $\Omega(K) = K'$ [show that d_x maps K' into itself; conclude that, for any $t \in T$, Λ_t maps K' into itself; prove by induction on n that Ω maps $K \cap T_n$ onto $K' \cap T_n$]. Let (E, ψ) be an exterior algebra on M, and (C, ζ) a Clifford algebra for q; show that there exists an isomorphism J of the module (not the algebra!) E with the module C such that $J \circ \psi = \zeta$. Conclude that ζ induces a monomorphism of M into C and that the unit element of C constitutes a base of the module it generates.

Show that, if M is a free module with a finite base, then, for any given quadratic form on M, the assumption of the existence of a bilinear form β with the postulated property is satisfied.

15. Let M be a module over a commutative ring R, E an exterior algebra on M and E^* the dual algebra of E. Denote by E_m the module of homogeneous elements of degree m of E and by E_m^* the module of elements of E^* which map E_n upon $\{0\}$ whenever $n \neq m$. Show that, if φ is an element $\neq 0$ of E_m^*, with $m > 0$, there exist m derivations $d_1, \cdots, d_m$ of degree -1 of the algebra $G = \sum_{m \geqslant 0} E_m^*$ such that $(d_1 \circ \cdots \circ d_n)(\varphi) \neq 0$. Show that, if λ and μ are any elements of E_1^* and d a derivation of degree -1 of G, then $(\lambda \wedge \mu) \wedge d(\lambda \wedge \mu) = 0$. Let S be the set of elements of the form $\lambda \wedge \mu$, with λ, μ in E_1^*. Show that, if $u_1, \cdots, u_r$ are elements of S whose sum is 0, we have $\prod_{i=1}^r (1 + u_i) = 1$ [show that, if v is the homogeneous component of degree m of this product, and $m > 0$, then $d(v) = 0$ for every derivation d of degree -1 of G]. Let A be the subalgebra of E^* generated by S, and K the additive group generated by S; show that there exists a homomorphism ρ of the additive group of K into the multiplicative monoid of elements of A which maps every $u \in S$ upon $1 + u$.

16. Let M be a module over a commutative ring R and E an exterior algebra on M. To every alternating bilinear form γ on $M \times M$, associate an automorphism Ω_γ of the module E in the manner described in Sect. 14. Show that $\Omega_{\gamma+\gamma'} = \Omega_\gamma \circ \Omega_{\gamma'}$ if γ, γ', are any two alternating bilinear forms on $M \times M$ [prove that, if $\Omega_\gamma(\Omega_{\gamma'}(t)) = \Omega_{\gamma+\gamma'}(t)$ for some $t \in E$, then the same formula holds for xt if $x \in M$]. Let E^* be the dual algebra of the algebra E, and ${}^t\Omega_\gamma$ the transpose mapping of Ω_γ. Show that, if E^* is

generated by its homogeneous elements of degree 1, then ${}^t\Omega_\gamma$ is the operation of right multiplication by an element ω_γ of E^* [use the following facts: Ω_γ commutes with the derivations of degree -1 of E, and the transpose mappings of these derivations are the left multiplications by the homogeneous elements of degree 1 in E*]; show that ω_γ is uniquely determined and that $\omega_{\gamma+\gamma'} = \omega_\gamma \omega_{\gamma'}$ if γ, γ' are any two alternating bilinear forms on $M \times M$; denote by φ_γ the element of E_2^* such that $\varphi_\gamma(xy) = \gamma(x, y)$ for any x, y in M; show that ω_γ and φ_γ have the same restriction to E_2; denoting by A the subalgebra of E^* generated by E_2^* and by S the set of elements of the form $\lambda \wedge \mu$ (with λ, μ in E_1^*), show that, under our assumption on E^*, S is a set of generators of A and that the squares of the elements of S are 0; show that $\omega_\gamma = \rho(\varphi_\gamma)$, where ρ is the mapping of ex. 15 [first consider the case where φ_γ is of the form $\lambda \wedge \mu$].

Assume now that M has a finite base $(x_1, \cdots, x_n)$, and set $\gamma(x_i, x_j) = a_{ij}$; denote by A the matrix (a_{ij}). Show that the homogeneous component of degree n of ω_γ is $(\text{Pf } A)(x_1^* \wedge \cdots \wedge x_n^*)$ (where $(x_1^*, \cdots, x_n^*)$ is the base of the dual module M^* of M dual to the base $(x_1, \cdots, x_n)$). Show that, if $m = 2n$, then $\text{Pf } A = \Sigma_p \chi(p) a_{p(1), p(2)} \cdots a_{p(2m-1), p(2m)}$ where the summation is extended to all permutations p of $\{1, \cdots, 2m\}$ such that $p(2k-1) < p(2k)$ for $1 \leqslant k \leqslant m$, and where $\chi(p)$ is the signature of p.

Generalize the result to the effect that ${}^t\Omega_\gamma$ is a right multiplication in E^* to the case where it is not assumed any more that E^* is generated by its homogeneous elements of degree 1 [first consider the case of a free module; then, in the general case, represent M as a homomorphic image of a free module].

17. Let A and B be graded algebras over a commutative ring, having $\underline{Z}$ as their group of degrees. Let d_A (resp.: d_B) be a derivation of degree i_A (resp.: i_B) of A (resp.: B), and let I_B be the identity mapping of B into itself. Show that $d_A \otimes I_B$ is a derivation of degree i_A of $A \otimes B$. Let J_A be the main involution of A; show that $J_A^{i_B} \otimes d_B$ is a derivation of degree i_B of $A \otimes B$. Show that

$$(d_A \otimes I_B) \circ (J_A^{i_B} \otimes d_B) = (-1)^{i_A i_B} (J^{i_B} \otimes d_B) \circ (d_A \otimes I_B).$$

Show that if $i_A = i_B$ is an odd number and $d_A \circ d_A = d_B \circ d_B = 0$, then the operation $d = d_A \otimes I_B + J_A^{i_B} \otimes d_B$ is a derivation of $A \otimes B$ and that $d \circ d = 0$.

18. Let A, B, M be modules over a commutative ring R and E an exterior algebra on M. Denote by E_m the module of homogeneous elements of degree m of E; if C is any module, denote by $\text{Hom}_m(E, C)$ the module of linear mappings φ of E into C such that $\varphi(E_p) = \{0\}$ for every $p \neq m$. Let φ be an element of $\text{Hom}_m(E, A)$ and ψ an element of $\text{Hom}_n(E, B)$. Denote by ζ the isomorphism of $A \otimes B$ with $B \otimes A$ which maps $a \otimes b$ upon $b \otimes a$ if $a \in A$, $b \in B$. Show that $\zeta \circ (\varphi \wedge \psi) = (-1)^{mn} \varphi \wedge \psi$.

19. Let E be an exterior algebra on a module M, and E_n the module of homogeneous elements of degree n of E. Let f be a linear mapping of E into itself with the following property: there exists an even number n such that $f(E_p) = \{0\}$ for every $p \neq n$, $f(E_n) \subset E_1$. Let μ be the linear mapping of $E \otimes E$ into E such that $\mu(t \otimes u) = tu$ if $t, u \in E$; let I be the identity mapping of E; set $g = \mu \circ (f \wedge I)$, $h = g \circ g$. Let E^* be the dual algebra of E, E_p^* the module of homogeneous elements of degree p of E^* and G the subalgebra $\sum_{p \geqslant 0} E_p^*$ of E^*. Show that the transpose mapping th of h induces a derivation of degree $2(n-1)$ of G [use the fact that ${}^th = {}^tg \circ {}^tg$]. Let U be the analyzing mapping of E; show that $U \circ h = (h \otimes I + I \otimes h) \circ U$

20. Let the notation be as in ex. 19, and assume now that h maps E_{2n-1} upon $\{0\}$. Show that $f \circ g = \{0\}$. Using formula (4), sect. 11, show that $h = \mu \circ (f \otimes g) \circ U$. In this expression, replace g by its expression $\mu \circ (f \otimes I) \circ U$. Denote by ω_E the isomorphism of $(E \otimes E) \otimes E$ with $E \otimes (E \otimes E)$ which maps $(t \otimes u) \otimes v$ upon $t \otimes (u \otimes v)$ if t, u, v are in E. Show that

$$\mu \circ (f \otimes (\mu \circ (f \otimes I))) \circ \omega_E = \mu \circ ((\mu \circ (f \otimes f)) \otimes I).$$

Show that $\mu \circ (f \otimes f) \circ U = 0$ [if $t \in E$, set

$$U(t) = \textstyle\sum_{p,q} U_{p,q}(t), \quad U_{p,q}(t) \in E_p \otimes E_q;$$

use the fact that, if $t \in E_{2n}$, then $U_{n,n}(t)$ is a linear combination of elements of the form $u \otimes v + v \otimes u$, with u, v in E_n]. Conclude that $h = 0$. Give a short proof of the fact that ${}^th = 0$ in the case where E^* is generated by its homogeneous elements of degree 1.

21. Let L be a Lie algebra over a commutative ring R; denote by $(x, y) \to [x, y]$ the multiplication in L. Let E be an exterior algebra on L; denote by E_n the module of homogeneous elements of degree n of E. Show that there exists a linear mapping f of E into $E_1 = L$ such that $f(xy) = [x, y]$ if $x, y \in L$, and $f(E_p) = \{0\}$ if $p \neq 2$. Let g be the mapping $\mu \circ (f \wedge I)$, where μ and I are defined as in ex. 19. Show that $g \circ g = 0$ [use ex. 20]. Show that ${}^tg$ induces a derivation d of the algebra G defined in ex. 19, and that $d \circ d = 0$.

22. Let L be a Lie algebra over a commutative ring R and M a module over R. Let there be given a linear mapping ρ of L into the algebra A of endomorphisms of M such that $\rho([x, y]) = \rho(x) \circ \rho(y) - \rho(y) \circ \rho(x)$ for any x, y in L (where $[x, y]$ is the product of x and y in the Lie algebra L); such a mapping is called a representation of L on the module M. Let α be the linear mapping of $A \otimes M$ into M such that $\alpha(a \otimes m) = a(m)$ for all $a \in A$ and $m \in M$. Denote by E an exterior algebra on L and by E_p the module of homogeneous elements of degree p of E; let the mapping g of E into itself be defined as in ex. 21. Denote by ρ_1 the mapping of E into A which extends ρ and which maps E_p upon $\{0\}$ if $p \neq 1$. If $\varphi \in \text{Hom}(E, M)$, set $\delta\varphi = \alpha \circ (\rho_1 \wedge \varphi) - \varphi \circ g$. The sets $\text{Hom}_p(E, M)$ being

defined as in ex. 18, show that δ induces a linear mapping of $\mathrm{Hom}_p(E, M)$ into $\mathrm{Hom}_{p+1}(E, M)$. Denote by ρ_2 the linear mapping of $E \otimes E$ into A which maps $x \otimes y$ upon $\rho(x) \circ \rho(y)$ if $x, y \in M$ and which maps $E_p \otimes E_q$ upon $\{0\}$ if $(p, q) \neq (1, 1)$. Denote by ω the isomorphism of $(E \otimes E) \otimes E$ with $E \otimes (E \otimes E)$ which maps $(t \otimes u) \otimes v$ upon $t \otimes (u \otimes v)$ if t, u, v are in E. Show that

$$\alpha \circ (\rho_1 \otimes (\alpha \circ (\rho_1 \otimes \varphi))) \circ \omega = \alpha \circ (\rho_2 \otimes \varphi)$$

and that $\rho_2 \circ U = \rho_1 \circ g$. Setting $\delta_1 \varphi = \alpha \circ (\rho_1 \wedge \varphi)$, show that

$$\delta_1(\delta_1 \varphi) = \alpha \circ (\rho_1 \otimes \varphi) \circ (g \otimes I) \circ U.$$

Using the formulas $U \circ g = (g \otimes I + J \otimes g) \circ U$ (formula (4), Sect. 11) ang $g \circ g = 0$ (ex. 20), show that $\delta(\delta\varphi) = 0$ for any $\varphi \in \mathrm{Hom}(E, M)$.

23. The notation being as in ex. 22, let σ be some other representation of the Lie algebra L, on a module N. Denote by I_M and I_N the identity mappings of M and N respectively, and set, for $x \in L$, $\tau(x) = \rho(x) \otimes I_N + I_M \otimes \sigma(x)$. Show that τ is a representation of L on $M \otimes N$. Let σ_1 and τ_1 be defined as the mapping ρ_1 of ex. 22, using σ and τ instead of ρ. Let A, B and C be the algebras of endomorphisms of M, N and $M \otimes N$ and θ the linear mapping of $A \otimes B$ into C which maps $a \otimes b$ upon the tensor product $a \otimes^m b$ of the mappings a of M into M and b of N into N. Let ζ_M (resp.: ζ_N) be the linear mapping of E into A (resp.: B) which maps 1 upon I_M (resp.: I_N) and E_p upon $\{0\}$ if $p > 0$. Show that

$$\tau_1 = \theta \circ ((\rho_1 \wedge \zeta_N) + (\zeta_M \wedge \sigma_1)).$$

Let β be the linear mapping of $B \otimes N$ into N which maps $b \otimes n$ upon $b(n)$ ($b \in B$, $n \in N$) and γ the linear mapping of $C \otimes (M \otimes N)$ into $M \otimes N$ which maps $c \otimes q$ upon $c(q)$ ($c \in C$, $q \in M \otimes N$). Let φ be an element of $\mathrm{Hom}_m(E, M)$ and ψ an element of $\mathrm{Hom}_n(E, N)$ (cf. ex. 18). Show that

$$\gamma \circ (\theta \circ (I_M \otimes I_N)) \circ ((\rho_1 \wedge \zeta_N) \wedge (\varphi \wedge \psi)) = (\alpha \circ (\rho_1 \wedge \varphi)) \wedge \psi$$

[compute $\zeta_N \wedge \varphi$ and $\rho_1 \wedge (\zeta_N \wedge \varphi)$, and use the associativity formula (5), Sect. 8]. Show that

$$\gamma \circ (\theta \circ (I_M \otimes I_N)) \circ ((\zeta_M \wedge \sigma_1) \wedge (\varphi \wedge \psi)) = (-1)^m \varphi \wedge (\beta \circ (\sigma_1 \wedge \psi))$$

[use ex. 18]. The operator δ being defined as in ex. 22, show that

$$\delta(\varphi \wedge \psi) = (\delta\varphi) \wedge \psi + (-1)^m \varphi \wedge \delta\psi.$$

24. Let M be a commutative algebra over a commutative ring R, and let L be the module over R formed by the derivations (of degree 0) of M (where M is considered as a graded algebra in which every element is homogeneous of degree 0). If $x, y \in L$, set $[x, y] = x \circ y - y \circ x$; show that the multiplication $(x, y) \to [x, y]$ turns L into a Lie algebra. If $m \in M$ and $x \in L$, denote by mx the mapping $m' \to mx(m')$ of M into itself. Show that $mx \in L$ and that the mapping $(m, x) \to mx$ is the scalar multiplication of a module structure over M on the additive group L. Prove the formula $[mx, y] = m[x, y] - y(m)x$.

25. Let the notation be as in ex. 24. Denote by $\overline{L}$ the module over M which was defined in ex. 24. Let E be an exterior algebra on L; if $x \in L$, set $\rho(x) = x$; show that ρ is a representation of the Lie algebra L (cf. ex. 22), and let the mapping δ of Hom (E, M) into itself be defined as in ex. 22 The set Hom_m (E, M) being defined as in ex. 18, let Φ_m be the set of elements φ of Hom_m (E, M) with the following property: the mapping $(x_1, \cdots, x_m) \to \varphi(x_1 \cdots x_m)$ of L^m (the product of m modules identical to L) is an m-linear mapping of the module $\overline{L}^m$ over M (the product of m modules identical to $\overline{L}$). Show that the condition $\varphi \in \Phi_m$ implies $\delta\varphi \in \Phi_{m+1}$. Let $\overline{E}$ be an exterior algebra on $\overline{L}$; denote by $\overline{E}_p$ the module of homogeneous elements of degree p of $\overline{E}$ and by $\overline{E}_p^*$ the module of linear forms on the module $\overline{E}$ which map $\overline{E}_q$ upon $\{0\}$ for every $q \neq p$. Denote by $\square$ the multiplication in $\overline{E}$; show that there exists a bijection $\varphi \to \overline{\varphi}$ of Φ_m on $\overline{E}_m^*$ such that $\overline{\varphi}(x_1 \square \cdots \square x_m) = \varphi(x_1 \cdots x_m)$ if $x_i \in L$ $(1 \leqslant i \leqslant m)$. Set $\overline{G} = \sum_{p \geqslant 0} \overline{E}_p^*$; show that there exists a mapping d of $\overline{G}$ into itself with the following properties: d maps $\overline{E}_p^*$ into $\overline{E}_{p+1}^*$; if $m \in M$ and if ε is the unit element of the algebra $\overline{G}$, then $(d(m\varepsilon))(x) = x(m)$ for every $m \in M$; if $\varphi \in \overline{E}_m^*$, $\psi \in \overline{E}_n^*$, then $d(\varphi \wedge \psi) = d\varphi \wedge \psi + (-1)^m \varphi \wedge \psi$; $d \circ d = 0$ [use ex. 23].

26. Let N be the module $2\underline{Z}_4$ over the ring $\underline{Z}_4$, and set $M = N \times N$. Let $E(M)$ and $E(M^*)$ be exterior algebras on M and on its dual module M^*. Show that the canonical homomorphism of $E(M^*)$ into the dual algebra of $E(M)$ is neither an epimorphism nor a monomorphism.

27. Let M be a free module and M^* its dual module; let $E(M)$ and $E(M^*)$ be exterior algebras on M and M^*. Show that the canonical homomorphism of $E(M^*)$ into the dual algebra of $E(M)$ is a monomorphism; in which case is it an isomorphism?

28. Let N be the module $2\underline{Z}_4$ over the ring $\underline{Z}_4$; set $M = \underline{Z}_4 \times N$, $M' = N \times N$; let E and E' be exterior algebras on M and M'. Show that the prolongation to E' of the identity mapping of M' into M is not a monomorphism.

29. If $A = (a_{ij})$ is a rectangular matrix of type (n, m) with elements in a commutative ring R, and σ a strictly increasing sequence of length m of integers between 1 and n, denote by $D(\sigma, A)$ the subdeterminant of type $(\sigma, (1, \cdots, m))$ of A. Show that $\det {}^tA \cdot A = \Sigma_\sigma D^2(\sigma, A)$ (Lagrange identity). [Introduce a free module with a base $(x_1, \cdots, x_n)$; let $(x_1^*, \cdots, x_n^*)$ be the dual base of the dual module M^*; set $y_i = \sum_{j=1}^n a_{ji} x_j$, $y_i^* = \sum_{j=1}^n a_{ji} x_j^*$; compute the element $(y_1^* \wedge \cdots \wedge y_m^*)(y_1 \cdots y_m)$ in two different manners].

30. Let $a_1, \cdots, a_n$ be elements of a commutative ring R. Set $a_{ij} = a_j^{i-1} (1 \leqslant i, j \leqslant n)$ show that $\det (a_{ij}) = \prod_{i > j} (a_i - a_j)$.

31. Let V be a finite dimensional vector space over a field R. Let E be an exterior algebra on V and E_p the space of homogeneous elements of degree p of E. Let t be an element of E_p (with $p > 1$). Let W be the subspace of

V generated by the elements of the form $(d_1 \circ \cdots \circ d_{p-1})(t)$, where $d_1, \cdots, d_{p-1}$ are any derivations of degree -1 of E. Show that t belongs to the subalgebra of E generated by W [proceed by induction on p, or use theorem 49, sect. 15]. Assuming that $t \neq 0$, show that dim $W \geqslant p$ and that dim $W = p$ is a necessary and sufficient condition for t to be decomposable. Show that another necessary and sufficient condition for t to be decomposable is that $wt = 0$ for every $w \in W$.

32. Let V be a vector space of finite dimension n over a field, and E an exterior algebra on V. Show that every homogeneous element of degree $n-1$ of E is decomposable.

33. Let V be a vector space of dimension 4 over a field R, and (x_1, x_2, x_3, x_4) a base of V. Let E be an exterior algebra on V; set $t = \sum_{i<j} a_{ij} x_i x_j$, where the a_{ij}'s are elements of R. Set $a_{ij} = -a_{ji}$ if $i > j$, $a_{ii} = 0$, and denote by A the matrix (a_{ij}). Show that a necessary and sufficient condition for t to be decomposable is that Pf $A = 0$.

34. Let the notation be as in ex. 33. If W is any 2-dimensional subspace of V, let $u(W)$ be a representative bivector for W. Let K be the set of 2-dimensional subspaces W such that $tu(W) = 0$. Assume that t is not decomposable. Show that, if X is any 1-dimensional subspace of V, the spaces W which belong to K and which contain W are all the 2-dimensional subspaces containing X and contained in a certain 3-dimensional space H. Show that, if H' is any 3-dimensional subspace of V, the spaces W belonging to K and contained in H' are all the 2-dimensional subspaces of H' which contain a certain 1-dimensional space X'.

35. Show by an example that a system of homogeneous linear equations $\sum_{j=1}^{n} a_{ij} x_j = 0$ $(1 \leqslant i \leqslant n)$ with coefficients in a commutative ring R may have a non-trivial solution although the determinant of the matrix (a_{ij}) is $\neq 0$ [take $n = 1$].

36. Let R be a commutative ring with at least 2 elements, and let $A = (a_{ij})$ be a square matrix of degree n with elements in R such that det $A = 0$. Show that the system of equations $\sum_{j=1}^{n} a_{ij} x_j = 0$ $(1 \leqslant i \leqslant n)$ has a solution composed of elements not all zero of R. [Assume that the subdeterminant of type $((1, \cdots, p), (1, \cdots, p))$ of A is $\neq 0$, but that all subdeterminants of order $> p$ of A are 0; show that there is a non-trivial solution for which $x_j = 0$ for $j > p + 2$.] Show that the same conclusion remains valid if, instead of assuming that det A $= 0$, we assume that there is an exponent r such that $(\det A)^r = 0$ and also if we assume that, for any element a of R which does not belong to the ideal generated by det A, there is an element b of R such that $(\det A)b = 0$, $ab \neq 0$ [show that there exist elements $x_1, \cdots, x_n$ of R, which do not all belong to the ideal K generated by det A, but are such that the elements $\sum_{j=1}^{n} a_{ij} x_j$ $(1 \leqslant i \leqslant n)$ belong to K].

37. Let M be a module over a commutative ring R and (S, ψ) a symmetric algebra on N. Proceeding in the same manner as for exterior algebras, define an "analyzing mapping" U of S into $S \otimes_c S$ and the structure of an algebra on the dual S^* of the module S; show that this algebra is commutative. Let M^* be the dual module of M, and (T, θ) a symmetric algebra on M^*; define a "canonical homomorphism" η of T into S^*. Assume now that S has a finite base $(X_1, \cdots, X_n)$; show that, if $P \in S$, then we have $U(P) = P(Y_1 + Z_1, \cdots, Y_n + Z_n)$, where $Y_i = X_i \otimes 1$, $Z_i = 1 \otimes X_i$. Assuming further that R is a field, show that η is an isomorphism if R is of characteristic 0, while, if R is of characteristic $p > 0$, then η maps the p-th power of every homogeneous element of degree > 0 of T upon 0.

Index